THE
ROSEATE
SPOONBILL

Roseate Spoonbill

THE ROSEATE SPOONBILL

by Robert Porter Allen

Dover Publications, Inc., New York

Published in Canada by General Publishing Company, Ltd., 30 Lesmill Road, Don Mills, Toronto, Ontario.

Published in the United Kingdom by Constable and Company, Ltd., 10 Orange Street, London W.C. 2.

This Dover edition, first published in 1966, is an unabridged and unaltered republication of the work originally published in 1942 as Research Report Number 2 of the National Audubon Society.

In the 1942 edition the frontispiece was reproduced in color, but is here reproduced as a black-and-white halftone.

This edition is published by special arrangement with the National Audubon Society.

Library of Congress Catalog Card Number: 66-19043

Manufactured in the United States of America
Dover Publications, Inc.
180 Varick Street
New York, N.Y. 10014

FOREWORD

THE National Audubon Society considers facts obtainable through scientific research the essential basis for wise policies governing the conservation of wildlife resources.

The Roseate Spoonbill is one of the most exquisitely beautiful birds in the world. Bayard Christy has in his charming style written:

Of the Spoonbills it is impossible to withhold an enthusiastic word more. Sailing in the sunlight, from translucent bill to toe, and from wing tip to wing tip, they are suffused with color, and such color! Flame birds! Birds of the dawn! Rosy pink, with wing and tail coverts of deeper carmine. The tail tawny orange. It is as though an orchid had spread its lovely wings and flown. The sight of this beautiful creature is an event, an experience; a thing to be carried in memory, with the sight of Fujiyama in the dawn, with an eclipse of the sun.

It is a sorry fact that man's persecution reduced the Spoonbill to the verge of extinction throughout its normal range in the Gulf region of the United States. It was killed to provide commercial traffic in its feathers for use in fans, millinery and screens; it was killed to provide meat for commercial fishermen and Indians. Its chosen habitats were encroached upon by civilization, and are now threatened with disturbance and ruin through commercial operations for the development of oil.

The National Audubon Society has been involved in furnishing protection to Spoonbills in the United States since 1902, and to a concentrated degree in the past ten years. All known Spoonbill breeding, feeding and resting concentrations of importance in our Gulf states have been protected by Audubon wardens; such protection in Texas has produced favorable results, but as a nester in Florida the Roseate Spoonbill is still losing ground despite protection.

In seeking up-to-date life history and ecological data on rare birds threatened with extinction, the Society has employed two methods. One involves the coöperation of universities and is known as the Audubon Research Fellowship Plan; this has resulted in the publication of the Society's Research Report No. 1 on the Ivory-billed Woodpecker, and will in due course result in publication of research report on the California Condor. The other plan, followed in research as to the Roseate Spoonbill, involves the Society's capitalizing on the ability and particular qualification of members of its own staff.

Robert Porter Allen had well served the Society in the capacity of Director of Sanctuaries; he was thus already familiar with the Spoonbill and many of the problems connected with its preservation. He had made numerous expeditions to the Texas and Florida coasts and had made thorough surveys of their bird populations. He was intensely interested in undertaking the field research on which this report is based.

The job involved living midst the Spoonbills day and night, twenty-four hours a day, week after week, month after month; it spelled physical exposure and hardship, necessitated endurance, perseverance, boundless energy, and enthusiasm. These qualities Robert Allen possesses in ample measure.

I

Upon completion of this report, he volunteered for service as a private in the armed forces of our country; he is now a sergeant in the Mine Planters Unit of the Coast Artillery Corps of the United States Army, and on sea duty.

New York, N.Y.
November 10, 1942

JOHN H. BAKER
Executive Director
National Audubon Society

PREFACE

IN 1939, I was asked by John H. Baker, Executive Director of the National Audubon Society, to undertake a study of the life history of the Roseate Spoonbill and make a report including recommendations as to its restoration as a common breeding bird throughout its former range in the United States. This meant obtaining precise knowledge of its habits, a thorough investigation of its ecological niche, its food relations, its choice of nesting sites, its wanderings, its reactions to excessive high and low temperature and precipitation. Would it react favorably to a protective formula limited to laws plus sanctuaries plus wardens? Was its food supply at fault? Was possible inbreeding in a small, isolated population impairing the virility of the race? Guesses, suggestions and 'explanations' there were aplenty. If there were ever a bird in need of a thorough study of its life history and ecological relationships that species was the Roseate Spoonbill.

When, in 1902, the National Audubon Society (then the National Committee of Audubon Societies) became aware of the Roseate Spoonbill's need for special protection, its first warden was employed to guard the Florida breeding colonies that then existed in Alligator Lake and Cuthbert Lake, as well as the handful of egrets that were the last hope of those persecuted birds in the United States. In spite of protective laws and increased efforts to save them, the Spoonbills gradually decreased, one breeding colony after another disappearing with what seemed like tragic finality.

In recent years, however, this decline in numbers has been distinctly a Florida problem. After its gradual reappearance as a breeder on the Texas coast during the 1920's, the Spoonbill has been increasing in that state under the vigilant protection of Audubon wardens. In Florida, though, its status as a nesting species has gone from bad to worse, in spite of redoubled efforts to prevent its destruction or any disturbance in its chosen habitat.

The writer accordingly left his post as Sanctuary Director for the National Audubon Society in October 1939 to spend a total of twenty-five months making an intensive study of the Spoonbill—sixteen in the field in the bird's Florida and Texas habitats, and nine in museum, library and office. The first base of operations was established at Tavernier on the lower tip of Key Largo, Florida. This location is some six miles from the only remaining breeding colony of Spoonbills in Florida—lonely, mangrove-studded Bottlepoint Key in Florida Bay. The breeding colony was on the southern end of Bottlepoint; on the northern end a camp was built from which the initial ecological field work was conducted during the five months from November 1939 through March 1940.

During the three months that followed, April through June 1940, a second camp was established on the shores of San Antonio Bay, Texas, one mile from the successful Spoonbill colony on the Second Chain-of-Islands. Here, study of breeding-cycle behavior was of primary importance, although considerable ecological research was also accomplished.

After nine months in the field, I returned to the New York office for a period of museum, library and office work; there were innumerable specimens of insects and small fish to be identified, field notes to be written up, museum skins to be examined for plumage sequences.

Field studies were resumed in October 1940, when a camp was set up on Low Key near Bottlepoint Key, in Florida Bay.   For five months I concentrated research on the food and feeding habits of Spoonbills in that area, and on ecological investigations of some of the animals and environments with which the Spoonbill is most closely associated.   Then, in April 1941 I transferred my 'camp' to an 18-foot motor skiff, the *Croc*, which was outfitted for a three months' survey of Spoonbill flocks inhabiting the southwest coast of Florida during the spring and summer, from East Cape Sable to Little Patricio Island below Charlotte Harbor.   Living on the *Croc* during these investigations, I sometimes went nine and ten days without setting foot on shore.   Except when navigating the boat from one point on the coast to another, full attention was devoted to a study of the plumages and feeding habits of these flocks, and many new data were obtained.   Eventually, after sixteen months of concentrated field work in Florida and Texas under all sorts of conditions, I again returned to the New York office to prepare my report on this stately, strange and beautiful bird, the Roseate Spoonbill.

In this report I have not hesitated to mention in detail all locations on our Gulf coast where Spoonbills may currently be observed.   I am fully conscious of the fact that some people will consider this indiscreet, but it has been done deliberately, with two thoughts in mind:

1.   Experience has long taught us that anyone who, for one reason or another, desires to kill a Spoonbill or take its eggs will know where to find them without a guide book.

2.   All known breeding colonies and concentrations of importance in the United States are guarded by competent wardens.

It is the hope of the author that publication of this report will help to clarify the problem of restoration of the Roseate Spoonbill as a common breeder in Florida and serve to arouse new interest in its future welfare throughout its range.   It seems obvious that more research, much careful planning and, above all, a program of coöperative effort with certain of our neighbors to the south must be undertaken if the Spoonbill is to be permanently maintained as a nesting bird in our Gulf states.   Furthermore, the maintenance of protective services in areas where Spoonbills concentrate will require continued public support.   If this report encourages the accomplishment of these ends, its preparation will have been well worth while.

ROBERT PORTER ALLEN

Tavernier, Florida
April 30, 1942

ACKNOWLEDGMENTS

DURING the preparation of this report and throughout my experiences in the field, I was fortunate in having the varied and cheerful assistance of many able and unselfish persons, each of whom deserves all possible thanks and a proper acknowledgment in these pages. If, through mischance, any such acknowledgment is omitted, the oversight will be entirely unintentional.

I am indebted most of all to John H. Baker, Executive Director of the National Audubon Society, who initiated the project and rendered essential help and encouragement throughout its progress. I am also grateful to the Society's Board of Directors, collectively and individually, for their interest and support.

Thanks are due Mrs. Margaret M. Nice for her kindness in making suggestions with regard to my material on breeding-cycle behavior and for bibliographic assistance. I am grateful to A. C. Bent for critical assistance in the preparation of the chapter on plumages and molts; to J. T. Nichols of the American Museum of Natural History for his patient work with my collections of fishes and for other encouragement; to Dr. C. Brooke Worth for his port-mortem work and for distributional data; and to Dr. T. Gilbert Pearson for a variety of data and for many helpful suggestions.

I am indebted to Ludlow Griscom for having critically read the entire manuscript and made valuable suggestions.

For critical aid and other assistance I wish to thank J. J. Hickey, D. S. Lehrman and R. H. Pough; also Mrs. Marie V. Beals, who identified botanical specimens and helped with translations and other bibliographic matters.

Special thanks are due James O. Stevenson of the United States Fish and Wildlife Service, and Everett Beaty and Ray Custer of the Aransas National Wildlife Refuge for much practical assistance and encouragement in the field.

In Louisiana I received coöperation from Messrs. Landry, Bienvenu, Schexnayder and Gordon, and for their kindness I am deeply grateful.

So many individuals assisted me in the field by providing transportation in boats or automobiles, and in giving freely of their time, that I feel a brief acknowledgment here is scarcely adequate reward. Edward M. Moore, Audubon warden in Florida Bay during my researches there, did much more for me than his job required and my gratitude and indebtedness to him are considerable. Alexander Sprunt, Jr., helped in a number of ways, and I am also grateful to him for the interest he has shown throughout the study. Lester L. Karcher has given much assistance and has been especially helpful during the course of field work in south Florida. Other help in Florida was given me by J. Ray Barnes, who provided boat transportation and gave of his own time as well. In Texas, Gordon Gunter assisted with fish collections and with helpful discussions of certain of my problems.

Others in Texas who assisted me in the field and to whom special thanks are due are Judge and Mrs. O. F. Hartman, Mr. and Mrs. Albert Nutt, Robert Hopper, E. T. Dawson, Van Harris, Ernest G. Marsh, Jr., Raymond Redding, the late J. G. Fuller, H. C. Blanchard, W. T. Friddell and John O. Larson.

In Florida, assistance in the field was provided by many persons. I am especially grateful to Augustus S. Houghton, who was kind and helpful in many ways; also to Claude F. Lowe, James Earle Moore, Arthur O. Eifler, Howard Sharp, Harry Brown and Judson Barnes, who gave cheerfully of both time and energy.

I am indebted for various kinds of encouragement and help to many residents of Tavernier and the adjacent Florida keys; and to a number of fishermen at Turkey Key on the southwest coast, particularly to Charlie Bodiford and Capt. Barney Manning.

Data and advice on distribution, abundance or migration were provided by the following individuals, to whom I owe grateful thanks: L. C. Scaramuzza, S. C. Bruner, Dr. Armando Dugand, Dr. F. Carlos Lehmann, Dr. Thomas Barbour, W. H. Phelps, J. D. Smith, Ernesto R. Runnacles, F. W. Miller, Dr. Oliverio Mario de Oliveira Pinto, D. S. Bullock, Fred A. Flanders, Frank Cothern, Dr. H. R. Mills, James L. Peters, Laurence M. Huey, Charles Greene, Edward J. Reimann, Mrs. Jack Hagar, Dr. George B. Saunders, Clinton Sherman, Jr., Mrs. Bessie M. Reid, Mrs. Robert J. Kleberg, Jr., Joseph Cadbury, John B. Semple, Capt. W. A. Card, Capt. Cliff Carpenter, Lt.-Comm. C. C. von Paulsen, Bayard H. Christy, Dr. Walter P. Taylor.

Help and advice of various kinds have been given me by Dr. Harold E. Anthony, Daniel B. Beard, Dr. R. C. Murphy, Aldo Leopold, Arthur H. Schmidt, Dr. Ernst Mayr, Joost ter Pelkwyjk, John H. Davis, Jr., Dr. Carlton M. Herman, Samuel C. Harriot, Henry M. Kennon, and T. T. Waddell.

Various members of the museum staffs coöperated by identification of specimens, and for this assistance I am grateful to John C. Armstrong of the American Museum of Natural History; C. R. Shoemaker, J. O. Maloney, I. Fox, Dr. Waldo L. Schmitt, Dr. Paul Bartsch and Dr. Raeder of the National Museum. I am also indebted to Dr. Herbert Friedmann of the National Museum, Dr. W. E. Clyde Todd of the Carnegie Museum and Dr. Frank M. Chapman and Charles O'Brien of the American Museum for giving me access to their collections of study skins.

I wish to thank F. M. Uhler and Clarence Cottam of the United States Fish and Wildlife Service for analyzing the contents of the Spoonbill stomach which I sent them.

To Mrs. Margaret Brooks Hickey I am grateful for invaluable help in preparing the manuscript for publication, for proof-reading and preparation of the index; also to Miss Barbara Coulter for her enthusiastic assistance in getting the manuscript in shape and for final preparation of the bibliography.

Photographs used in the published report have been provided through the generosity of Allan D. Cruickshank for Plates 1, 6–7, 10, 12–18, and 20; John O'Reilly for Plates 2–5, and 9; Karl Maslowski and Peter Koch for Plates 11 and 19; and Theodore Childs for Plate 8. I wish also to thank Katherine Van Cortlandt who contributed original pen and ink drawings of fish made from specimens in my collection. Frederick P. Mangels very kindly prepared the plumage-cycle charts.

To Roger Tory Peterson I am indebted for much assistance, in addition to his excellent painting which appears as the color frontispiece of this report. During the writing of the text and the drawing of the numerous maps and sketches, his advice and encouragement were invaluable. Mr. Peterson also did the half-tone drawings of spoonbill plumages, including those of the five species occurring outside the Western Hemisphere.

                                                    ROBERT PORTER ALLEN

Fort Monroe, Virginia
October 1, 1942

TABLE OF CONTENTS

LIST OF ILLUSTRATIONS

FIGURES

INTRODUCTION

SPOONBILLS have long stirred the interest and admiration of man. Crude images of spoonbills are to be found among birds depicted on the walls of Neolithic caves in Spain, drawn by artists who have been dead for six or eight thousand years.[a] In the tombs of the kings of ancient Egypt at Thebes, there are figures of spoonbills—the flat, spoon-shaped bill drawn as seen from above, but the remainder of the bird in profile![b] In a stone carving from the Han Dynasty (220–206 B.C.), a spoonbill is distinctly recognizable.[c]

These early examples of appreciation for the spoonbill show a contrast that has its counterpart today. The rough, uncouth artist seeking self-expression on the walls of Neolithic caves in Spain, and the two relatively cultured individuals who indulged their skill by appointment, perhaps, to royalty in ancient centers of civilization, all three found something striking, something unusual and worth preserving in the outlines of the spoonbill. These delineations were of the White or European Spoonbill, a species of striking appearance, but in no degree so colorful and startling in its beauty as the Roseate Spoonbill of the Western Hemisphere.

The subject of the present study, the Roseate Spoonbill, is classified in the order *Herodiones*, which includes the herons, storks, ibises, etc., and in the family *Threskiernithidae*, the ibises and spoonbills. All six species of spoonbills inhabit the warmer portions of the world, but only one occurs in the Western Hemisphere. This species, *Ajaia ajaja*, the Roseate Spoonbill, is the lone member of its genus, and breeds from the Gulf coast of the United States southward as far as the Pampas of the Argentine, south of Buenos Aires. Details of this distribution are discussed in the body of the report.

Other spoonbills are widely distributed over parts of Europe, Asia, Australia and islands in the southwest Pacific. The most far-flung range is that[d] of the White Spoonbill (*Platalea leucorodia*). There are three subspecific forms: the European (*P. l. leucorodia*), the Asiatic or Japanese (*P. l. major*) and the White Nile or Red Sea form (*P. l. archeri*). In the genus *Platalea* there are three additional species: the Black-faced (*P. minor*); the African (*P. alba*); and the Royal, sometimes called Black-billed (*P. regia*).

In addition to *Ajaia* and *Platalea*, there is a third genus, *Platibis*. Only one species has been described, the Yellow-billed or Yellow-legged Spoonbill (*P. flavipes*).

The **White Spoonbill** (*Platalea leucorodia*) is the most northerly as well as the most universally distributed species. The European form (*P. l. leucorodia*) once bred in England (*Norfolk, Suffolk, Sussex, Middlesex*) and in Wales, but is now only an occasional visitor. In 1928 a group nested in Denmark. There are also colonies in the Netherlands (*Buiten-Muy, Texel; Zwanenwater, Vlieland; Naardermeer, Vlieland*); in southern Spain (*Guadalquivir delta, Cano de la Junqueria*); in Yugoslavia (*Obedska Bara* and possibly *Dalmatia*); Rumania (*lower Danube*); Albania; and from southern Russia (possibly north to 56°) to Transcaucasia (*Georgia* and *Azer-Baidzhan*) and Asia Minor.

In migration this form reaches Equatorial Africa (*Niger River, Nigeria; Central Sudan; Cameroon* below Lake Chad; *Somaliland*). It is an uncertain migrant in Egypt.

Jourdain (Witherby, *et al.*, 1939, 'Handbook of British Birds,' III, 120) states that the migration routes carry them through France, Belgium and the Mediterranean region. They are also said to follow the coasts of Portugal and Spain, crossing to Africa at Gibraltar. In Italy they occur (chiefly in spring) in the Province of Veneto, in the Province of Puglia, in Sicily (Craveri, 1927, 'Atlante Ornitologico,' XV), Capitanata and at Lago di Lesina (Degli Oddi, 1929, 'Ornitologia Italiana,' 460). Accidental occurrences have been recorded in the Faroes, Norway, Sweden, Finland,

---

[a] Gurney, 1921, 'Early Annals of Ornithology,' pp. 1–7.

[b] Whymper, 1909, 'Egyptian Birds,' p. 140.

[c] Sowerby, 1940, 'Nature in Chinese Art,' p. 29.

[d] Basic data from Peters, 1931, 'Check List of Birds of the World,' I, 139–140. Details from numerous sources, most of which are given in the text.

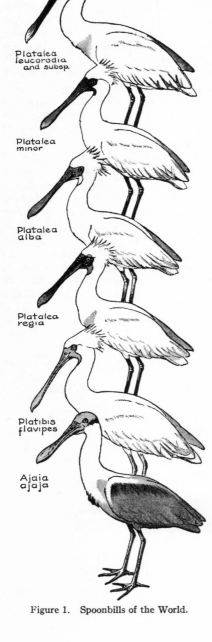

Platalea
leucorodia
and subsp.

Platalea
minor

Platalea
alba

Platalea
regia

Platibis
flavipes

Ajaia
ajaja

Figure 1. Spoonbills of the World.

the Baltic states, Germany, Switzerland, Czecho-slovakia, Poland, northern Russia and on the Azores, Canaries and Madeiras (Jourdain, see above).

The Asiatic form (*P. l. major*) inhabits central Asia (*Caspian Sea* to *Kirghiz Steppes*), China, southern Transbaikalia (*Bury-At Mongol,* U. S. S. R.), Ussuriland (*Ussuri area,* east of *Manchukuo* and immediately north of *Vladivostok*) and Japan[e] (*Yetorofu,* Kurile Islands; *Hokkaido* or *Yezo; Shimosa, Mukojima* in Tokyo, *Yokohama, Tamashiro* all in Hondo; *Tokushima,* Shikoku; *Ariaka Bay, Kagashima* in Yatsushiro Bay and *Higo,* Kiusiu; *Korea; Sho,* Riu Kui Islands; *Formosa*) south to India (*Deccan; Sind; northwest provinces* and *Ceylon*), Afghanistan, Baluchistan, Syria, Iraq and Egypt.[f]

This form is migratory in the northern part of its range. Delacour and Jabouille (1925, *Ibis,* 229) reported an immature specimen of "*Platalea leucorodia*" from Hailang, Quang-tri, Annam. It was also said to occur in the provinces of Vinh and Hatinh.

The third form of the White Spoonbill (*P. l. archeri*) occurs on the coasts of the Red Sea and Somaliland and along the White Nile (*Bahr-el-Abiad*), Anglo-Egyptian Sudan.

The **Black-faced Spoonbill** (*P. minor*), sometimes called the Lesser Spoonbill (*La Petite Spatule*), is found in southern Japan (*Shimosa,* Hondo; *Nagasaki* and *Satsuma,* Kiusiu; *Goto Island:* Korea (*Fusan*); *Ishigaki,* Riu Kui Islands; *Formosa*) to southern China, Hainan and occasionally to the Philippines (*Obando,* Balacan Province; *Dagupan,* Pangasinan Province). Delacour and Jabouille (1931, 'Les Oiseaux de l'Indochine Francaise,' I, 79) record *P. minor* in Tranninh (*Laos*), Thua-Thien and Kontoum, French Indo China.

The **African Spoonbill** (*Platalea alba*) inhabits the African continent from Gambia and the Egyptian Sudan south to Cape Province.   It is

[e] Japanese localities from 'Handbook of the Japanese Birds,' 1932, Orn. Soc. of Japan, Tokyo.

[f] Meinertzhagen (Nicoll's 'Birds of Egypt,' 1930, II, 434–435) states that the Asiatic form is apparently a migratory visitor to Egypt. There are, however, April and July records for the Sinai peninsula.

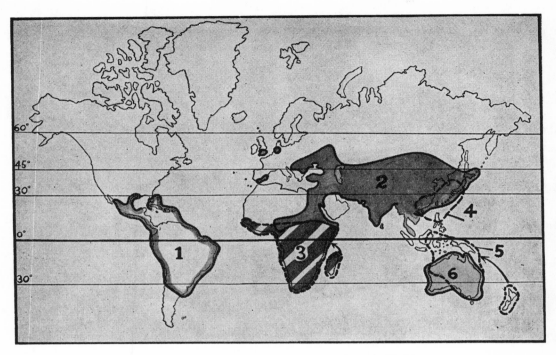

Figure 2.   Distribution of Spoonbills throughout the World:

1. Roseate Spoonbill (*Ajaia ajaia*)
2. White Spoonbill (*Platalea leucorodia* and subsp.)
3. African Spoonbill (*P. alba*)
4. Black-faced Spoonbill (*P. minor*)
5. Royal Spoonbill (*P. regia*)
6. Yellow-billed Spoonbill (*Platibis flavipes*)

also found in Madagascar. South of the Zambesi it is rare (Bannerman, 1930, 'Birds of Tropical West Africa,' I, 123–125). Locations mentioned by Bannerman are Casamance, Portuguese Guinea, Sierra Leone (*Yawry Bay*), Gold Coast, Nigeria, Bagirmi (*Shari* region, Chad Territory) and Gabon (Gabun). They also occur in Rhodesia, the Transvaal and Zululand.

The **Royal** or **Black-billed Spoonbill** (*Platalea regia*) occurs in Australia[g] (except western Australia south of North West Cape) and occasionally in New Guinea, Celebos, Timor and the Moluccas, also in Borneo and accidentally in New Zealand. Oliver (1930, 'New Zealand Birds,' 372–373) gives only four records for

New Zealand: 1876, 1892, 1905 and 1922. The species is known to the Maoris, who have a name for it, so it must have occurred there on previous occasions.

The **Yellow-billed** or **Yellow-legged Spoonbill** (*Platibis flavipes*), a lone species in the genus *Platibis*, inhabits Australia generally.

In general appearance the Old World spoonbills resemble each other, with white or black and white plumage and the feathers of the nauchal crest relatively long and pointed. The most striking differences in color are to be found in the soft parts. Our species is the only spoonbill with brilliant plumage characteristics. In the adult *Ajaia ajaja* the head and throat are bare, the neck and upper back white with tinges or suffusions of pink. The tail is ochraceous-buff, and yellow-buff suffusions appear on the sides of the breast

---

[g] Australian data from Cayley, 1931, 'What Bird Is That?' and Peters, 1931.

in front of the wings. The rest of the plumage is pink, the lesser wing coverts and upper and lower tail coverts rich carmine. In the chapter on plumages and molts, details of adult and various immature plumages are fully discussed.

Following are brief descriptions of the plumage of the other spoonbills:

The **White Spoonbill** is slightly larger than *Ajaia*. In summer the plumage is white throughout, except for a collar of yellow buff at the base of the neck. Feathers of the nauchal crest are long and pointed. The bill is black with a yellow tip, and the bare skin on the forepart of the lores is also black. The base of the lores, chin and throat are yellow. The legs and feet are black, and the iris is red. In the juvenile the bill is flesh colored and the feet and legs are yellowish to slate colored. The adult plumage is acquired by a complete molt in the period from January to March and another complete molt appears to take place in late summer or early autumn. Winter adults do not have the yellow collar and the crest feathers are shorter. As in our species, the primaries and primary coverts in the juvenile show varying amounts of brownish black.

The **Black-faced Spoonbill** is a smaller species. The plumage of this 'Japanese Spoonbill' is white, except for the tips of the inner primaries and outer secondaries which are fuscous, and the

[h] Data from 'Handbook of British Birds' (1939) and other authorities.

shafts of the remiges, the alula, and the upper and under tail coverts, all of which are fuscous black. The 'face,' including the skin around the eyes and throat, is black. The mandibles are whitish gray, and the eyes dark gray.

The **African Spoonbill** is a bird of striking appearance because of contrasting colors of the soft parts. The plumage is entirely white, although the crest is cream colored at the breeding season. The upper mandible is red, the lower slate black with yellow spots and edgings. In younger birds the bill is evidently blue gray clouded with pink. In the adult the skin on the forehead is a bright red, the chin yellow, and the iris a pearly white. The legs and feet are bright pink and red.

The **Royal Spoonbill** is the Australian and East Indian representative of the genus *Platalea*. Its plumage is entirely white except for a tinge of sandy buff on the lower foreneck. The bill is black with the tip brown. The bare skin on the forehead and rest of face is black. The gular pouch is leaden brown. Above the skin of the eye is a yellow spot. The iris is brown and the legs and feet blackish.

The immature bird has a shorter bill, lacks the crest and shows brown on the tips of the primaries.

The **Yellow-billed Spoonbill,** a large Australian species, is white throughout but has black-edged, plume-like feathers on the back. All of the soft parts, including the bare skin of the face, are yellow.

THE
ROSEATE
SPOONBILL

Part I. Distribution

THE distribution of a species is a dramatic subject, reaching out over space. It not only commands distances but it echoes with strange names; we hear of unexplored rivers, of unknown valleys, of islands where pirates careened their ships between voyages. When it deals with the past, it calls to our minds a vision of unspoiled wildernesses. We can almost see the broad expanses of unbroken swamp and forest and imagine the clear, ringing depth of the vast, pristine silence. The teeming abundance of wildlife is an inspiration; we rededicate ourselves in our determination not only to protect the heritage that is ours against further decimation but to restore to past glory all forms that can still respond to our efforts at rehabilitation. Thus, our interest in the distribution of the Roseate Spoonbill (*Ajaia ajaja*) is more than mere curiosity, more than a bald inventory of place names. It is the beginning of any thorough inquiry into the well-being of a species that has come close to disappearance from our avifauna. It is the first step that we must take.

A. FORMER DISTRIBUTION IN THE UNITED STATES

In order that we may understand the present distribution of the Roseate Spoonbill, it is important that we reconstruct its past distribution as accurately as possible. This has been divided into various periods, because the history of the Spoonbill's decimation in this country carries it through certain phases of good and bad fortune, each of which has a discernible connection with the march of human activities and events.

As a basis for this reconstruction, there are really only two available sources. The first of these is the published literature, and the second is our present understanding of the bird and its habits. This understanding, coupled with a more than speaking acquaintance with recent and current records of occurrence and nesting, is of incalculable help in this job of reconstruction. Even so, the results in many instances cannot be presented as anything more than my interpretation. This particular account is biographical and sub-ject to all the errors, misjudgments and involuntary prejudices which inevitably victimize and trap the would-be historian. A majority of the observers quoted are long since dead, and we cannot ask them their precise meaning when they used such general terms as "large numbers," "great bodies," and similar intriguing but often unsatisfactory phrases.

There should be no misunderstanding, however, of the importance of this research into the past, this thumbing of dusty pages and scrutinizing of the published word of men long since passed away. For it seems obvious that many of the habitats in which Spoonbills once flourished, and which they deserted, were given up under pressure from man and not because they no longer provided the essentials of Spoonbill existence. The more we can learn about these localities and the manner in which they were deserted the better fitted we will be to prevent further losses. Looking into the future, we should be more adequately equipped, as a result of our understanding of past events, to cope with the problems of rehabilitation.

1. Earliest Times to 1850

Published references from the earliest period down to about 1850, during which Spoonbills presumably occupied suitable portions of the Gulf coast unhampered and undisturbed, are not only few in number but leave great gaps to baffle the researcher. We can be fairly sure that the Indians, conservationists by instinct or at least by habit, did not seriously disturb breeding colonies of these birds until white men created a demand for wild bird feathers. They probably made occasional use of the brilliant plumage, especially the wings, for decorative purposes and ceremonial dances, just as they are said to have used the strikingly contrasted head and bill of the Ivory-billed Woodpecker. These demands must have been relatively small and no doubt harmless to the species as a whole. Furthermore, there is considerable difference between a bow and arrow and a shotgun in the effect produced upon a nesting colony of birds.

1

Early travelers and ornithologists who mention the Spoonbill within our borders include Bartram, Barton, Wilson, Audubon, Nuttall, Williams and Gambel. From their comments it is apparent that Spoonbill colonies originally existed over much of south Florida and along the Texas coast. There were also records of the species having been seen or reported as occurring north of the Altamaha River in Georgia (Bartram, 1791); at the mouth of the Cape Fear River, North Carolina (Barton, 1799); along the shores of the Alabama River and in other parts of that state (Nuttall, 1834); the Mississippi River valley as far as Natchez (Wilson, 1829); and in 1845 in the vicinity of Janesville, Wisconsin (Bent, 1926). John Lee Williams (Williams, 1837) described rather extensive journeys he made along the coasts of Florida prior to 1827; although one of his accounts devotes a paragraph to the Spoonbill, he gives no details as to where he saw them or the numbers that then existed. Gambel (1847–49) reported the species at San Francisco, but these records were doubted by Cooper (1877), who suggested that Gambel may have been "deceived by hearing *Spatula clypeata* called Spoonbill." However, subsequent California observations suggest that Gambel may have been correct, although there are no records north of the San Bernardino region.

For this early period Audubon alone tells of the nesting of the species, but it would appear that his first-hand experience with a nesting colony may have been confined to Galveston Island, Texas, where he went ashore in April 1837. In so far as they refer to Florida, Audubon's comments concerning the massing of Spoonbills "to form great bodies" at the approach of the breeding season seem to have been based on what others told him. There is no doubt that he saw them breeding in Texas, but our wish today is that he might have explored farther south along the Texas coast where he would most assuredly have met with a number of flourishing Spoonbill colonies. But these were perilous times in Texas, which had broken away from Mexico less than two years before Audubon's visit, and traveling in remote parts of the new republic must have been both difficult and hazardous. The Alamo massacre

was only a year old; although Santa Anna had been defeated by Sam Houston in April 1836, it was still a wild and dangerous country for ornithologists between the Rio Grande and San Antonio Bay in April 1837.

Audubon refers to Spoonbills breeding in flocks among the Florida keys; although he spent some days between Indian Key (on the Atlantic Ocean side near the upper tip of Lower Matecumbe Key) and Sandy Key near East Cape, he did not indicate that he actually visited a Spoonbill colony in that region. His only reference is to "Rose Coloured Curlews" stalking gracefully beneath the mangroves on the margin of Sandy Key. Others have expressed regret that he did not go ashore at Cape Sable, except for one brief visit to fill a cask with water "from a fine well, long since dug in the sand of Cape Sable, either by Seminole Indians or pirates."[1] Arthur H. Howell (1932) suggested that by failing to collect on the mainland "he thus missed the opportunity to secure the Cape Sable Seaside Sparrow, which was not discovered for nearly a hundred years." He likewise missed the possibility of finding the splendid colony of Roseate Spoonbills that must have existed at that time on the shores of Alligator Lake, a few miles inland.

There appear to be no early records from Louisiana, and the few birds mentioned for Alabama by Nuttall (1834) are not coupled with evidence that they were breeding on the Alabama coast or elsewhere in that state.

An unfortunate feature of this attempt to gain some general idea of the early distribution of the Spoonbill is the distressing fact that a great many, and perhaps even a majority, of the Gulf coast colonies must have been destroyed before ornithologists could record their existence. In truth, we know less about the original distribution of the Roseate Spoonbill on the Texas coast south of Galveston, for example, than we do of the distribution of some of the giant reptiles of preglacial epochs. However, on the basis of our present knowledge of the Spoonbill's habitat requirements and our current records of its presence once more

[1] This was only nine years after Commodore David Porter of the United States Navy was sent to Key West to rout buccaneers from the keys.

as a breeding species in many areas where for decades it was unknown, we are doubtless safe in assuming that colonies were scattered along most of the Gulf coast. Bearing in mind Audubon's matter-of-fact comments regarding their large numbers, we are inclined to picture these unknown, unspoiled and unrecorded colonies as flourishing and well populated.

It would seem to be significant that no evidence exists to suggest the breeding of Spoonbills northward of the present breeding range, except for those areas in Florida which were known prior to their desertion by Spoonbills and one location in West Feliciana Parish, Louisiana, reported at a later date.

Thus, down to about the 1830's the Spoonbill's distribution in the United States was probably little affected by man. Some commercialization of Spoonbill feathers may have broken up a few colonies prior to 1850, but in general its distribution was not restricted until approximately the Civil War period.

2. *Period of Decline: 1850–1890*

The period from 1850 to 1890 was one of violence and change. It witnessed the destruction of nearly all Spoonbill colonies within our borders, from Pelican Island on the east coast of Florida, southward around the tip of the peninsula to the Florida west coast and thence along the great sweep of the Gulf to the most distant Texas lagoons. Quite naturally we have a more accurate picture of the progress of this destruction and the manner in which it was carried out, than we have of the status of the colonies before the white man appeared upon the scene in any numbers. In fact, from certain writings of this time we gain our only hints as to the location and size of many of the early colonies.

The end of the Civil War resulted in widespread shifts of the human population, particularly from southeastern states to western areas, including Texas. The postwar depression and activities of the despised carpet-baggers had, in a fortuitous and indirect way, a significant effect upon the Roseate Spoonbill. Settlement of the Gulf coast wildernesses was bound to come sooner or later; the end of the Civil War was merely the instru-

ment of a fate that could not be forestalled much longer. The economic and political situation in a deflated Confederacy produced an epidemic of unrest, a general movement toward greener fields. It wasn't a force of numbers, however, that spelled doom to wildlife so much as the pioneer aspect of these settlers, their uninhibited spirit. It was what Jack London, I believe, called the "inevitable white man." Everyone carried a gun, an ax and a determination to wrest a living from the wilderness. And most of them did, whether they grew tomatoes on land cleared with their own hands or shot plume birds.

The impact of the times resulted in destruction of wildlife, in large-scale redistribution and in some cases in extinction or extirpation. These same years laid the groundwork for the quick decline of the Passenger Pigeon, the Carolina Paroquet, the Ivory-billed Woodpecker. The American and Snowy Egret were nearly extirpated, the Reddish Egret and Roseate Spoonbill were dealt such blows in Florida alone that they have not since recovered.

Perhaps the greatest single influence in the decrease of bird life during this period was the fashion for the use of feathers in millinery creations, which reached a peak in the 1890's. Oddly enough, the beautiful feathers of the Spoonbill were never in millinery demand as were plumes of the Egrets. According to Dr. T. Gilbert Pearson (1925), "the Roseate Spoonbill . . . was never extensively killed for the millinery trade . . . the feathers begin to fade in a short time and for this reason have little commercial value." But there are other considerations. Anyone familiar with Spoonbills in breeding colonies can testify that they are inordinately shy at such a time and easily disturbed. The shooting of egrets in colonies that these birds shared with the 'Pink Curlews' would have had an effect on both species, even though no Spoonbills were actually killed. Death of the egrets would, in my opinion, coincide with desertion of the area by the Spoonbills.

Colonies along the northern limit of the breeding range in Florida may have been broken up as early as the 1830's. Audubon spoke of the wings being made into fans, which were a "regular article of trade" at St. Augustine. The colony on

Pelican Island in the Indian River was being raided as early as 1858 (Bryant, 1859).

Three years after Bryant's visit to Pelican Island, George Cavendish Taylor went to the same place. He found the species greatly diminished (Taylor, 1862). Taylor's note in *The Ibis* is the last published reference that I have found to Pelican Island as a Spoonbill colony. Later, in March 1898, Dr. Frank M. Chapman visited the island and found only Brown Pelicans (Chapman, 1908). Instead of the good-sized mangrove trees described by Bryant, Pelican Island had become a treeless waste.[2]

Meanwhile, there is an indication that the Spoonbill was beginning to lose ground in Texas. In June 1864, Dresser saw two or three birds on Galveston Island and commented that they formerly bred there, but no longer did so as they "have been too much disturbed" (Baird, Brewer and Ridgway, 1884). In May 1877, George B. Sennett visited the Brownsville region and collected in the vicinity of Point Isabel. He wrote (1878) that "but little was seen of this magnificent and wonderful bird." Merrill, who was in the same region at this time, suspected the species might be breeding, which suggests the important fact that he did not find any nesting Spoonbills (Griscom and Crosby, 1925).

In Florida a few years earlier there were still breeding colonies in Brevard County and on Lake Okeechobee, but the numbers of Spoonbills in these colonies were small and from all accounts must have soon disappeared. Frederick Albion Ober went to the Okeechobee colony in the spring of 1874 (Ober, 1874) and found breeding Spoonbills on Goodshore Island.

In the same year, Frederick Tingley Jencks located two Spoonbill nesting groups in Seventeen Mile Swamp, Brevard County, and farther north near Lake Poinsett (Jencks, 1884).

In 1877, Edward Howe Forbush made a trip to Florida and traveled by river steamer on the St.

------

[2] According to John H. Davis, Jr. (*in litt.*), killing frost is the principal factor in determining the geographic limits of mangrove. There was a severe 'freeze' in 1886 that was accompanied by record low temperatures on the Gulf coast. This freeze may have destroyed the Pelican Island mangroves.

John's and the Oklawaha River. He wrote (May, 1929): "Great flocks of White Egrets and Ibises, among them the lovely Roseate Spoonbills, possessed the land." He spoke of his fellow travelers, practically all of whom were armed with "rifles, shotguns, revolvers, or all three." These men lined the rails of the steamboats and shot at birds, alligators, or anything that made a target. The boats never stopped to gather in the 'game,' and it was left to lie where it had fallen. Scott found Spoonbills along the banks of the Oklawaha in 1876 (Howell, 1932).

One of the most favorable locations for Spoonbills has long been the general region of Tampa Bay. Spoonbills still occur there in small numbers, but there has been no record of nesting since 1912 (Howell, 1932). When this region was visited by W. E. D. Scott in 1879–80, Spoonbills were found in what he termed "particular abundance" (Scott, 1887). This was inside of John's Pass, just north of Tampa Bay, where he observed a 'rookery' in April 1880. Scott used the word rookery in describing a large nesting group of herons, egrets, and ibises, among which were Roseate Spoonbills. He does not state, however, that the Spoonbills were nesting; I do not believe that they were, and this likewise appears to be the interpretation that was given his comments by Arthur H. Howell.

Scott also found hundreds of Spoonbills feeding and roosting near rookeries at Boca Grande, at the 'Maximo Rookery' in Boca Ciega Bay and elsewhere along that part of the coast. He is not definite with regard to their actual nesting, but he does speak of their tameness and says that on this early visit he found them so "fearless that one could approach so as to almost touch the birds." Today we would consider this behavior as typical of nonbreeding as opposed to breeding Spoonbills.

Bear in mind that these were conditions met with chiefly in the spring of 1880. Six years later Scott saw relatively few Spoonbills in these same locations, which he visited during April and May 1886. On this trip he spoke of the Spoonbills as being very wild as a result of being frequently fired upon by plume hunters. In the town of Pinellas he told a resident of seeing a flock of Spoonbills at Rocy Creek. The man would hardly believe him, as he had not seen any of the birds in that region for a couple of years.

Although Scott was a first-hand witness to the dramatic change that took place in the status of the Spoonbill in this six-year period, he apparently visited Florida too late to see the great colonies that were said to have existed in the region about Cape Romano and south along the coast. Speaking again of the Roseate Spoonbill, he wrote (1889): "The birds bred in enormous rookeries in the region about Cape Romano and to the south of that point. These rookeries have been described to me by men who helped to destroy them, as being frequently of many acres in extent." These localities doubtless included Blue Hill Bay and the Marco region, also areas still favored by Spoonbills from Fakahatchee Island to Wood Key Bight immediately north of the mouth of Lostman's River (Joe's Grasses, Duck Rock, Alligator Cove, etc.). In this article Scott states that he did not believe the species ever bred to the north of Charlotte Harbor.

In the same year, 1886, Horace A. Kline, a collector, was eagerly hunting Spoonbill specimens on the shores of Wakulla County. He found the birds roosting on an island eleven miles west of the St. Mark's Lighthouse and in the vicinity of Shell Point, which is in the same general area (Kline, 1887).

Meanwhile, the growing scarcity of Spoonbills on the Texas coast is described by George B. Benners, who went there on a collecting trip in May 1884. On the Nueces River near Corpus Christi, he shot eight Spoonbills on May 11 and May 18, six males and two females. He wrote that they were extremely shy and "the only way we could shoot them was by crawling through the reeds. This mode of progress was very slow as it took us about two hours to go 300 yards" (Benners, 1887). This exhibition of patience testifies to the rarity of the birds.

Benners was told that they bred in colonies on the Brazos River, but he did not see these at first hand. A few years earlier Nehrling wrote that the Spoonbill was "common in the breeding season" in Texas, particularly on ponds in the northern part of Harris County. However, he goes on to say that they were never seen in companies but always singly, associated, with herons, ducks, and other water birds (Nehrling, 1882). This does not suggest breeding.

The literature contains a few additional references which help to round out our conception of the Spoonbill's distribution during this period, sometimes in regions far outside the breeding range. The locations are listed below, dates of occurrence being given in chronological order.

1854—Collected in Calcasieu Parish, La. (G. Wurdemann)—(Oberholser, 1938).
1856—East of Vincennes, Ind.—(Butler, 1897).
1859—'American Bottoms' along Mississippi River below St. Louis (Alexander Wolle, Sr.)—(Ridgway, 1895).
1865 (circa)—Lancaster, Pa.—(Warren, 1890).
1869—Georgia (Murphy)—(Sprunt, 1936a).
1874—Island in Lake Okeechobee, Fla. (Dr. I. I. Shores)—(Henninger, 1917).
1877 (circa)—Chokoloskee Region, Fla.—(Ellis, 1917).
1879—Lucas Mill Pond, Charleston, S.C. (Dr. T. G. Simons)—(Sprunt, 1936b).
1879—Salt Lake, Fla.—(*The Oölogist*, 1879).
1880—Near Pueblo, Colo.—(Smith, 1896).
1883—Taken in Cameron Parish, La.—(Oberholser, 1938).
1883—Taken on Kissimmee River and at Gadsden, Fla.—(Howell, 1932).
1884—One taken St. John's River, Fla. (F. S. Webster, label in Am. Mus. Coll.).
1884—Two taken below New Orleans, La.—(Beyer, Allison and Kopman, 1908).
1885—Near Yemassee, S.C. (Eugene Gregorie)—(Sprunt, 1936b).
1886—Cameron Parish, La.—(Oberholser, 1938).
1887—Near Gainesville, Fla. (Bell)—(Chapman, 1888).
1887 (circa)—Waverly Plantation, La. (George Bains); breeds sparingly (Judge Lawrason)—(Beckham, 1887).
1888—Howardsville, Colo.—(Bent, 1926).
1888—? Lockwood's Folly, N.C.—(Pearson, Brimley and Brimley, 1919).
1888—Indian River, Fla. (Hoxie)—(Howell, 1932).
1889—Near Portland, Ind. (R. E. Kirkman)—(Butler, 1897)

By the end of this period startling changes had occurred in the distribution of the Spoonbill within the United States. In Florida it would appear that this change, once under way in earnest, was more rapid than elsewhere. We have Scott's evidence of the species' relative abundance as late as 1880 and of its scarcity six years later. In February, March and April 1889, Dr. J. A. Henshall[3] journeyed through the Florida keys, around

---

[3] 1889. *Forest and Stream*, **32** (16): 316.

Cape Sable and up the west coast as far as Tampa. Everywhere the scarcity of plume birds was noted and only two Roseate Spoonbills were observed. Scott (1889) wrote that by 1886 the Spoonbill in Florida had become so rare that it "is almost as great a stranger to me as to my fellow workers who live the year round in Massachusetts." In Texas shortly after the close of this period, James J. Carroll indicated that the Spoonbill had disappeared as a breeding bird, and he rarely saw even a single individual (Carroll, 1900).

During this forty-year period the Roseate Spoonbill all but disappeared from its original United States range. Although the destruction of colonies appears to have begun in Florida, the species was first driven out of Texas, probably because the coastal lagoons of that country were more accessible than the mangrove swamps of south Florida.

3. Low Ebb: 1890–1919

It is difficult to decide arbitrarily on a date marking the end of the period of decline and the beginning of this present phase. Certainly, the low point had been reached in many localities prior to 1890, and there was a growing public consciousness of this situation. Many of our birds, particularly water birds, were being rapidly destroyed by professional hunters for the millinery trade. Shortly before the beginning of this last decade of the Nineteenth Century, various movements were started with the avowed purpose of putting a stop to the slaughter of our wild birds. By 1890 the decline of the Spoonbill had spread like a plague into all regions where they had previously occurred. During the present period the downhill plunge continued and the Spoonbill was more seriously reduced over the country as a whole than at any time before or since. It reached the slack of the tide, and no one knew if that tide would flow again or not.

There are a good many records in the published literature, during these years, many more than for the period just preceding. This reflects the growing interest in birds and bird protection, the greater number of publications devoted to ornithology and conservation matters, and the increased facility with which ornithologists and others were able to journey to even the most remote areas. In spite of this greatly improved coverage, one fact stands out with considerable clarity: there were relatively few Spoonbills to be seen anywhere. Only in Florida were fair-sized flocks still reported, and these continued to diminish or they disappeared entirely.

A great majority of the reports during these years are from Florida, where in May 1902 the first warden[4] was employed by the National Audubon Society for the purpose of guarding Roseate Spoonbills.

There were no nesting colonies or concentration areas that might have been protected in Texas. As for Louisiana, there was evidently a group nesting in the southwestern parishes of that state, but such nesting was probably irregular and was not reported conclusively until the very end of this period. Writing in 1900, George B. Beyer spoke of the species as resident only in the southwest portion of the state, chiefly in Calcasieu and Cameron Parishes. There, according to E. A. McIlhenny, they were common breeders at that time. Beyer added that prior to 1900 McIlhenny had collected from this colony (or colonies?) "numerous specimens and eggs."

In Alabama two Spoonbills were killed on Dauphin Island in 1897 (Howell, 1924).

It will be of interest to list some of the Florida records for these years in chronological order, together with localities where the birds were observed. These are as follows, the names referring to the authority for each record:

1891—Horse Prairie, Ledwith Lake, Alachua County—Pearson (*in litt.*).
1896—Tampa Bay—Pearson (1897).
1896 (circa)—Old Tampa Bay—Hoyt (1906).
1901—Micco—Butler (1930b).
1903—Cuthbert Lake—Dutcher (1904).
1903—Alligator Lake—Dutcher (1904).
1904—Riding Key—Fowler (1906).
1905—Alligator Lake, Cuthbert Lake and Bottlepoint Key (?)—Job (1905).
1906—Old Tampa Bay—Hoyt (1906).
1907—Turtle Bay, Tampa Bay area—Bowdish (1909).
1908—Cuthbert Lake—Chapman (1908).
1912—Indian Key, Tampa Bay, and Corkscrew rookery—Howell (1932); Green (unpublished).

---

[4] Guy M. Bradley, murdered by a plume hunter near East Cape Sable, July 8, 1905.

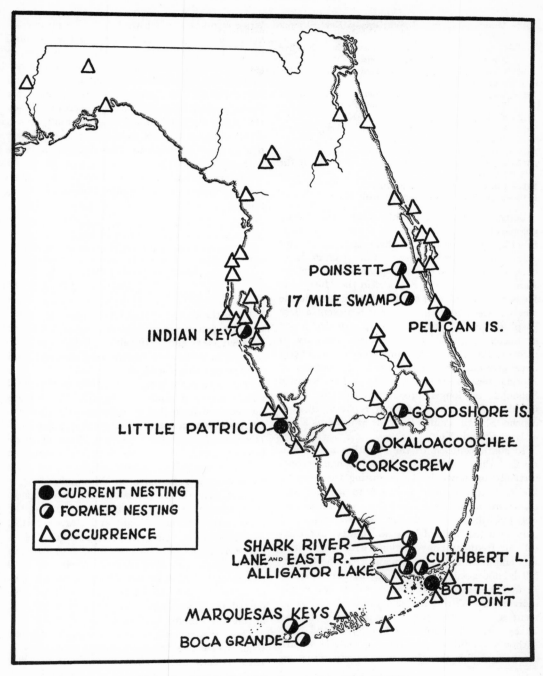

Figure 3. Distribution of the Roseate Spoonbill in Florida.

1913—Marquesas Keys and Boca Grande (Key)—Howell (1932).
1913—Corkscrew rookery and Okaloacoochee Slough—Phelps (1914); Green (unpublished).
1914—Corkscrew rookery and Florida west coast (?)—Pearson (1914).
1914—Corkscrew rookery and Okaloacoochee Slough—Kennard (1915); Green (unpublished).
1915—Corkscrew rookery—Pearson (1915).
1916—Kissimmee River and Corkscrew rookery—Howell (1932); Green (unpublished).
1917—Mosquito Lagoon—Howell (1932).
1917—Mosquito Lagoon opposite Oak Hill—Butler (1930a),
1917—Chokoloskee area—Ellis (1917).
1918—Bush Key, Tampa Bay—Howell (1932).

Some of the above localities were still nesting colonies even in this period of low ebb. In fact, the history of certain of them appears at first glance to constitute evidence of an attempt at recovery, for example: the sporadic nestings on Indian Key in Tampa Bay and in the Marquesas Keys region. It does not seem possible to decide whether these particular records represent a 'last gasp' at the tag end of the period of decline or significant examples of the species' inability to recover, for it must be understood that several dates given above mark the death of a number of Florida nesting colonies. Today the Roseate Spoonbill no longer breeds at Alligator Lake, Cuthbert Lake, the Corkscrew rookery, Okaloacoochee Slough, Tampa Bay, the Marquesas Keys, or Boca Grande Key.

In sharp contrast to the situation in Florida, we find that the Roseate Spoonbill had become virtually unknown in Texas during these years. We have already had occasion to mention the comments of James J. Carroll; although his article published in *The Auk* in 1900 was concerned only with the birds of Refugio County, Mr. Carroll, in frequent conversations with the writer, was emphatic in his statements that the Spoonbill did not breed in Texas during this entire period. In fact, he seldom observed so much as a single individual. Writing in 1892, Samuel N. Rhoads[5] mentioned that the species was seen in southwest Texas during the months of May, June and July. Although he did not give plumage details, we are safe in assuming that these were chiefly immature

[5] 1892. *Proc. Acad. Nat. Sci. Phila.* (Jan. 26).

birds wandering northward from Mexican colonies. Austin Paul Smith, writing of the Spoonbill in *The Condor* (1910), says: "It is to be seen at times in large flocks in the vicinity of Point Isabel, particularly during the months of August and September." The only other comment from Texas is that of Mrs. Florence Merriam Bailey (1916), who saw several Roseate Spoonbill skins in a collection at Priour's Ranch northwest of Corpus Christi. Apparently these specimens were without dates or other data.

The species has had an erratic career in Louisiana; arranged chronologically, the record is as follows:

1900—A common breeder—(Beyer, 1900).
1907—Common in Calcasieu Parish—(Oberholser, 1938).
1917—Two at Avery Island—(Bailey and Wright, 1931).
1919—Fourteen observed June 16 on Black Bayou, no nests—(Bailey and Wright, 1931).
1919—Twenty-five observed June 18 at Bird Island, no nests—(Figgins, 1923).

From these reports it would appear that there were no definite records of nesting in Louisiana between 1900 and 1919, although there still remains the possibility of sporadic nestings that went unreported during this interval.

It is interesting to note that there were several widely scattered Spoonbill records from regions far removed from the usual range of the species. In April 1899, a single specimen was taken near Douglas, Kansas (Lantz, 1900). Another single bird appeared in Sedgwick County, Kansas, in 1900 and was collected (Isley, 1912). In 1911, a Spoonbill was reported from Savannah, Georgia (Sprunt, 1936a). In the same state of Georgia in 1913, feathers of the Spoonbill were found in the Okefenokee Swamp (Wright and Harper, 1913). For the first time since 1799, a Spoonbill was reported from the mouth of the Cape Fear River in North Carolina. This was on April 17, 1919 (Pearson, 1919); (Fleisher, 1920). Captain Willis of the Smith's Island Life Guard Station reported two Spoonbills seen at the same location during the summer of 1918 (Fleisher, 1920).

There is a remarkable record from Wendover, Utah, where five Spoonbills appeared on July 2, 1919 (Barnes, 1919). Wendover is close to the Nevada line in the midst of an arid region. A

series of reports from California appears to vindi-
cate the early Spoonbill records of Gambel. Although Joseph Grinnell in 1902 stated that the
species was unknown in California except for the
Gambel record, it was reported for that same year
in the Riverside vicinity by H. E. Wilder and four
miles south of San Bernardino valley by R. B.
Heron in 1903 (Stephens, 1904). There are also
reports from the Imperial valley in 1909, and in
1918 Leo Wiley was quoted as claiming that
Spoonbills appeared along the banks of the lower
Colorado River near Palo Verde during the hot
months of summer (Grinnell, Bryant and Storer,
1918).

In order that we may have a clear picture of the
general status of the Roseate Spoonbill during
these years, it will be well to quote directly from
general statements made at the time. These
quotations serve a double purpose, by acquainting
us with opinions as to status and with the manner
in which the birds were destroyed.

Montague Chamberlain wrote of the Spoonbill
in 1891:

They were abundant in Florida not many years ago, but
the plume hunters have almost exterminated them there.

In April 1902, a member of the Audubon Society wrote William Dutcher that Cape Sable,
Florida, was "the paradise of plume hunters and
the purgatory of birds." He added that Spoonbills were steadily diminishing, although still
numerous in that area. Their "speedy extinction"[6] by plume hunters was feared (Dutcher,
1903).

In 1903, A. C. Bent and Herbert K. Job[7] wrote
Mr. Dutcher that herons and egrets in south
Florida were being killed in large numbers by
gunners in the winter and the young sought after
by natives for food. They wrote:

The Roseate Spoonbills are steadily decreasing in numbers
from the same cause and certainly need most stringent
protection to save them from extinction.

Mr. Bent wrote in *The Auk* for January 1904:

The Spoonbill will probably be the next to disappear from
the list of Florida water birds; they are already much
reduced in numbers and restricted in habitat; they are

_____
[6] I.e. extirpation.
[7] 1904. *The Auk,* **21** (1): 22–25.

naturally shy and their rookeries are easily broken up.
Their plumage makes them attractive marks for the
tourist's gun, and they are killed by the natives for food.

He goes on to say that their breeding places are remote and almost inaccessible and speaks of the
recently initiated warden service.[8]

In 1906, R. D. Hoyt wrote:

The Spoonbill is rapidly diminishing in numbers from no
apparent cause, as they are not, like the Egrets, being
exterminated for their plumage.

Mr. Hoyt remarks in this same article that his
party took a single specimen on the southwest
coast.

Writing in 1909, Frank H. Knowlton said that
the Spoonbill was "formerly abundant in Florida,
but the persecutions of plume hunters have so
nearly exterminated it, that during four winters
recently spent in various parts of the state, Mr.
Chapman did not observe a single specimen."
In a letter to the writer (September 9, 1935), Dr.
Chapman listed the following places in Florida
where he did *not* observe Spoonbills during various
trips to that state between 1887 and 1904:

Gainesville..............................1887 and 1888
Caloosahatchee River Mouth......................1888
Micco, Oak Lodge, and the Sebastian River........1889
Suwannee River................................1890
St. Mark's to Cedar Keys.........................1904
Kissimmee to Okeechobee to Fort Pierce............1904

Spoonbills have been reported from Micco
(1901), Gainesville[9] (1887), the Kissimmee River
(1883 and 1916). There are no records for the
coast from Cedar Key, to St. Mark's, or for the
Suwannee River. The region west of St. Mark's
(Wakulla County) is where Kline had his experiences with the species in 1886. The Caloosahatchee River mouth is near the present-day
Spoonbill concentrations in San Carlos Bay and
Pine Island Sound, but the bird is not apt to be
seen frequently either at the mouth or along the
river inland.

Writing from Chokoloskee, Florida, in 1917,
J. B. Ellis said that it was then "rare to see half a
dozen" Spoonbills. He added:

_____
[8] Warden Bradley, employed in 1904 by the (then)
National Committee of Audubon Societies.
[9] But not observed by Chapman.

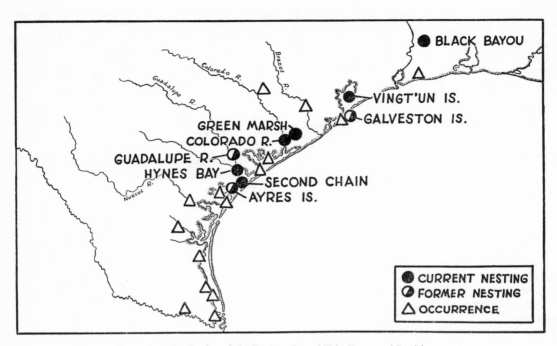

Figure 4.   Distribution of the Roseate Spoonbill in Texas and Louisiana.

If they decrease in the next five years as rapidly as they have in the last five, they will be classed with the Ivory-billed Woodpecker, Carolina Paroquet, etc.

He overlooked the essential differences in the range limits of the three species compared.

A final comment is by R. A. Sell, who in 1918 wrote in *The Condor* regarding the authenticity of sight records of the Scarlet Ibis on the Texas coast. He found that Roseate Spoonbills were occasionally reported as Scarlet Ibises and told of one such record of a Spoonbill killed by a doctor from Houston, " in order to get a feather for his best girl." This adds romance to the list. The Spoonbill, we may record, was killed for money, for 'amusement,' for food, for science, and now, for love!

From these various accounts we gain the impression that during this thirty-year period there was a general feeling of the Spoonbill being a doomed species. Actually, we can see signs of recovery, at least in Texas and Louisiana. It is significant that between 1890 and 1919 more

people discussed the Spoonbill and its "perilous condition." The pendulum was rapidly swinging in the other direction. On its own, the species was shortly to gain lost ground in some quarters; in others, it was still giving way slowly and stubbornly. Growing interest in its welfare ultimately provided the necessary spadework of protection that eventually made its comeback in Texas and Louisiana a reality.

In reviewing these events, the most important fact to have in mind is that the Roseate Spoonbill is not limited in distribution to the United States. If it had been, there is no doubt that it would have become finally and irretrievably extinct before 1900.

B.   THE YEARS BETWEEN

There is little to the story of distribution from this point until the present. Spoonbills were recorded here or there, in this location and that, but the places in themselves are not especially significant. From this point on, it is the *numbers*

Plate 1.   The Spoonbill exhibits paradoxical glamour and drollery.

Plate 2.   All flights and movements from key to key were carefully recorded.

Plate 3.   Initial ecological field work was conducted at this first camp on
Bottlepoint Key, Florida (1939–40).

of Spoonbills that are of interest. How many, we want to know. We note, of course, that when birds did appear they were usually to be found in certain bays or on certain islands time after time, and we rightly suppose that these habitual rendezvous have a special importance. They are ancient nesting or roosting or feeding sites used from the very beginnings of time (Spoonbill time, that is). They exert a hereditary attraction, we like to think, or perhaps they simply provide the 'life form' that is the Spoonbill's niche, his place out of all the many types of habitat that make up our remaining wilderness areas.

The ponds and lagoons near Point Isabel, in Cameron County, Texas, are one of these locations, although the species has never nested there. The Second Chain-of-Islands, on the edge of San Antonio Bay, is a notable example, also Black Bayou in southwestern Louisiana, Bush Key in Tampa Bay, Alligator Cove on the southwest Florida coast, and the mud holes back of East Cape Sable.

It is fortunate that such areas continued to exist, continued to provide a suitable environment. All of them are still comparatively remote. Even today one can anchor a boat inside the curve of Alligator Cove and stay there for some days without another boat of any kind coming within hailing distance.

When Spoonbills began to migrate once more to the Texas coast in numbers, there were laws to protect them and wardens to enforce these laws. There were, in a very short time, sanctuaries. We must profit by our knowledge of what we may term the 'natural distribution' of the species. If we are to keep these splendid birds we must be sure that *permanent* sanctuaries are provided that encompass the more important areas in which Spoonbills naturally congregate.

In the chapter on abundance, the return of Spoonbills to a portion of the old range and their continued decline in another portion are described in detail. The place names mentioned in that discussion are the key to this natural distribution of the species.

Our job, then, is twofold: to know where these places are; and to preserve, if we can, every one of them.

C. PRESENT DISTRIBUTION: WESTERN HEMISPHERE

Evidently the Old World's first acquaintance with the Roseate Spoonbill was achieved through specimens brought back from South America and Mexico. In 1678 Francis Willoughby in his 'Ornithology' wrote of the "Brazilian Spoon-bill, called Aiaia, and by the Portuguese, Colherado" which he said was very common about the river of St. Francis and "elsewhere in Fenny places." He thought it to be the same as the "Tlauhquechul, or Mexican Spoon-bill of Hernandez." Of this second bird he simply states that it lived about the seashores and rivers.

It is entirely appropriate that this species should be recorded at this early date from South America where it is still widely distributed and where today we find important areas of apparent maximum density. The classification of the Roseate Spoonbill as *Platalea Ajaja* by Linnaeus in 1758 was based mainly on this or another early specimen from Brazil, evidently first described by Marcgrave (spelled by Willoughby: Marggrav).

The present limit of distribution of the Roseate Spoonbill to the north is approximated by a line extending through the Mexican province of Sonora; thence across Mexico in an irregular line to Texas in the vicinity of Brownsville; thence northeastward along the curving Texas Gulf coast and inland so as to pass through Colorado County; then on into Calcasieu Parish, Louisiana. Here the line breaks but is resumed again on the west coast of Florida at Tampa Bay from which point it dips southward toward Charlotte Harbor and thence across Florida at the southern end of Lake Okeechobee and northward so as to meet the Atlantic Ocean in the neighborhood of Oak Hill near Mosquito Lagoon. Spoonbills occur more or less regularly up to this line, breed along it only in Texas and Louisiana. From here to the south and east the exact position of the line is uncertain, as we do not know if it should drop southward to the Cuban coast or sweep off in a wide curve so as to take in the Bahamas. It does, however, run north of Great Inagua Island and Hispaniola. Its further progress to the north and east of the Leeward Islands and Windward group as far as Trinidad is likewise uncertain. The accompanying map indicates the approximate location of this current distribution line.

The southern limit may be approximated by another line drawn through Colchagua Province, Chili, and thence eastward across Argentina to a point in Buenos Aires State below Dolores.

The northern and southern limits of the Spoonbill's distribution are thus more than 4500 miles apart. If we consider the fact that the species wanders well to the north and south of this line, which represents in large part the limits of the breeding distribution, we may state that the Roseate Spoonbill is found in the Western Hemisphere at points 5000 miles apart.

The occurrence of wandering individuals to extreme points both north and south of the breeding range will be discussed under a separate heading. It will be enough to mention here that the Spoonbill has been recorded north to southern Wisconsin (approximately 42° N. latitude) and south to the Straits of Magellan and the Falkland Islands[10] (approximately 53° S. latitude).

We have already gone into some detail in discussing Spoonbill distribution within the United States. As already indicated, it breeds at the present time in several locations along the Gulf coast of Texas, in southwestern Louisiana, in Florida Bay and casually in a few scattered locations on the Florida mainland. I cannot at this time give a detailed account of the Spoonbill's distribution in Mexico, Central America, the West Indies, and South America. It may be useful, however, to list the following locations to the south of the United States where Spoonbills have been observed and in some cases collected. This is not a complete list. Some of these localities are known or suspected breeding colonies (indicated by *); others are merely areas or localities where the species has occurred. The accompanying map shows this distribution, the breeding locations designated by triangles, occurrence localities by dots.

Mexico

a. Laguna de San Andrés, Tamaulipas*
b. Pájaro Isleño, Laguna de Tamiahua, Vera Cruz*
c. Colony on Tamesin or Panuco River, Tamaulipas*
d. Vera Cruz (area)*

[10] Bent, 1926.

e. Guaymas, Sonora*
f. Río Moctezuma (?) (75 m. s.w. Tampico)
g. La Barca, Jalisco
h. Volcano Lake, Lower California
i. Manzanillo, Colima
j. Tlacojalpan, Vera Cruz
k. Keeno Bay, Sonora
l. Toburi Lagoon, Sonora
m. Mazatlan, Sinaloa
n. Laguna del Rodeo, Morelos
o. Tierra Caliente (State?)
p. Pantla Guerroro
q. Yucatan, Ascensión Bay and Chunyaxche Savannahs

Cuba

a. Cayo Romano, Camaguey*
b. Ciénaga de Zapata, Matanzas*
c. Cayos de los Indios (Isle of Pines) (Bond suggests: casual)*
d. Oriente Province*
e. South coast of Camaguey near Baragua*
f. (Another) South Coast of Camaguey near Baragua*
g. Camaguey Province, east of Cayo Romano (?)
h. Cayo Coco, Camaguey

Bahama Islands

a. Bimini (Bond says: formerly)
b. Great Inagua (Alfred Sound; Sheep Cay Creek)
c. Andros Island (?)

Jamaica

a. (Bond says: formerly; Peters lists with ?)

Hispaniola

a. Trou Caiman Lake, Haiti
b. Gonaive Island, (?) Haiti
c. Saona Islands, Santo Domingo

Windward Islands

a. Grenadines (Bond says: formerly)

Trinidad

a. Caroni River, ?

Guatemala

a. Hacienda California, near Ocos
b. Lake Yzabal

Nicaragua

a. San Juan del Sur
b. San Juan River

Costa Rica

a. La Palma
b. Bebedero

Honduras

a. Castilla

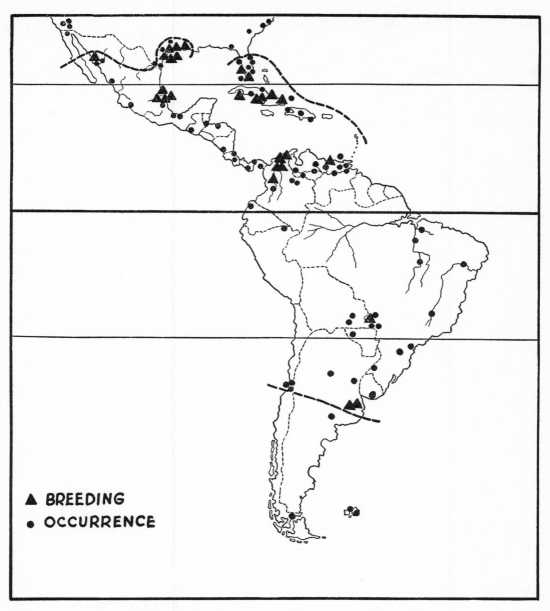

Figure 5.   Distribution of the Roseate Spoonbill in the Western Hemisphere.

Panama

   a. Rio Juan Diaz
   b. Gatun Lake

Colombia

   a. Cienaga Grande de Santa Marta*
   b. Cienaga de Guajaro*
   c. Cienaga de Manati*
   d. Cienaga de Zapayan*
   e. Cauca Valley*
   f. Brazo de Loba, Magdalena River
   g. Magangue, Magdalena River
   h. Tacaloa, Magdalena River
   i. Meta River
   j. Yumbo Valle (Cauca River)
   k. Punto Caiman (Santa Marta)
   l. Neguauge

Venezuela

   a. Laguna Tacarigua*
   b. Delta of Orinoco
   c. Rio Apure
   d. Rio Portuguesa
   e. Llanos of western Venezuela (southern portions)
   f. Calabozo (Rio Guarico)
   g. Barrancas, Monagas
   h. La Boca, Adicora
   i. El Morro
   j. Margarita Island, Nueva Esparta
   k. Isla Plata (Rio Manamo)
   l. Merida region
   m. Aruba

Ecuador

   a. Esmeraldas

Peru

   a. Rio Ucayali

Brazil

   a. Lake Gaiba, Corumba, Salobra, Cuiaba (Matto Grosso)
   b. Boavista, Rio Tocantins
   c. Rio Araguaya
   d. Para, Rio Guama
   e. Iguape and Cananea (São Paulo)
   f. Cidade de Barra (Baia); Pirapora (Minas Gerais) on Rio San Francisco
   g. Porto Epitacio, São Paulo (Rio Parana)
   h. Itaqui, Rio Grande do Sul (Rio Uruguai)

Bolivia

   a. Chaco (llanos)
   b. Buena Vista, Santa Cruz

Uruguay

   a. Laguna del Sauce

Paraguay

   a. Chaco Boreal

Chile

   a. Santiago area
   b. El Almahue, Colchagua
   c. Laguna Cauquenes, O'Higgins
   d. Province of Valparaiso

Argentina

   a. *Los Yngleses*, near Dolores, Buenos Aires State*
   b. N. w. of Dolores, Buenos Aires State*
   c. Rio Parana
   d. Cordoba

D. SUMMARY

1. The original distribution of the Roseate Spoonbill in the United States was evidently the same as it is today, except that it included a large part of the southern mainland of Florida and a portion of Louisiana that is now deserted. This distribution probably remained more or less unchanged down to about 1860–1865.

2. During the period from 1850 to 1890 the Spoonbill was virtually driven from its entire United States range. Except in a few remote locations in Florida it became a rarity in this country, a situation that reflected the rapid exploitation of unsettled Gulf coast areas after the Civil War.

3. Between 1890 and 1920 the Spoonbill's range was reduced to a minimum. If a reservoir of supply had not existed in countries to the south, it would probably have become extinct in the United States before 1900.

4. Following their virtual extirpation from Texas, Louisiana and much of Florida, Spoonbills that moved north once more to our shores have enjoyed protective laws, warden patrols and sanctuaries. The remarkable recovery in Texas is doubtless due to this protection.

5. The present range of the Roseate Spoonbill in the Western Hemisphere extends from Sonora, Mexico, the coasts of Texas and Louisiana; Tampa Bay and Mosquito Lagoon, Florida, south to Colchagua Province, Chile, and the Pampas in Buenos Aires State, Argentina.

Part II.   Abundance

1. Earliest Times to 1850

In the first Part, I reached the conclusion that Audubon's matter-of-fact comments with regard to abundance prompt us to think of the early Spoonbill colonies as flourishing and well populated. But only once does he use actual figures. In writing of the appearance of the adults following their spring molt, he says: "The sight of a flock of fifteen or twenty of these full-dressed birds is extremely pleasing to the student of nature, should he conceal himself from their view...." How much *more* pleasing would have been the sight of two or three hundred! If Audubon had seen groups larger than fifteen or twenty it seems logical that he would have mentioned it. Writing at a much later date, W. E. D. Scott (1889) repeats the accounts given to him by plume hunters who described rookeries many acres in extent in which "thousands of Roseate Spoonbills" were said to have nested.

In the light of this somewhat meager evidence, how numerous was the Spoonbill in early times? Perhaps the best evidence is to be found in the growing Spoonbill population on the Texas coast today, where present conditions and future outlook suggest rather strongly that the species occurred on that coast by the thousands when Audubon landed there in 1837.

Because Scott's reference to "thousands" of Spoonbills in Florida colonies is second hand, it loses much of its value. We are well aware of the native fisherman's tendency to be over-zealous in describing the numbers of birds, especially in his own 'back yard.' When such numbers are a matter of history, it is impossible to check on them. On the other hand, if we find ourselves convinced that Spoonbills once existed by the thousands on the Texas coast, it is bound to strike us as logical that they enjoyed contemporaneously an equal abundance in Florida.

There are additional records of a later date that suggest fairly large numbers along the Indian River on the Florida east coast and comparatively small numbers at inland locations. For various reasons it is difficult to compare these figures, and in any case, we will do no more than mention them in their proper chronological order.

2. Decline in Numbers: 1850–1890

It is not surprising that the period of decline in the fortunes of the Roseate Spoonbill went hand in hand with man's settlement of outlying portions of Florida and the Gulf coast states. This decline began somewhere in the pristine wilderness of the Florida peninsula, the Florida in which there were still great stands of cypress and long-leaf pine and vast stretches of mangrove-fringed coast that knew man only as an occasional visitor in a dugout canoe or as a transient creature who sailed by in a slow-moving sloop or schooner. The tremendous numbers of birds and other wildlife then inhabiting these wildernesses must have been a stirring spectacle. In addition to Audubon's early narratives, we have the account, already mentioned, of Edward Howe Forbush, who journeyed along the St. John's and Oklawaha rivers as late as 1877 and found "uncounted swarms of waterfowl of many species" that inhabited the water in "innumerable multitudes." Forbush mentions Spoonbills among these flocks, and a year earlier Scott reported Spoonbills as being "conspicuous" along the banks of the Oklawaha.

Few men could realize how quickly these multitudes were to disappear. Such inspiring scenes had unfolded season upon season, perhaps for a million years, unwitnessed and unappreciated by white men; and then, just as they were about to fade, at almost the very moment of their oblivion, a few small voices were raised in protest. In the darkness of past ages other scenes had flourished for a time and then withdrawn, never to reappear. In this same Florida, sabre-tooth tigers had stalked beside jungle glades, where herds of one-toed Pleistocene horses grazed and the imperial mammoth trumpeted from the nearby savanna. All of these are gone, and many others with them. Perhaps no man ever saw the terrible beauty of the Pleistocene; and if there did exist in that dim age a shambling, beetle-browed creature cast vaguely in the mold of modern man, we can be sure that his reactions to the wonders about him were not of a spiritual nature.

But 'progress' had reached the Florida wilderness as early as the 1830's. Feathers of the Roseate Spoonbill, if made into fans, could be sold for good hard cash. The Indians and runaway Negroes learned this, and Audubon's voice was the first to tell of it. Then, much later, came other protests: Bryant, Scott, Forbush. It was too late. The momentum of decline was gathering speed and size. It spread to Texas where the Spoonbill grew scarce by the 1880's and all but disappeared entirely by 1895.

The Indian River colony on Pelican Island must have been fairly large in 1858 when Dr. Bryant found the feather hunters killing as many as sixty Spoonbills in a day for their wings, which were sent to St. Augustine to be made into fans (Bryant, 1859). These fans were thus an 'article of trade' at St. Augustine for at least twenty years, probably much longer.

Taylor, it will be recalled, found the species "greatly diminished" at Pelican Island in the spring of 1861.

John Hoxie (Howell, 1932) spoke of the Spoonbill as "fairly numerous" along the Indian River in November 1888, but these may have been flocks of immature wanderers. Hoxie does not elucidate.

In Florida we get only glimpses of the colonies that inhabited Okeechobee Lake and the swamps of Brevard County before they too went 'over the hill.'

In 1874 Frederick Albion Ober, with great difficulty, reached the shores of Lake Okeechobee. This region was at that time considered to be extremely isolated. Few white men had visited it due to the swampy nature of the surrounding country and because for many years it was a land filled with hostile Indians. Soldiers had crossed the lake on two occasions during the Indian War of 1835–43. In the war of 1856–58, forts or military stations were built near it. It seems possible that the lake and its shores were pretty thoroughly explored, but only one record remains of these explorations. In 1842, during the Seminole War, an expedition under the United States

Navy, consisting of eighty-three sailors and marines with a few Indians and one Negro crossed Lake Okeechobee, paddling in sixteen canoes along the southern and western shores as far as the Kissimmee River. One of the party, Midshipman George Henry Preble, kept a diary that was published many years later (Preble, 1905). On March 6, at Fisheating Creek, Preble saw "immense flocks of Cranes, Pink Spoonbills, Curlew and Wild Turkeys in plenty." By cranes he doubtless meant herons and the curlews were, of course, ibises. In 1855 the state engineer of Florida, in writing of the country around Lake Okeechobee said: "These lands are now, and will continue to be, nearly as much unknown as the interior of Africa, or the mountain sources of the Amazon" (Ober, 1874). This gentleman may have been a good engineer but he wasn't much of a prophet.

When Ober and his party reached the lake in 1874, they spent five weeks "in exploring every inlet and bayou." On Goodshore Island (now Observation Island), they saw several Roseate Spoonbills and found *two breeding pairs*. We do not know if this represented the primeval condition of the Spoonbill in the Okeechobee area or whether the decline in numbers was already under way, begun possibly, during military expeditions between 1856 and 1858. Ober was told by the Seminoles that Spoonbills bred "abundantly" on Fisheating Creek, which flows into the lake about midway along its west shore. It is evident that Ober did not find this colony nor did he mention the presence of Spoonbills at this location. Possibly the "Pink Spoonbills" seen by Midshipman Preble in 1842 were no longer there.

In the same year of 1874, Frederick Tingley Jencks was in Brevard County north and east of Lake Okeechobee on a collecting trip, the object of which appeared to be the taking of specimens of the Roseate Spoonbill. Jencks had provided himself with native guides who were familiar with the location of Spoonbill colonies. He had small hope of a successful trip, however, because he realized that the species was already growing scarce. Jencks talked to a member of another party who told him that "their destruction had been so great that probably not 100 remained in Florida." Jencks believed him, although this figure was obviously an exaggeration.

Being primarily a collector, Jencks determined to take as many clutches of eggs and as many skins as he could secure. He even shot adult birds as they sat on their nests! Each day he collected as many birds as stayed within gunshot, going back again and again until no Spoonbills remained in either of the two colonies visited. A total of eleven adults were taken from the colony in Seventeen Mile Swamp and fifteen from the colony up-river near Lake Poinsett. We have no record to indicate that either of these colonies survived such slaughter.

The total number of twenty-six birds collected by Jencks does not at first glance suggest very large nesting groups. On the other hand, it seems likely that a Spoonbill flock will scatter pretty widely after the first shot; and there must have been a good many Spoonbills present to permit him to secure that many birds. In addition to the skins taken, others were shot which fell into the water and were devoured by alligators.

We have already mentioned that another collector, Horace A. Kline, found a few Spoonbills on the shores of Wakulla County. This was in May and June of 1886, and only a small number was observed, the largest group being a flock of fifteen. There is no evidence that there was a nesting colony in that area. Kline's account gives ample proof of the value that the collector of that day placed upon even a single Spoonbill skin. The first group that he approached was a flock of five that alighted on the edge of an island a few hundred yards off and commenced feeding. He wrote:

By looking carefully we see that they are the most beautiful species of the south, one that we have tried many times to capture—Roseate Spoonbills. The sail is lowered once more and a paddle substituted, and we approach carefully. They seemed to pay very little attention to us so intent were they feeding. To my dismay I discovered I had forgotten all the heavy shot at the camp except the two loads I fired at the Pelicans, and had nothing but No. 6's. It was too dark for a successful shot with the rifle. They let us approach within 50 yards before flying. As they arose, I fired two shots but to no avail and we would have to be contented by thinking how nearly we had come to killing a Roseate Spoonbill.

Mr. Kline was not to be outdone, however; that night he slept in his boat, thinking that more Spoonbills would show up the next morning. He did secure a single specimen, describing his success with considerable enthusiasm.

As he passed within 30 yards a charge of No. 6 caused him to reel in the air; but catching his balance, he started to move on when a charge from the second barrel brought him to the earth. I shall never forget how we admired him as he lay dead. His bright rose colored wings, delicate pink breast and back, snowy white neck, bald head and wondrous bill. Many a time have ladies in looking over my birds here exclaimed, "Oh, how lovely you have got that pink bird colored!"

If we take the words of such observers as Jencks and Kline at their face value, we get the impression that by 1890 the Spoonbill must have disappeared entirely from Florida, as it very nearly had in Texas by that date. Such an assumption would overlook two facts: (1) the Spoonbill is migratory and the population curve climbs upward with each spring and summer; (2) certain colonies and concentration localities were still isolated enough to be generally unknown (Big Cypress, Alligator Lake, etc.). It is clearly evident, however, that the species had lost a vast majority of its breeding range by 1890.

3. Minimum Numbers: 1890–1919

Obviously it is impossible for us to know even approximately the number of breeding pairs of Spoonbills that remained in the United States during the poorest season of this present period; but we can form an estimate of this figure. There is a good deal of published data, and evidently there were but few portions of the range that were not inspected at one time or another during these years.

We are reasonably certain that there were no breeding Spoonbills in Texas during this period. In Louisiana there was evidently a small colony in the southwest part of the state, at least during the first decade of the period; but two decimating factors were known to be in operation; and these probably resulted in the absence of breeding birds there during 'the poorest season' between about 1900 and 1920. These factors were: (1) collectors, and (2) the erratic, uncertain nature of this colony at the northernmost breeding location.

More properly, this second factor is an 'influence,' but however we classify it the fact remains that it can limit distribution and numbers.

Bent and Job visited Alligator Lake in 1903 and found an immense colony of many species, including "large numbers" of breeding Spoonbills. However, as the Spoonbill had very nearly deserted Alligator Lake by 1924, we can assume that in the 'poorest season' between 1890 and 1919 there were no more than a half dozen nests. Estimates for Cuthbert Lake and Bottlepoint Key have some basis in fact, although it is conceivable that Spoonbills may not have nested in these locations every year. To the best of our knowledge the species deserted the Corkscrew rookery and Okaloacoochee Slough prior to 1919.

Thus, during the poorest season there may have been no more than three Florida colonies and an aggregate total of twenty to twenty-five nests in all of the United States.

Our concept of abundance during these thirty years should quite properly stem from a consideration of breeding pairs alone. From these figures we gain a true picture of the seriousness of the situation. A majority of other records of occurrence was made up of birds that had no connection with breeding activities. Large flocks of 'summer birds' were still to be seen in Texas in 1891, when Samuel N. Rhoads estimated 600 at the mouth of the Nueces River on May 28. He remarked that "none have been known to breed on the Texas coast of late years," and considered that the birds he observed were "raised somewhere on the coast south of Brownsville." Even these postnuptial wanderers must have discontinued their annual visits to Texas soon after this date, for there is a long gap in the records from 1891 to 1920. Rhoads tells us the reason for this: "The reception accorded these birds by Corpus Christi gunners is far from encouraging."

The following list presents a chronological record of numbers of Spoonbills observed in Florida during this period as reported in the literature or in unpublished reports.

1891..........................3 (1)
1895..........................1 (2)
1896..........................40 to 50 (3)
1896 (circa)....................several hundred (?) (4)

1901..........................1 (5)
1903..........................12 (3 nests) (6)
1903..........................1 large colony (100 nests?) (7)
1904..........................1 (8)
1905..........................8 (9)
1906..........................40 (10)
1907..........................18 (11)
1908..........................30 to 40 (12)
1912..........................165 (13)
1912..........................50 (14)
1913..........................112 (15)
1913..........................about 50 (16)
1913..........................10 (17)
1914..........................147 (18)
1914..........................30 to 40 (19)
1914..........................50 (20)
1915..........................63 (21)
1916..........................12 (22)
1916..........................29 (23)
1917..........................80 (24)
1917..........................1 (25)
1917..........................6 (26)
1918..........................30 (27)

1. (Pearson, *in litt.*)	12. (Chapman, 1908)	20. (Rhett Green, unpublished)
2. (Butler, 1930b)	13. (Howell, 1932)	21. (Pearson, 1915)
3. (Pearson, 1897)	14. (Rhett Green, unpublished)	22. (Howell, 1932)
4. (Hoyt, 1906)	15. (Howell, 1932)	23. (Rhett Green, unpublished)
5. (Butler, 1930b)	16. (Phelps, 1914)	24. (Howell, 1932)
6. (Dutcher, 1904)	17. (Rhett Green, unpublished)	25. (Butler, 1930a)
7. (Dutcher, 1904)	18. (Pearson, 1914)	26. (Ellis, 1917)
8. (Fowler, 1906)	19. (Kennard, 1915)	27. (Howell, 1932)
9. (Job, 1905)		
10. (Hoyt, 1906)		
11. (Bowdish, 1909)		

Several items in this list require special comment. The forty to fifty birds observed by Pearson were in Tampa Bay and may have been summer wanderers. Pearson did not find any nesting Spoonbills. Hoyt's figures are simply his recollection of the numbers observed around Old Tampa Bay about 1896. These seem to have been quite definitely summering birds, probably immatures for the most part. The large colony mentioned for 1903 was at Alligator Lake.

Figures for 1912 represent two groups, the larger having been observed on Indian Key in Tampa Bay, and the smaller in the Corkscrew rookery. P. J. Pacetti, who reported the Indian Key colony, said that there were eighty-five Spoonbills nesting at this location. A later report by Warden Pillsbury stated that eighty young were raised. It is not clear if eighty-five pairs or eighty-five individuals were seen by Pacetti. Probably a total of eighty-five Spoonbills was counted or estimated on the key, and the eighty young suggest a total of about thirty nests. The thirty-seven young counted on the Marquesas Keys and on Boca Grande Key by Warden Ashe would indicate about a dozen nests at these two places.

Of the 147 birds listed by Pearson in 1914, sixty-five adults and twenty-five young were located in the Corkscrew rookery, apparently the only Spoonbill colony under warden protection at that time. All of the figures for 1914 and 1915 refer to this same rookery.

The eighty Spoonbills reported by Howell for 1917 were observed along Mosquito Lagoon during the summer by "a local hunter." What this unnamed individual was hunting for in the summer months was not stated. In 1929, Mrs. S. W. Sweett of New Smyrna reported to Amos W. Butler (1930a) that a flock of about 150 Spoonbills was said to have been present in the Mosquito Lagoon region around 1893. Mrs. Sweett made this report on the authority of Wallace Cook, who had been warden for the Canaveral Club. It is difficult to decide where to draw the line in accepting bird counts from untrained observers, especially when the observation is a quarter of a century old.

From the point of view of abundance, this period is quite definitely one in which the Spoonbill was at its lowest ebb in the United States. As mentioned in my discussion of distribution, we cannot with certainty put a finger on the precise event or situation that brought about the desertion of each individual colony. In our record of actual numbers of birds observed, however, we have something quite tangible, lacking only our cautious interpretation to provide us with abundant signposts indicating both the way out and, perhaps, the way back.

Obviously it is of the utmost importance for us to learn why Spoonbills ceased to nest on the Marquesas Keys, on Boca Grande Key, on Indian Key in Tampa Bay, in Alligator Lake, Cuthbert Lake, the Corkscrew rookery, and Okaloacoochee Slough—all of them having been deserted as breeding locations. On the face of it, causes for desertion appear easy enough to describe, but how can we be sure that we are right? What I have

done is attempt to learn in the field why these areas were chosen or used as nesting sites in the first place, and further along in this report I will discuss the relationship of the Spoonbill to its environment and under that heading an attempt will be made to answer these important questions.

B. RECOVERY IN TEXAS AND LOUISIANA: 1920–1941

In evaluating published records of bird observations we must take into account the ever-present possibility that many gaps in the record may sometimes be caused by a total absence of ornithologists from the area during certain months and years. The compiler risks the error committed by the bird student whose peaks of migration abundance coincided with week-end dates! In spite of the occasional lack of published reports, the fact remains that the Spoonbill reappeared in ever-growing numbers on the Texas coast during the 1920's, and since then has increased steadily right up to the present time. In this same period the Spoonbill also returned as a breeding species in both Texas and Louisiana. Although we do not know exactly when this upward trend began, we are perfectly aware of when it became apparent, and we can recognize the aptness of certain factors that appear to have contributed to this recovery.

1. Return in Texas

For many years Spoonbill flocks, generally of inconsequential size, had been reported from the vicinity of Point Isabel near Brownsville. These flocks were generally thought to be immature birds, plus a small percentage of adults, that had wandered north along the Gulf coast after the breeding season in Mexico (Bent, 1926). After some thirty 'lean years' and beginning with the 1920's, these flocks increased in the total number of birds involved. Shooting of plume birds along the coastal areas of Texas had become a thing of the past, and through the years, as the pioneer settlers became established on farms and ranches, the number of meat hunters gradually diminished. Coupled with these events was a growing consciousness on the part of the general public that birds were deserving of protection. Furthermore, the presence of wardens and increased legal restrictions on hunting tended to reduce indiscriminate gunning.

The part that Mexican colonies played in this recovery of Texas Spoonbills is not certain, but their role would seem to have been of paramount importance. Presumably remote colonies on the Mexican Gulf coast were successful enough to send once more a regular overflow of post-breeding-season flocks northward to the Texas islands and lagoons. It is also possible that certain Mexican colonies were so much disturbed that birds from them fled northward to Texas in search of safer nesting locations. That this latter explanation is not altogether baseless is attested by the large-scale nesting of White Pelicans in Laguna Madre, Texas, in the spring of 1941, following the reported breaking-up of a nesting group of this same species on the Mexican coast in Laguna de la Madre, south of the Rio Grande.

Whatever the factors involved, we have an unmistakable record of this recovery in the published accounts and reports of numerous observers. To consider Texas alone, we have only to glance back through our present discussion prior to 1920 to appreciate the significance of observations made in May and June 1920 by T. Gilbert Pearson and the William L. Finleys (Pearson, 1921). Between May 24 and June 2, this party traveled from Matagorda Bay to Point Isabel and counted Spoonbills in nine separate flocks, totaling 179 individuals. They may have missed other groups north of Matagorda Bay, particularly in the vicinity of Galveston Bay where local observers were beginning to see more and more of these birds and suspect the presence of nesting colonies (Bessie M. Reid, *in litt.*).

It was significant, as proved by later events, that all save eleven of the Spoonbills observed by the Pearson-Finley party were located between Matagorda Bay and Aransas Pass. All told, eighty of the total number of Spoonbills were seen at or near the Second Chain-of-Islands, which a few years later was to become the site of the greatest Spoonbill nesting colony in the United States.

In May of the following year, J. R. Pemberton journeyed to the Reddish Egret colony that had already been described by Dr. Pearson on Green Island in Laguna Madre. Just before he left Green Island, a flock of fifty Spoonbills arrived and settled on a shallow bar off the north end of the island (Pemberton, 1922). It is probable that Spoonbills had been coming to this same place for some years, chiefly during the period from late April to September, with numerical peaks during July or August. The writer has observed them there on several occasions and most of them are immature birds.

In 1923 there were several expeditions to the Texas coast. Early in that year Ludlow Griscom and Maunsell Crosby were in the Brownsville region, but they were too early to see the Spoonbill flocks; nevertheless they recorded the birds as being regular and often common summer visitors in that area (Griscom and Crosby, 1925).

Arthur Cleveland Bent found a large flock of Spoonbills that "consistently frequented the chain of islands between Mesquite and San Antonio Bays on May 15 and 16" (1923). He wrote: "We spent some time chasing them from one island to another, but could not drive them away from that vicinity." This was the Second Chain-of-Islands; in June of that same year, George Finlay Simmons evidently found the species nesting there and described what he took to be Spoonbill nests on the ground[11] (Bent, 1926).

Bent also went to the Vingt'un Islands that same year, but did not find Spoonbills nesting (*in litt.*, September 8, 1935). However, he did locate a nesting colony in Victoria County "in an immense tract of swamps and heavily forested country in the lowlands along the Guadalupe River." We do not know how many years elapsed between the last definite nesting record in Texas and the year 1923. Dresser wrote that in 1864 they had ceased to breed on Galveston Island. Merrill and Sennett did not find them nesting in the Brownsville region in 1877. Benners found them scarce on the Nueces River in 1884 and failed to locate a colony. He was told that there were 'colonies' on the Brazos River, but this was not substantiated. Nehrling (1882) did not find evidence of nesting.

---

[11] This is the only American colony in my experience where the Spoonbill nests on the ground.

The species occasionally wandered inland at this time, a sign of increasing numbers perhaps, and during the wet year of 1926 one was observed near Kingsville (Eifrig, 1930).

In 1928 James J. Carroll found Spoonbills nesting on the Second Chain-of-Islands; with the interests of the birds at heart, he told no one of his discovery. Meanwhile, the Guadalupe River colony was deserted, possibly because it was disturbed by collectors,[12] and these same birds may have been responsible for the nesting of the species on the Second Chain (subsequently, at Mr. Carroll's request, the Second Chain was made an Audubon sanctuary in 1934).

Thereafter, Spoonbill stocks on the Texas coast showed a steady gain. They nested on the Vingt'-un Islands in Galveston Bay where an exploring party of the Outdoor Nature Club of Houston found nests on June 8, 1931 (Bull. 1, Outdoor Nature Club of Houston, 1931). This location was established in 1932 as an Audubon sanctuary. In June 1931 flocks of nonbreeding birds near the delta of the Arroyo Colorado, a few miles from the Society's Green Island Sanctuary in Laguna Madre, totaled no less than 500 birds (*Bird-Lore*, 1931, p. 484). In May 1934, the writer traveled from Galveston Bay to lower Laguna Madre and at seven locations counted a total of 879 Spoonbills (Allen, 1935).

In the twenty years since 1923, there have been seven Texas breeding locations occupied by Roseate Spoonbills. The list is as follows:

1. Guadalupe River bottoms....1923
2. Second Chain-of-Islands......1928 to 1941 (inclusive)
3. Vingt'un Islands............1930 to 1941 (inclusive)
4. Hynes Bay Island...........1935, 1936, 1937, 1938, 1941
5. Ayres Island................1938, 1939
6. Green Marsh................1939, 1940, 1941 (?)
7. Colorado River bottoms......1940, 1941 (?)

Down to the present time, the National Audubon Society has established sanctuaries at Vingt'-un Islands (now a Texas State Sanctuary with an Audubon warden in charge), Second Chain-of-Islands, Ayres Island and Hynes Bay Island. In addition, feeding grounds and other concen-

---

[12] Bent's account of this colony was published in 1926 (Bull. 135, U. S. Nat. Mus.).

tration areas used by Spoonbills are included in Audubon sanctuaries at Green Island (in Laguna Madre), Crane Islands (near Corpus Christi Pass), Lydia Ann Island (at the lower end of Aransas Bay), and islands at the western end of Copano Bay (Swan Lake). The Society also maintains a warden patrol in Cameron County, including the Bahia Grande area near Brownsville where large flocks of Spoonbills congregate in the late summer and fall.

With the increase of Spoonbills along the Texas coast, there have been reports of numbers of birds in areas where they have not been seen before, or from which only a few individuals had been previously recorded. Mrs. Robert J. Kleberg, Jr. (*in litt.*), reports that her husband observed 300 Spoonbills on September 25, 1940, on the Rincon de la Salle, which is about forty miles south of Corpus Christi on the edge of Laguna Madre, and approximately midway along the length of the Laguna between Corpus Christi Bay and the mouth of the Arroyo Colorado.

Other areas where Spoonbills have recently been seen in fair numbers are located in the general vicinity of Rockport. At Red Fish Point on Copano Bay, Spoonbills drop in regularly to feed in tidal ponds. Farther west, close to Rincon de la Cera, large numbers of Spoonbills were observed by Mrs. Jack Hagar and the writer in June 1941. These birds were feeding on marshy islands on the edge of Swan Lake, islands now incorporated in an Audubon sanctuary. They have been using this area for some time and appear to be coming for the most part from the Second Chain-of-Islands and from the Mission Bay region.

An interesting winter record was the presence of five Spoonbills near Mission, Texas, January 1, 1940. These birds were seen by Mr. Hale and reported by Irby Davis (*Bird-Lore*, 1940, p. 222).

The discovery of two breeding colonies in Matagorda County in 1939 and 1940 was not only a gratifying extension of the breeding distribution of the Spoonbills, but also may have constituted return of this species to fresh-water habitats. These two areas are Green Marsh (Hawkins Ranch), where the presence of nesting Spoonbills was first reported by the Texas Game, Fish and

Oyster Commission, and an island in the Colorado River bottoms located by the writer with the aid of State Warden Van Harris of Bay City.

Another location where Spoonbills have been observed is Lydia Ann Island just north of Aransas Pass. On this island, which is an Audubon sanctuary, the writer counted 340 Spoonbills on June 3, 1940. A great many of these birds were in immature plumage, and they were using the island simply as a feeding place.

Twenty years ago Pearson and the Finleys saw 179 Spoonbills in six scattered locations on the Texas coast, but none of the birds were nesting. Now they are not only nesting in at least four Texas colonies, but the locations where they can be seen are innumerable. The greatest recovery has taken place since 1930, with a really amazing impetus over the last five years. In midsummer the 1941 population in Texas alone reached more than 5000 Roseate Spoonbills. This is one of the most remarkable recoveries in the history of wildlife protection in this country, and the establishment of Audubon sanctuaries on the Texas coast since 1931 has been a major factor.

2. *Return in Louisiana*

In Louisiana irregular records of Spoonbill occurrence and nesting had been reported over a period of some years. Except for one or two reports, the species does not seem to have been observed in recent times outside of Calcasieu and Cameron Parishes in the southwestern portion of the state. The only nesting reported beyond these two parishes was in 1887 on Bayou Sara in West Feliciana Parish, which is up the Mississippi nearly thirty miles north of Baton Rouge (Oberholser, 1938).

In 1920, T. Gilbert Pearson visited Bird Island on May 18. This location is in Cameron Parish on the Cameron Farm some fourteen miles south of Vinton. It is south of the old Black Bayou colony where no Spoonbills were reported that year. At Bird Island he counted 104 Spoonbills and examined five[13] of their nests. He has told me that there were probably additional nests.

In 1925, E. S. Hopkins observed two Spoonbills on the Paul J. Rainey Wildlife Sanctuary in Vermillion Parish (Oberholser, 1938). The following year Mr. Hopkins collected an early set of Great Horned Owl eggs in Black Bayou (which he called "Bayou Black")[14] and, in his report of this in *The Oölogist* (1926), mentioned the bird colony there and expressed the hope that he might get back in the spring and collect a few eggs!

A. M. Bailey and E. G. Wright (1931) observed "a small band" of Spoonbills in the general locality of Bird Island on November 1, 1928. There were no nests. In 1930 these same observers were at Bird Island, apparently during the nesting season, but they did not see a single Spoonbill.

In a list of sanctuaries of the National Audubon Society published in *The Florida Naturalist* (1931, p. 11), Alden H. Hadley mentions that as many as 300 Spoonbills were reported from the Lake Charles area.

In 1932 T. Gilbert Pearson and Ernest G. Holt investigated bird colonies in Louisiana. On May 22 at Bird Island, they found ten nests "positively ascribed to the Spoonbill" (Holt, *unpublished report*). Edward Woods, who was with the party, counted fifty Roseate Spoonbills. In 1935 there is no record that the species nested in Louisiana, although on June 10, George H. Lowery, Jr., saw seventeen birds at Johnson Bayou in Cameron Parish (Oberholser, 1938).

The writer visited the site of the nesting colony near Black Bayou in 1934 without seeing a single Spoonbill. I again went there in July 1940. According to Messrs. Landry and Bienvenu of the Stanolind Oil and Gas Company, there must have been at least twenty-three occupied nests that season; although at the time of my visit the birds had finished nesting and departed. Several of the nests were observed, however, and the remains of Spoonbill eggs that had hatched were examined. This location is in an island of

---

[13] Through a printer's error this is given as "75 nests" in *Bird-Lore*, 22: 259. It is correctly reported in *The Auk*, 28 (4): 516 (1921).

[14] It is not always certain which of the two nesting sites in southwestern Louisiana are referred to by different observers; both sites are near Black Bayou but in different parishes. The one referred to as Bird Island is evidently that south of Vinton in Cameron Parish, and the other is north along the same bayou but in Calcasieu Parish.

mixed growth in the midst of a wet marsh some five miles east of Black Bayou proper and two miles south of the Calcasieu Parish line.

It may be well to add here two records from outside the usual range of the Spoonbill. One of these is for Alabama, a section of the Gulf coast where Spoonbills have not been seen very often. An adult was collected June 1, 1930, by Oliver Ladnier on Dauphin Island at the mouth of Mobile Bay (Edwards, 1930). It will be recalled that there were early records for this state reported by Nuttall and the two birds taken were shot on this same Dauphin Island in 1897.

California records have also been scarce, although Dawson (1923) seemed to believe that they might establish themselves in the Colorado valley if birds moving in there from Mexico were left to their own devices. He blamed the shooting of specimens for the fact that they do not establish themselves as breeders, but this seems an over-optimistic view of their abundance. J. R. Pemberton (1927), in describing a single Spoonbill collected at Salton Sea on May 20, 1927, writes: "This is apparently the first specimen of this species ever actually taken in California." They must still be considered a comparatively rare visitor in that state.

I have mentioned the possible role of Mexican colonies and of public point of view in the return of the Spoonbill to Texas. Probably these same factors had an important hand in the return of the species to Louisiana. Unfortunately a dearth of actual data prevents a more adequate discussion of the many factors that may have contributed directly and indirectly to this situation. We can be sure that once again there is a correlation between human events and viewpoints and the fortunes of the Roseate Spoonbill. I believe that this correlation should be emphasized because it illustrates a very important point: since man has come upon the scene, the bird and its environment have been subjected to factors and influences that are largely artificial. To quote Aldo Leopold:[15] "Every head of wildlife still alive in this country is already artificialized, in that its existence is conditioned by economic forces." It is important

───────
[15] 1933, p. 21.

that we recognize this fact when we attempt to interpret the Spoonbill's place in our avifauna, and especially when we plan for its further recovery.

C. CONTINUED DECLINE IN FLORIDA: 1920–1941

At the same time the Roseate Spoonbill was staging a recovery along the Texas coast and showing an improvement in Louisiana, it entered upon a further period of decline in Florida. Actually, this decline may be considered as simply a continuation of its long and gradual loss of ground on the Florida peninsula.

The history of these changes in relative abundance of the Spoonbill has been confused from time to time by the presence each summer of fairly large numbers of Spoonbills on the west coast, and of scattered individuals elsewhere on the mainland. It is necessary to belabor the point that a vast majority of the individuals in these 'summer flocks' are birds of immature plumage, evidently postnuptial wanderers from Cuba or elsewhere to the south. More will be said of them in other portions of this report; in this discussion of abundance the reader should clearly distinguish between actual breeding records and the mere occurrence of flocks and individuals that are predominantly juvenile.

By 1920 the Spoonbill had been shoved into the mangrove wilderness at the southernmost tip of the Florida peninsula, where a few pairs continued to nest irregularly at Alligator Lake and on the island in Cuthbert Lake. There was also a small isolated colony in Florida Bay, but this was not discovered until some years later. In these two decades since 1920, there have been more than a few reports of nesting, some of which may very well be authentic. Unfortunately, it has not been possible to investigate many of these reports, but on the basis of first-hand information regarding some of them, it seems likely that such nesting as has occurred has included only a few scattered pairs that have joined colonies of herons and ibises during the nesting season. Breeding records of this type do not represent a truly significant re-establishment of the Spoonbill as a nesting species in Florida. Only a nest or two are concerned; the locations are widely separated; and

years elapse without a repetition at the same location. This is quite a different situation from that
in Texas, where *all* breeding groups disappeared
in a short space of time and then returned as distinct colonies that rapidly became well established.

It will be helpful if we divide south Florida into
various sections in discussing this particular period. These sections are as follows (see accompanying map):

1. The Florida east coast from Oak Hill to Micco.
2. The Lake Okeechobee vicinity.
3. The Tampa Bay vicinity.
4. The southwest coast from Charlotte Harbor to
   Cape Sable.
5. The area from East Cape Sable to Cuthbert Lake,
   including Alligator Lake.
6. Florida Bay and the Florida keys.

There is also one isolated record for the region
west of the Apalachicola. F. F. Gander saw three
Spoonbills near Blountstown, June 27, 1928 (Weston, 1929).

1. East Coast Region

The return of Spoonbills to the region between
Oak Hill and Micco is especially interesting in view
of the fact that there were once breeding colonies
along the Indian River and in the marshes of Brevard County. Two or three Spoonbills were observed feeding along the Indian River near Cocoa
by Benjamin Redditt. This was in June of 1923
or 1924 (Nicholson, 1929). Along about this
same time, Spoonbills were seen in Mosquito
Lagoon near Oak Hill by Wallace Cook (Butler,
1930a). In June 1927 a Spoonbill was killed on
a highway east of Oak Hill by a motor truck
(Longstreet, 1929).

There were also Spoonbills observed in the
vicinity of Merritt's Island. On September 18,
1932, Benjamin C. Hiatt saw six adult Spoonbills
at this location (Hiatt, 1933). The following
May, Wray Nicholson and Charles Ross counted
seventeen Spoonbills on Merritt's Island, about
five miles east of Wilson. They were very shy,
flying when the observers were within 100 yards.
They rose out of a small salt pond, circled about
to a good height, and flew northwest (Nicholson,
1933). In September of 1933, R. J. Longstreet
saw a single Spoonbill in the Brevard Reservation
opposite Titusville. Warden W. E. Shannon had

seen four Spoonbills at the same place a few days
previous (Longstreet, 1933).

According to Charles R. Dawson, Spoonbills
have been observed in recent years in Seminole
County. He does not give details (Dawson,
1937). At Puzzle Lake, between the St. John's
River and the east-coast town of Mimms, a single
Spoonbill was seen by several people in July and
August 1936 (Mason, 1937). Three of the birds
were also seen in the Brevard Reservation that
same year, but the month is not mentioned (Woodhead, 1938). George Carter of Cocoa stated that
a single pair of Spoonbills nested among herons,
ibises and pelicans on a small island north of
Cocoa Beach in 1938 (Cadbury, *in litt.*). This
record was not substantiated.

2. Lake Okeechobee Region

The appearance of Spoonbills on the shores of
Lake Okeechobee reminds us that the species once
nested on Observation Island (Goodshore Island)
and also very likely along Fisheating Creek. In
the summer of 1923, W. R. Collins reported a
flock of seventeen at a point six miles north of
Okeechobee City, apparently on Taylor's Creek.
This same observer likewise saw a Spoonbill within
a few miles of Indiantown (Howell, 1932). In
1927 "an intelligent Seminole Indian" told Donald J. Nicholson of a nesting colony that included
Spoonbills on Fish Eating Lake in Hendry County
south of La Belle. Nicholson visited this location
in March of the following year, but saw no birds
there. However, it was a dry season and in his
opinion a lack of water prevented the birds from
nesting (Nicholson, 1929).

Henry Redding reported Spoonbills breeding on
a small lake in Palm Beach County in March 1928
(Nicholson, 1929). This report was not investigated.

The chief engineer in charge of the canal locks
at Moore Haven, Fred A. Flanders, has seen six
Spoonbills in the Lake Okeechobee and Caloo-
sahatchie areas over the past ten years (Flanders,
in litt.). Three "brilliantly colored" Spoonbills
were observed by him feeding in a slough three
miles north of Moore Haven in September or October 1931. They were quite tame and stayed
in the vicinity for several days. In November

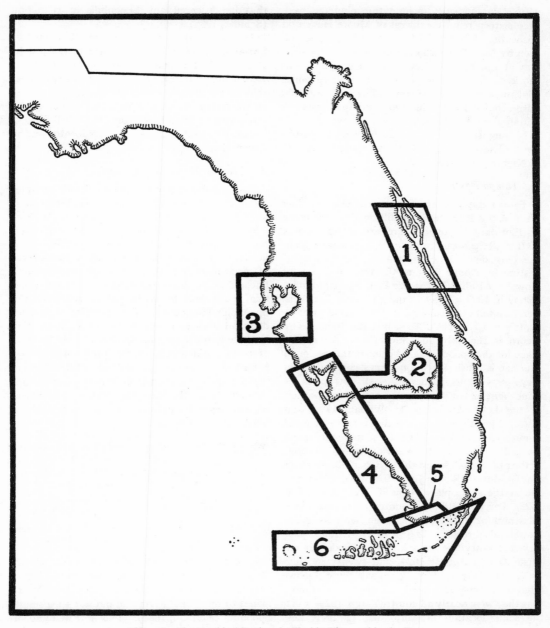

Figure 6. Geographical Regions in Florida Discussed in the Text.

1. Oak Hill to Micco
2. Lake Okeechobee Area
3. Tampa Bay Area
4. Charlotte Harbor to Cape Sable
5. East Cape to Cuthbert Lake
6. Florida Bay and Florida Keys

1936, two, evidently in immature plumage, were seen sixteen miles northwest of Moore Haven on Fisheating Creek. The most recent Spoonbill seen by Mr. Flanders was feeding along the highway at a place known locally as Nigger Jim Hammock, a location approximately twelve miles southwest of Moore Haven. The bird was 100 yards south of the road with a group of approximately fifty Wood Ibises.

In August 1940, Frank Cothern of Clewiston (*in litt.*) saw a Spoonbill about one-half mile east of Nigger Jim Hammock.

3. Tampa Bay Region

Tampa Bay is at the former northern breeding limit of the Roseate Spoonbill on the west coast of Florida. Although there are many records of the species' occurrence in that general region, the only definite description of the Spoonbills' nesting in Tampa Bay is the one given us by Howell for Indian Key where P. J. Pacetti found a colony in 1912. It seems quite certain that there were a number of colonies in that region prior to Scott's visits in the 1880's, but the Indian Key record is the only one since then. A favorite place for the Spoonbills that come to this region in summer is Bush Key, sometimes called Tarpon Key. Spoonbills gather in a shallow pond of some eight or ten acres in the east-central portion of the key. According to William G. Fargo (1926), Spoonbills appear in this vicinity in small numbers during April and become more numerous by July. He found no evidence of nesting. Arthur H. Howell found thirty Spoonbills on Bush Key in May 1918. In June 1922, Pacetti counted 143 at the same place (Howell, 1932). In May 1923, Perry Wetmore counted fifty-one birds there and forty the following June (Howell, 1932). Howell also records that Warden Bennett observed seventy-five to a hundred Spoonbills on Bush Key in August 1924, and twenty in July 1927. On May 1, 1928, Fargo saw forty Spoonbills on the Bush Key pond and was of the opinion that they were nearly all adults (Fargo, 1929). At the same location in May 1930, Francis Lee Jaques observed from forty to fifty Spoonbills (Howell, 1932). Fred W. Schultz was at Bush Key on August 4, 1935, but does not mention

that he observed any Spoonbills at that time (Schultz, 1936).

Dr. H. R. Mills has written me that fourteen Spoonbills were observed on Bush Key, April 18, 1941, and thirty-nine on May 15. These counts were made by William Lehman. I have also been told of the observation of fifty-three Spoonbills on the Indian Key reservation on May 30 of this same year. Both Bush Key and Bird Key, or Indian Key as it is also known, are located on this reservation.

4. Charlotte Harbor to Cape Sable

Perhaps the greatest nesting colonies occupied by Roseate Spoonbills down to the 1860's were located along the west coast of Florida from Charlotte Harbor to Cape Sable. Although there has been very little in the way of Spoonbill nesting activity there since those early days, this stretch of coast, more than a hundred miles in a straight line and many times that distance in actual coastline, is still host to the largest concentrations of Spoonbills that occur in Florida today. It seems doubtful if there has been any great fluctuation in these numbers during the last decade, in spite of certain differences in the total numbers reported by various observers. The following records from the literature describe observations through 1931, the year the National Audubon Society began its present intensive patrol of the southwest-coast area.

1921 (circa)—Pavilion Key.....many Spoonbills roosting (Nicholson, 1929).

1929—Goodland Point Road....three Spoonbills observed (August) (Kuerzi, 1931).

1930—Marco area.............large numbers of Spoonbills (Winecoff, 1930). (June)

1931—Marco area.............from 15 to 200 reported (Mitchell, 1931).

In January and February 1931, Dr. W. C. Herman traveled by auto and boat from Collier City to Key West and along the Gulf from Everglades to the Shark River and did not see a single Spoonbill (Herman, 1931). It is now well known that Spoonbills observed on the west coast are likely to be seen only during the period from April through October, inclusive, although they some-

Plate 4. A six-week-old youngster learns to feed in the sheltered pools of Bottlepoint Key, Florida.

Plate 5. An important place in the Spoonbill's food niche—shallow mangrove pools where it was possible to catch two or three quarts of fish after a short haul with a seine.

Plate 6. The route to Cuthbert Lake, Florida, showing typical red mangrove barrier.

times remain in the vicinity of East Cape Sable into December.

Audubon wardens in 1932 spent considerable time locating Spoonbill concentrations on this coast and searching for possible nesting colonies. J. V. Kelsey of the United States Fish and Wildlife Service (*Bird-Lore*, 1932, p. 106) reported large numbers of this species but said that they shifted their locations so frequently that they were hard to keep track of and therefore hard to protect.

In May 1933, Ernest G. Holt, then with the National Audubon Society, visited the southwest coast of Florida and observed 174 Spoonbills in the following locations:

Pink Curlew Flats (May 16)...............23
Blue Hill Bay (May 16)...................114
Alligator Cove (May 4)...................35
Lane River rookery (May 6–7)...............2

Audubon wardens reported four occupied Spoonbill nests in the Shark River rookery and twelve in the Lane River rookery that same year. Holt did not see Spoonbills at Shark River, but in the Lane River area ("about thirty acres of mangrove islets between Lane and East Rivers"), he saw one young Roseate Spoonbill just beginning to fly and also one of its parents (Holt, *unpublished report*).

Between April 10 and 15, 1935, the writer was in a part of this same area and saw a total of ninety Spoonbills—sixty-four in Alligator Cove and two flocks totaling twenty-six flying over the Shark River rookery. No nests were found.

Although there have been various reports of nesting from different locations along the coast, only one of these has been definitely established while a second is probably authentic. At the East River rookery (east of White Water Bay and in approximately the same area as the Lane River rookery previously mentioned) a single Spoonbill nest was found in process of construction on April 25, 1940. On May 5 it contained two eggs and on May 11 these eggs were taken by crows and the Spoonbills deserted (Sprunt, *in litt.*).

Spoonbills were also reported as nesting on a small island just south of Charlotte Harbor in 1939. In a letter to the writer, Clinton Sherman, Jr., of West Palm Beach, reported finding six nests

in that year and ten in 1940. I was unable to visit the island during the 1941 nesting season but managed to get there on August 7. That evening four Spoonbills flew in to the island to roost, coming from the direction of Jug Creek on Pine Island. Later, a single adult left the island and flew south across the Barras Islands. The next morning at daylight three Spoonbills were located feeding along the shore of the island. Two of these appeared to be adults, probably in a postnuptial molt. The third was an immature bird. In the spring of 1938, Edward J. Reimann (*in litt.*) reported Spoonbills roosting on Little Patricio Island. He found no nests. This is the same island where I found them in August 1941, and where Mr. Sherman reported nests.

5. East Cape to Cuthbert Lake

One of the regions in which Spoonbills have continued to nest in Florida down to very recent years is that section of mainland from East Cape Sable to Cuthbert Lake, including the old site on Alligator Lake. The story here is a rather discouraging one, for in addition to the construction of roads and canals which have facilitated man's access to this otherwise remote territory, considerable damage to the nesting cover resulted from the hurricanes of 1929 and 1935. On January 26 and 27, 1924, Ernest G. Holt (1929) visited Alligator Lake and on the second day saw a single Spoonbill. Although he does not mention Alligator Lake by name, it was in this colony that Bayard H. Christy (1928) found four pairs of Spoonbills nesting in February 1927. All told there were ten species of birds nesting in the colony that year, to the total number of 879 pairs. The following year John B. Semple (*in litt.*) visited Alligator Lake and found it "abandoned" except for some Wood Ibises.

In January 1929, Eugene R. Pike found twelve Spoonbill nests in Alligator Lake, and forty along the East Cape Canal not far distant (Pike, 1931). The following September a tropical hurricane swept across this region and killed large areas of mangrove. Pike again visited Alligator Lake on January 26, 1940, and found no birds there. He counted twenty-six Spoonbills on the East Cape Canal. A. C. Bent (*in litt.*) visited Alligator Lake that same year and did not see any Spoonbills. In 1931, Pike found no Spoonbills on the lake on January 25, but counted fourteen along the canal. The following March, John B. Semple counted forty-one Spoonbills near Cape Sable, apparently along the East Cape Canal (Howell, 1932).

In January 1938, there were thirty-eight Spoonbills roosting in the southwest corner of Alligator Lake (Reimann, *in litt.*). They were present for a total of eight weeks. At this same time a number of species were roosting on islands in the lake, but the nesting birds were some forty pairs of Wood Ibises. On January 4, 1940, the writer, accompanied by J. Ray Barnes, found three Spoonbills roosting in this same part of Alligator Lake and thirteen at the nearby Fox Lakes. Only one of these sixteen birds was in adult plumage.

Late in October 1940, Alexander Sprunt, Jr., was at the East Cape Canal (*Bird-Lore*, 1941, p. 64). He counted twenty-six Spoonbills that were so tame they fed right up to the net racks adjacent to the fish house, and within a few feet of the house itself. At the same place the next month I saw an equal number of Spoonbills and most of them appeared to be in the first winter plumage. On April 7, 1941, I was again at East Cape Canal and spent parts of two days in the vicinity. There were no Spoonbills in the area. My next visit was May 14 when I counted thirty-five Spoonbills, most of them in immature plumage, on ponds southwest of the fish house. I counted thirty-nine immature birds on August 11 that were feeding in a tidal run just south of the fish house. A few additional Spoonbills were noted feeding in nearby tidal creeks and pools. All told, there may have been as many as fifty birds there at that particular time.

Spoonbills have not nested in Cuthbert Lake since 1937 when there were approximately 150 birds of this species using the island and ten or fifteen occupied nests.[16] However, since that year, Audubon wardens have occasionally observed Spoonbills on the lake, chiefly in spring and summer. I visited the lake in August 1941, but no Spoonbills were present.

---

[16] This same season the number of nesting birds at Bottlepoint Key in Florida Bay dropped to five pairs.

6. *Florida Bay and Florida Keys*

It was not until 1935 that we learned of the presence of nesting Spoonbills on Bottlepoint Key in Florida Bay. The largest concentrations at that location have not exceeded 100 birds (December 1939), and the average number of nests is between fifteen and sixteen.

Small groups of Spoonbills may be seen at various places in the Florida Bay vicinity, chiefly feeding areas. Those most frequently resorted to are discussed in detail in the chapter on 'Food and Feeding Habits.'

An unverified report was made of the nesting of eleven pairs of Spoonbills on the Marquesas Keys in 1934, and a few birds have actually been observed there since then, but no nests found.

There is an interesting concentration area on Boot Key, east of Key Vaca, the flocks numbering from one to fifteen individuals. Small groups have also been reported from Torch Key (von Paulsen, *in litt.*).

Our greater fund of information now enables us to correct a feeling that existed only recently to the effect that the species was headed for oblivion so far as Florida was concerned. In 1925, Dr. T. Gilbert Pearson wrote: "The Roseate Spoonbill of the southern states was never extensively killed for the millinery trade, and yet today it is largely approaching extinction" (Pearson, 1925). In that same year Harold H. Bailey wrote: "The end of this beautiful and peculiar shaped bird in Florida is not many years distant" (Bailey, 1925). C. J. Pennock wrote in 1929 of the Roseate Spoonbill in Florida: "These and other birds are doomed unless prompt and vigorous efforts are made to save them" (Pennock, 1929). In 1931 Arthur H. Howell, writing in *The Quarterly Bulletin of the Department of Agriculture* (Florida) said: "Once quite abundant and well-distributed over this state, it [the Spoonbill] is today so rare that it hardly ever is seen and in some sections of the state, never."

It is difficult to cut a pattern to fit the status of the Spoonbill in Florida during the past twenty years. The facts indicate that it has continued to lose ground as a nesting species, but there seems to be a good possibility that the presence of nonbreeding flocks on the west coast in summer has become more regularly established over this period and has included larger numbers of Spoonbills in recent years. Although at present nearly all of these summer birds are immatures, this situation may change at some future time. Just now there is no way for us to know what to expect in this regard. Of this we can evidently feel certain: so long as the species continues to thrive in Cuba and to the south of Cuba, we will have Roseate Spoonbills in Florida. The annual appearance of some 500 immature Spoonbills on the Florida mainland indicates successful breeding at some location or locations outside of that state. We should know *where* these places are; their continued success is the backbone of our hope for rehabilitating the Spoonbill in Florida.

It is not a simple task, nor an easy one, to analyze the desertion of nesting sites during this period. One could indulge in rationalization, of course, but this would prove little or nothing. The proper place for such analyses is not here, but in that part of our discussion in which we are deliberately preparing the groundwork for future activities aimed directly at rehabilitation. Whatever the factors and influences are that cause Spoonbills to desert an established nesting place, they must be considered decimating factors that are present and active, plus welfare factors that are absent or deficient. An entire chapter is devoted to this subject.

D. PRESENT ABUNDANCE: WESTERN HEMISPHERE

It would be convenient if we could list all places where Spoonbills occur in the Western Hemisphere and enter opposite each locality the number of Spoonbills to be found there. No inventory such as this is possible. Although there are a certain number of instances in which we know the exact or approximate number of Spoonbills in a given locality, for the most part we are faced with a sort of unsolved algebraic problem. Because there are so many unknowns, it will be impossible for us to dispose of the subject of present abundance by writing out a partial list of places and numbers. Some of the unknowns will be explored further along in this chapter.

It has required some years of experience to learn the technique for accurate Spoonbill counts in certain of the localities included. There are, for example, coves along the southwest coast of Florida where Spoonbill counts can be made quite easily on the high tide. The birds are then roosting and when disturbed they fly up in such a manner that a one-two-three count can be made. However, they will then move along the coast a short distance to a similar cove or creek; and unless the observer is alert, he will count them over again several times before the ebbing tide prevents further investigations or he runs out of coves. Such duplication has been carefully avoided in obtaining the present counts.

1. Actual Numbers

The following figures are a reasonably accurate index to the present total abundance of Roseate Spoonbills in this country and are based on counts and estimates made during 1940 and 1941. It should be understood that these are maximum figures and include the large flocks of immature, young, and adult Spoonbills that spend the summer on both the Texas and Florida coasts, arriving after our breeding season is under way.

Maximum Numbers: Summer of 1941

Florida:
  1. Bottlepoint Key (Florida Bay)............. 6
  2. East Cape Sable (Alligator Lake, etc.)...... 60
  3. Alligator Cove (Auger Hole, Turkey Key, Buzzard Key)........................ 80
  4. Duck Rock (Joe's Grasses, Duck Rock Cove). 157
  5. Blue Hill Bay (Pink Curlew Flats, Goodland Point)................................ 100*
  6. Pine Island Sound (Little Patricio Island, San Carlos Bay, Jug Creek, etc.).......... 50*
  7. Tampa Bay (Bush Key, Indian Key, etc.)... 60

  Florida Total   513

Louisiana:
  8. Cameron and Calcasieu Parishes (Black Bayou) (1940 figure)................... 150*

  Louisiana Total   150

Texas:
  9. Vingt'un Islands........................1475
  10. Matagorda County (Green Marsh, Colorado River bottoms, etc.) (1940 figure)........ 200

11. Second Chain-of-Islands...................3000
12. Hynes Bay Island........................ 60
13. Aransas Bay area (Lydia Ann Island, Rock-
    port vicinity, etc.)...................... 200
14. Laguna Madre (Green Island, etc.).......... 100†

                        Texas Total   5035

                        Grand Total   5698

_____

* May be somewhat higher in some seasons.

† Higher early and late in season during migratory movements.

The grand total of more than 5600 Spoonbills is unquestionably gratifying, although this figure by itself is by no means the whole story. In the first place 89% occurred in Texas and only 9% in Florida. Furthermore, the number of breeding birds amount to about 33% of the Texas total in that state and only 9% in Florida. There is only one Louisiana concentration but the 2% that it represents is not significant since the location, just over the Texas line, is an extension of the Texas group. If there is doubt in anyone's mind as to the area where the most intensive work is needed, these figures give the answer. The full significance of these and other totals in a comparative and historic sense are graphically represented on the accompanying charts.

How do the number of Spoonbills in the United States compare with those in other parts of the hemisphere? In Mexico the colonies would appear to be fairly large in view of the abundance of postnuptial flight birds from that direction. Dr. Chapman estimated 200 pairs in the Pajaro Island colony thirty years ago, but we do not know if these have increased or decreased. In the West Indies the species has disappeared from many of the islands. On Great Inagua, Klingel (1940) found Spoonbills, describing the flock as a long wedge-shaped formation but not giving an actual figure. In Haiti, Folk (*in litt.*) counted twenty-eight at Trou Caiman Lake in March 1940.

Although Dr. Barbour (1923) said it was a "very rare bird" in Cuba and knew of no "rookery" in that territory, I have learned of from three to six breeding places, so possibly it is not as rare as he supposed. However, numbers there cannot compare with our Texas flocks. Pearson (*in litt.*) saw scattered birds on the north coast of Cuba in May 1924, and the largest group numbered more than eighty birds. These were seen at Cayo Coco.

Central American reports do not indicate any sizable concentrations. Brooke Worth's report (*in litt.*) of six Spoonbills observed at Castilla, Honduras, in June 1930 is very likely typical. Evidently, from Mrs. Sturgis' remarks, there is no migration through the Panama Isthmus.

In South America the largest concentrations reported occur in the Matto Grosso of Brazil, close to the Bolivian border. F. W. Miller (*in litt.*) witnessed evening roost flights along the Paraguay River that involved several thousand Spoonbills. The *Los Yngleses* colony south of Buenos Aires, Argentina, contained 500 pairs in 1938 and even greater numbers in 1940 (Runnacles, *in litt.*). In November 1939, Pearson (*in litt.*) saw a single Spoonbill along the Parana River, between Argentina and Paraguay. In Argentina he came across fair-sized groups on four or five occasions south of La Plata, and near Dolores saw three individuals.

Apparently there are fair numbers in both Venezuela and Colombia, and at least five breeding locations are reported in the latter country (Dugand, *in litt.*). Dugand speaks of them as "rather frequent" but not very abundant in Colombia. Lehman (*in litt.*) writes that he has found "flocks of 6 to 50 or more" in the Valle del Cauca Department. In the *llanos* he never found "more than a pair at a time" but adds that he did not reach the larger marshes.

In Venezuela, J. D. Smith (*in litt.*) observed a concentration of 500 Spoonbills (with Scarlet Ibises and Flamingos) on Laguna Tacarigua, Miranda, east of Caracas. He says that the Spoonbills nest in this lagoon during May, but the flock of 500 was seen in August (1941) and probably included many immatures.

Obviously there is still much to be learned as to the relative abundance of Roseate Spoonbills over their entire range. It would seem that our Texas population, however, is beginning to compare very favorably from a numerical point of view with other concentrations. In Holland the largest colony of European Spoonbills is said to have contained from 100 to 200 pairs annually, a fluctuation that is reported without explanation (Haverschmidt, 1938). The largest of all European Spoonbill colonies, located in the great morass of Obedska Bara in Yugoslavia (Kirkman, 1913), contained an estimated 1000 pairs when visited by Herr Schenk in 1908. Jourdain (Kirkman, 1913) reported a Spanish colony of only eighteen nests; Beetham (1927) one of fifteen. A Rumanian colony "some miles from the Danube" (Kirkman, 1913) contained 100 nests. Jourdain (Witherby, *et al.*, 1939, 'Handbook of British Birds,' III, 120), is of the opinion that the Spoonbill is *rare* in southern Spain, and that there are *many* in Holland. Joost ter Pelkwyjk (*in litt.*) believed that in 1940 the three Dutch nesting colonies totaled ±400 pairs (8, 100 and 300).

2. Maximum Density

Optimum conditions may result in a species attaining what is sometimes termed 'maximum density' of numbers. What are optimum conditions with relation to the Roseate Spoonbill? The discussion of limiting factors (in another chapter) suggests a number of conditions that seem essential to Spoonbill success, but I am not sufficiently acquainted with the range as a whole to attempt an adequate appraisal of 'optimum.' Evidently it can be found to a considerable extent on the Texas coast, in spite of occasional failures. In fact, optimum conditions in the complete sense is an ideal that very likely is never actually attained but only approached. Some regions in the range of the species come closer to attainment than others, and these are the areas of maximum density.

In addition to Texas coastal lagoons, there may be similar areas on the Mexican Gulf coast. In South America the wilderness of the Matto Grosso evidently provides optimum conditions (of quite a different sort, perhaps!) and likewise certain portions of the Chaco.

We must not attempt to simplify a subject like this too much. The range of the Roseate Spoonbill is not a convenient circle with a nicely located center of abundance. There may be any number of optimum areas, as I have suggested. Optimum is a dynamic condition, it is a state of balance between the animal and its environment.

It is a condition subject to change, to fluctuation.

Further discussion of this important subject in relation to the Spoonbill is found in the chapters, 'Limiting Factors' and 'Food and Feeding Habits.'

3. Population Curves

I have charted breeding-population curves for two colonies of Roseate Spoonbills on the Texas Gulf coast at the northern periphery of the species' range. The curves cover a period of seven years, which is none too long for such purposes. However, the irruptive nature of both is evident. Perhaps the most interesting point in connection with these two curves is their tendency to follow an identical pattern. The Vingt'un Islands and the Second Chain-of-Islands are approximately 200 miles apart, yet the number of nesting pairs in each colony reached peaks in the same years and dropped to occasional 'lows' at the same time. These similar trends strongly suggest that the factor concerned is an extremely broad, widespread influence, such as a climatic influence or a hereditary rhythm in the species itself.

The dip in the curve for 1936 was caused by gale winds and six-foot tides which swept over both Texas colonies, causing approximately a 30% loss of nests and eggs. Late in 1940 a severe storm, followed by a second blow of lesser proportions, resulted in a 92% loss of eggs and young at the Bottlepoint colony in Florida Bay.

There would appear to be an important difference between these colonies at the northern periphery of the Spoonbill's range and colonies that are located in the Matto Grosso, for example. Our colonies on the northern edge are situated along the Gulf of Mexico or at the tip of the Florida peninsula where they are directly in the path of the most violent tropical hurricanes. The fact that these colonies are almost invariably situated on islands increases the damage because of the great flood of water that sweeps over an area that is crossed by such a storm. No doubt there are severe storms in the Matto Grosso, but tropical hurricanes do not occur there and even if they did there would not be the accompanying threat of high water.

The severe dip in the curve in 1940 at both of

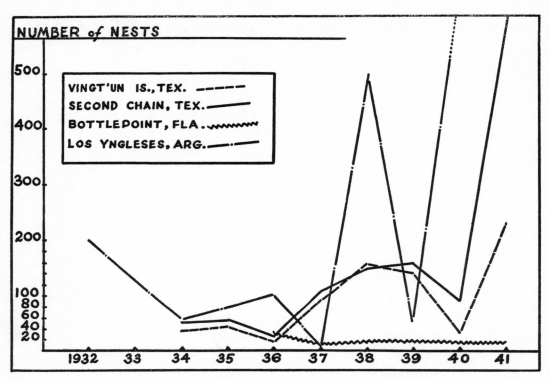

NUMBER of NESTS

VINGT'UN IS., TEX.	-----
SECOND CHAIN, TEX.	——
BOTTLEPOINT, FLA.	~~~~~
LOS YNGLESES, ARG.	—··—

Figure 7.   Breeding Population Curves.

these colonies is not so easily explained. Some influence or factor was evidently at work which I have thus far been unable to discern. Decimating factors that took a direct toll of eggs and young birds in 1940, i.e. grackles and ticks, were in operation only at the Second Chain colony, but the curve experienced a comparable drop at both locations.

Perhaps this is the most important fact to be learned from these data. I might have laid all the blame for the heavy losses experienced at Second Chain at the door of the grackle-tick combination if I had not also observed a similar drop in numbers and in nesting success at the Vingt'un colony. From the manner in which these breeding populations have kept pace, it is not conceivable that the major factors have been different in each separate colony, and the curves similar through mere coincidence.

At the southern edge of the Spoonbill's range there is a colony of herons, egrets and Spoonbills near *Los Yngleses* south of Buenos Aires. The fortunes of these birds have been observed for several seasons by Ernesto R. Runnacles of Estancia "La Esperanza." From information very kindly supplied me by Mr. Runnacles I have been able to chart the Spoonbill's breeding population curves for this colony. Although the length of the curve is fairly short (eight years), it will be seen that it is irruptive in character. Mr. Runnacles has written me that the absence of Spoonbills in 1937 was evidently caused by the extreme drought of that season. In the peak year of 1938, climatic conditions were normal. In 1940, another peak year, the season was unusual, and "began with much rain, culminating with a flood in July." The nesting season is ordinarily October and November with occasional December records, but in the fall of 1939 the Spoonbills failed to nest until very late, which apparently accounts for the dip in the curve in 1939 and the early 1940 peak. I assume that this peak was reached before the spring rains referred to above. This is a large colony during peak years, there being over 500 nests in 1938 and "fantastic numbers" early in 1940. In other words, the colony is somewhat comparable in numbers to the Second Chain group in Texas at the other extreme of the range. *Los Yngleses* is located in a fresh-water habitat, in a region not visited by tropical hurricanes. However, the influence of weather is such that under certain conditions nesting can be brought to a standstill.

Thus, we have evidence that the Roseate Spoonbill's population curve is irruptive at both the northern and southern peripheries, its irregularities subject in a large degree to climatic variations.

4. Other Fluctuations in Numbers

I have mentioned the presence of numbers of nonbreeding Spoonbills, both adults and immatures, in the neighborhood of breeding colonies and at other locations. Seasonal fluctuations in the numbers of these birds are of interest. In order to clarify our picture of Spoonbill numbers, I made a comprehensive count, in person and through correspondence with reliable co-workers, along the entire Gulf coast during April 1940. A similar count was again made in June 1940. The April count resulted in a total of 857 Spoonbills at nine United States locations, six being colonies in which nesting activities were in full swing. In another of the areas (Bottlepoint Key), nesting had been completed and the young on the wing by the middle of the preceding February.

A comparison with the actual number of breeding birds in these colonies demonstrates that 55% of the total number of Spoonbills in April were nonbreeders. This figure is probably high for two reasons: (1) 1940 was a poor breeding season, and (2) some of the birds counted in April on the Texas coast may have been early postnuptial arrivals from Mexican colonies. In 1941 a breakdown of the June figures indicated that 30% of the total United States population were breeding

birds, 70% immatures and birds that had bred elsewhere.

The June 1940 count showed a grand total of approximately 2300 Spoonbills for all areas; this reached 5698 in 1941. In Texas 1100 Spoonbills had arrived on that coast after the 1940 breeding season was under way, over 3000 after the 1941 season was advanced. In Florida it was estimated that some 375 additional birds reached the west coast between late April and about mid-June 1940. In 1941 nearly 500 were added in the same period.

E. BREEDING POTENTIAL

Aldo Leopold (1933) defines the *breeding* or *reproductive potential* as "the maximum or unimpeded increase rate of a species in an 'ideal' environment." This maximum rate is never attained in nature. The environment may appear to come close to it on occasion but it is never "ideal." Its perfection may be impaired by a storm, which temporarily reduces the value of cover, or by high tides which suddenly destroy what appeared to be an ideal nesting site. A host of factors are at work—human factors, disease, ticks, accidents, predators—and the impact of these upon the environment and directly upon the animal itself impede the rate of increase.

There are fundamental differences in longevity, breeding age, size of broods, etc. We speak of some animals as having a 'high breeding potential,' others as having a low. It becomes impossible to generalize. To quote Mrs. Nice (1937): "I have one chief criticism of theories on population questions... they all present too much theory based on too few facts. They all generalize too much, simplify too much. Each man looks at the world from his own special angle and assumes that all (or most) animal species behave in the same way as the few with which he is acquainted."

How much do we know about the characteristics of the Roseate Spoonbill that bear on this subject?

(a) The minimum breeding age is *apparently* thirty-three to thirty-six months. This statement is based on (1) my observation that only adults in full breeding plumage pair and rear young[17]; (2) according to Bent's description of the molts and my own plumage studies thirty-three to thirty-six months are required to attain this breeding plumage. In the European species the adult plumage is not fully assumed until the bird is more than two and possibly three years old.

(b) The average number of Roseate Spoonbill eggs per clutch is 2.7. Considerable variation has been noted in different seasons at Bottlepoint Key in Florida Bay: 1.9 (1939); 3.0 (1940); 3.3 (1941).[18] In Texas, at the Second Chain colony the average in 1940 was 2.6. The European species has an average clutch of 4.2 according to data given by several authors. In Spain this same species averaged 3.3. The West African species averages 2.7. Both species in Australia, the Royal and Yellow-billed Spoonbills, average 3.5 eggs per clutch.

(c) The Roseate Spoonbill has one brood per year. The European Spoonbill also has one brood annually but, according to Lodge (Kirkman, 1913), will lay a second and larger clutch if the eggs are taken from the nest before hatching. *Ajaia ajaja* will desert a nest that is disturbed.

(d) I cannot give an exact figure for the number of young per year produced by a pair of Roseate Spoonbills. In some seasons a colony appears to hatch and rear *all* eggs and young;[19] in other seasons I have recorded *nest mortality* as high as 98.5% (Second Chain-of-Islands, 1940), 92% (Bottlepoint Key, 1940–41), 80% (Florida Bay group, 1939–40). The average nest mortality for Florida Bay for the five seasons from 1936–37 to 1940–41, inclusive, is estimated at about 35%. In Texas the average nest mortality over a six-year period has been about 22%. Whether or not these averages will hold good for longer periods is, of course, not known. According to these average losses the number of young pro-

duced annually per pair is about 1.8 in Florida Bay; 2.1 in Texas. Comparative figures are not available for the European or other races of Spoonbills.

Mrs. Nice (1937) gives comparative figures on percentage of young fledged by certain passerine birds building open nests. In spite of the great difference in environments, habits, etc., between these birds and the Spoonbill, it is apparent that many decimating factors are similar (Mrs. Nice lists: flood; predators—including grackles; cowbirds; sterile and addled eggs; failure of parents;[20] man; parents killed; young starved). The Song Sparrows at Interpont laid four clutches, but there was only one record of four broods being raised in one season. The average number of young raised per "successful nest" was three (six years). The percentage of success for passerine birds building open nests is figured at 41% to 46% of eggs and nests and is considered "normal in temperate North America." This is a "normal" nest mortality[21] of 54% to 59%. In hole-nesting species Mrs. Nice found that the nest mortality is around 35%.

(e) The Roseate Spoonbill is evidently monogamous; both sexes incubate and share in care of the young. Jourdain (Kirkman, 1913) thinks that the European Spoonbill pairs for life but presents no proof. I believe that the Roseate Spoonbill finds a new mate each breeding season (see chapter on 'Breeding-Cycle Behavior').

(f) The incubation period of the Roseate Spoonbill is twenty-three or twenty-four days. Jourdain states that the period is "about three weeks" for the European species and Holstein (Witherby, *et al.*, 1939) is quoted as estimating twenty-one days for the same species.

(g) There is no longevity record for the Roseate Spoonbill. Among other wading birds a Louisiana Heron lived fourteen years,[22] another ten years.[23] A Black-crowned Night Heron lived at least ten years,[24] another was nearly ten years

---

[17] See description in the chapter on 'Plumages and Molts.'

[18] Goddard (*Jour. Animal Ecology*, 4 (2): 1935) correlated a decrease in nesting Short-eared Owls with a big decrease in voles. Previously Witherby (1920) had suggested that the size of broods of this owl might be related to vole abundance.

[19] A. D. Cruickshank (*in litt.*) believes that Double-crested Cormorants on the coast of Maine have a nesting success that is close to 100% for many consecutive seasons.

---

[20] Damage to eggs, loss of young pulled from nest, desertion of young.

[21] Loss of eggs and young before fledging.

[22] *Bird Banding Notes*, 1934, 2: 11.

[23] *The Auk*, 1934, 51: 3.

[24] *Bird Banding Notes*, 1935, 2: 13.

old when found with a broken wing.[25]   There is a record of the Grey Heron of Europe living almost seven years.[26]   The Herring Gull, which like the Roseate Spoonbill does not breed until its fourth year, has an expected life span of eight years, provided it reaches breeding age (Gross, 1940). Thus, the species is a breeding adult for an average of five years.   There are records of Herring Gulls that lived in a wild state for nearly twenty-five and twenty-six years,[27] eighteen years[28] and eleven years.[29]

In a consideration of the subject of breeding potential it would be of considerable interest to know not merely the age to which Spoonbills live under natural conditions but also the age to which they continue to breed.   There are few records for any species.   In *Bird Banding* (1936, **7** (4): 175) the story of the captive Herring Gull "Kaiser" is repeated.   This bird's mate laid eggs for forty-two consecutive years.   Also mentioned are three Canada Geese that laid annually until their deaths at twenty-nine, twenty-nine and thirty-three years of age.   Likewise there is the history of a pair of Eagle Owls that bred regularly for thirty-two years.   These cases are extremes. It would seem that the Spoonbill would more logically fall into the eight-to-ten-year life-span group and breed for something like five to seven years on the average, but this is a guess.

The importance of knowing these fundamental characteristics of a species is obvious.   If our knowledge of the survival, life span, etc., of the Roseate Spoonbill were even reasonably complete there would be little room left for speculation as to the probable fate of a small colony like the one on Bottlepoint Key.   We should *know* what to expect; we should be *certain* as to the trend of our program for the future.

I hesitate to indulge even briefly in hypothesis, but the present subject is such a vital one that I feel I must at least point out certain items in the life history of the species that urgently require information.

(a)   How long on the average does the Roseate Spoonbill live in a wild state?
(b)   What is the usual period in years that an individual breeds and produces young?
(c)   What is the average mortality of the young from fledging to maturity?
(d)   Do Roseate Spoonbills return to their natal colony to breed?   What evidence is there that the colony is also recruited from other areas?

Gross (1940) has been able to estimate the answers to these same questions as they apply to the Herring Gull.   To do so, he studied 773 Kent Island (N.B.) gull returns, representing 3.29% of the 23,434 birds banded at that station between 1934 and 1938, inclusive.   Spoonbills cannot be banded in such large numbers and follow-up is apt to be more difficult.   However, a few returns might serve as valuable indicators.

Meanwhile, the true status of the Bottlepoint group remains unknown.   Perhaps the most important single unknown is whether or not the adult Spoonbill population there maintains itself through its own reproductive efforts; this question may answer itself in time.   At least I would interpret the eventual disappearance of the colony as an answer in the affirmative.   We might possibly reassure ourselves in time by fairly large-scale banding of Cuban, Venezuelan and Colombian colonies.[30]

Darling (1938) suggests that, as a result of certain psychological influences, a very small nesting group is unable to breed regularly and eventually disappears.   He finds an important connection between initiation of pairing and the presence or absence of the stimulating effect of the sexual activities of other species, such as is observed in a large and diversified colony.   Pairing activities have a contagious effect beyond a doubt and thus we can account for the synchronized egg-laying of many colonial birds.   But pair formation among the Spoonbills at Bottlepoint Key takes place in November when *no other species are pair-*

[25] *Bird Banding Notes*, 1937, 8: 2.
[26] van Oort, *Zoologische Mededeelingen*, 1929, 17: 158.
[27] Schuz, *Der Vogelzug*, 1935, p. 6.
[28] Sleijser, *Ardea*, 1934, **23**: 173.
[29] *Bird Banding Notes*, 1935, **2**: 13.

[30] Nestlings cannot be banded because it has been demonstrated that such activities cause heavy losses in a colony.   Often it is possible to band many young when they are just learning to fly.   Colored celluloid bands one inch in width on one leg and one regulation government band on the other would be the combination.   Different colors could be used for different natal regions.

ing. In recent years only fifteen pairs (on the average) were formed at this location, but with complete success. Nevertheless it will do no harm to keep Mr. Darling's interesting theories in mind.

F. SUMMARY

1.   While there are no definite figures in the literature, we may find reasons for presuming that Spoonbills existed by the thousands along the Gulf coast prior to 1850, their numbers in Texas today serving as a realistic index to this past abundance.

2.   Between 1850 and 1890 the major destruction of Spoonbills by plume hunters and settlers took place in Florida and Texas. The decline in numbers was rapid and the species disappeared from north Florida by the 1880's, grew scarce throughout that state by 1890. In Texas it was no longer a breeding bird by the 1890's.

3.   The species reached an all-time low in the United States between 1890 and 1919, and during this time there may have been no more than three small colonies totaling twenty or twenty-five nests.

4.   The recovery in Texas and Louisiana between 1920 and 1941 has resulted from a combination of protective laws, wardens, sanctuaries and a changed attitude on the part of the public. Thriving Mexican colonies were probably the most important factor, however, but this correlation remains theoretical.

5.   The species continues to decline in Florida, and the explanation for this may be found in the present status of Cuban and South American colonies.

6.   The 1941 summer population in the United States exceeded 5000 individuals, but 89% of these were in Texas. These numbers in Texas compare very favorably with reports of members from all other ranges, including the great nesting groups to be found in the Balkans early in this century.

7.   'Optimum conditions' for the Roseate Spoonbill are unknown. There may be many areas of maximum density.

8.   Population curves appear to be affected by widespread climatic conditions or by hereditary rhythms in the species itself.

9.   Of the total United States population in 1941 (5698) some 3500 were nonbreeding birds that migrated to our shores from Mexico, Cuba (?) and possibly South America. Most of them were immatures.

10.   Apparently the breeding potential of the species may be classified as relatively 'low,' but many vital questions remain unanswered.

Part III. Migration and Postnuptial Wanderings

AUDUBON (1838) said that the Spoonbill wintered on the Florida keys near Cape Sable from whence it moved northward late in February. Dr. Elliott Coues (1887) spoke of it as "resident in Florida." Bent (1926) says that it is "resident throughout its breeding range," but also mentions the "theory" that large flocks of Spoonbills seen on the Texas coast in May are "birds which have bred on the coast of Mexico earlier in the season and wandered north after the breeding season." But such movements would involve postnuptial wanderings and would not constitute true or normal migration.

What is 'true' migration? According to Gadow it is "the wandering of living creatures into another, usually distant, locality in order to breed there; this implies a return, and the double phenomenon is annual. All other changes of the abode are either sporadic, epidemic or fluctuating within lesser limits." James Fisher (1939) gives this definition:

Normal migration of birds is essentially a movement, usually in north and south directions, from breeding place to wintering place. Naturally these movements are of different kinds in temperate, oceanic and tropical regions.

How do the movements of the Roseate Spoonbills fit these definitions? First of all we should realize that Spoonbills in the United States occur in two 'zones': the tropical zone in Florida, and the lower austral zone in Louisiana and Texas. We might be led to expect that certain aspects of the species' behavior would be different within these zonal divisions, and in other parts of its range in the Southern Hemisphere. Spoonbills on the *llanos* of Colombia, for example, may respond to the change from wet to dry season by migrating northward to breed during the summer season of equatorial rains and retreating southward with the rain belt when the parching trade winds advance in winter.

In Texas there is a very clear-cut migration concerned altogether with the breeding season in that state; there is also a somewhat regular movement of nonbreeding flocks that is presumably correlated with an earlier breeding season along the tropical Gulf coast of Mexico. There is a slightly more complicated pattern in Florida.

Spoonbills in other parts of the world undertake regular migrations from breeding to wintering grounds. For obvious reasons these are more apparent than the interhemispheric journeys of our species. For example, the European Spoonbill that breeds in Holland, Spain, Rumania, Yugoslavia, etc., differs in appearance from the African species with which it mingles on its wintering grounds. For this reason its presence in Africa is readily detected. Furthermore there is a migration bottle-neck at Gibraltar where the flights of these birds are observed. In the Western Hemisphere, Spoonbills of both continents are exactly alike in appearance and the presence of migrants from North America cannot be recognized.

It seems likely that the chief migration route between Florida and South America (if such route exists) would be along the chain of the Antilles,[31] but there are not many recorded observations from these islands. Records for the Isthmus of Panama are likewise few, and it seems possible that the Texas-Mexican group does not migrate to the south of Mexico. Of course it is equally reasonable to suppose that, while the species may trade between Cuba and Florida, there is no further movement south of Cuba and nearby West Indian points. Nevertheless, the relative abundance of Spoonbills in Colombia and Venezuela (especially in such locations as Laguna Tacarigua in Venezuela near the southern terminus of the Antillean chain) suggests the possibility of wanderings and migrations northward from those countries.

It should not be overlooked that the European Spoonbill annually migrates from Holland, etc., as far as Equatorial Africa (Nigeria, Central Sudan, Somaliland), a distance of at least 3000 statute miles. From the mouth of the Magdalena River in Colombia it is approximately 2600

---

[31] Ober reported the Roseate Spoonbill "a very rare migrant" on the Grenadines in 1878 (Lawrence, 1879, *Proc. U. S. Nat. Mus.*).

miles to the Florida keys via the Antilles and Cuba. From Trinidad the distance is about 1800 miles.

A. MIGRATION OF TEXAS SPOONBILLS

Spoonbills are normally absent from the Texas coast in winter, although W. T. Friddell of Smith Point reported to me that a group of ten immature birds remained at the Vingt'un Islands through the winter of 1938–39. First arrivals in spring may reach the vicinity of San Antonio Bay (Second Chain-of-Islands) as early as late February, and in 1940 a flock numbering some 300 Spoonbills was observed in this area on February 25 by J. G. Fuller and Raymond Redding. The usual date of arrival at the Vingt'un Islands in Galveston Bay is March 5. Arrivals at both of these locations are predominantly adult birds in breeding plumage, although in some instances they may still be completing their prenuptial molt.

Fishermen in the Galveston Bay vicinity (Smith Point) have told me that the first Spoonbills observed in the spring number ten or twelve individuals which come in flying low over the water, following a route close to the shoreline. Generally these first arrivals remain in the vicinity of the Vingt'un Islands for a day or two and then move on, evidently farther up the coast toward the Louisiana colony. The bulk of the breeding birds reach both San Antonio and Galveston Bays by early April.

Spoonbills were first noted at Hynes Bay on March 23 (1940) when Robert Hopper of Austwell observed twenty-seven flying south along the west shore of the bay. On the following day, Judge O. F. Hartman saw the first two Spoonbills of the year at the breeding site in the northeast corner of Hynes Bay.

During August the birds begin to leave the breeding colonies, and before the end of that month most of them have departed. Sometime in August, Spoonbills appear in the vicinity of Eagle Lake, Colorado County, where they remain through September. State Warden T. T. Waddell has observed Spoonbills in Colorado County during August and September since 1918. Of the 1940 season Mr. Waddell writes (*in litt.*):

The first ones showed up August 10. They are always here during August and September. They will drift away but will then come back again for a few days.

This dispersal, which precedes the real migration southward, is actually a postbreeding-season movement.

There are a few October and November dates that have been very kindly supplied to me by Mrs. Jack Hagar, of Rockport, and James O. Stevenson, of the United States Fish and Wildlife Service and formerly in charge of the Aransas National Wildlife Refuge below Austwell. Whether these involve Texas breeding birds or wanderers from Mexico is not certain.

October 5, 1937......Aransas Bay...................	4
November 4, 1938...Aransas Bay...................	1
November 7, 1938...Aransas Bay...................	1
October 17, 1939....Aransas Bay...................	9
October 27, 1939.....St. Charles Bay................	1
October 29, 1939.....St. Charles Bay................	1
October 17, 1940.....Mustang Lake..........small flock
October 17, 1940.....St. Charles Bay.........small flock
October 23, 1940.....Aransas Bay...................	15
October 2, 1941......Big Devil Bayou Lake.........200
October 8, 1941......Copano Bay...................	2

Apparently, with the one exception noted, there are no records of Spoonbills on the Texas coast between November 7 and February 25, and these constitute the dates of extreme occurrence. We can generalize that breeding Spoonbills reach the coast between late February and early April, desert the breeding sites during August, begin their southward migration during September, and for the most part disappear from the coast some time in October.

B. MIGRATION OF FLORIDA SPOONBILLS

Whatever may have been their original habit, the Roseate Spoonbill is now chiefly a migratory species in Florida. In fact, we can with reasonable assurance divide its current habits in this respect into three distinct groups:

(1) A spring migration of adults, presumably from Cuba and South America, reaching the Florida mainland in order to breed there;

(2) A fall migration of adults, presumably from areas to the south, reaching Florida Bay in order to breed there;

(3) A northward dispersal of mixed flocks of immatures and a few adults arriving on the Florida mainland in spring in order to spend the summer on the coast between Cape Sable and Tampa Bay.

This implies that there are at least two types of migration represented: the migration of breeding birds from nonbreeding grounds to nesting places, and the postbreeding-season wanderings characteristic of other groups of herons.

The group of breeding adults that arrives on the mainland in spring (April–May) may once have comprised the bulk of Florida Spoonbills. Today it is the smallest group, and it now seems quite possible that in some years no adult birds migrate to the Florida mainland in spring to nest there.

The group of nesting adults that arrives during the fall is small numerically, but has special importance because of its regularity in breeding each year in Florida Bay. The average number of breeding adults, which arrive in October and nest from November through February, has been thirty-one to thirty-two over the five-year period ending with the season 1940–41.

After the breeding season in Florida Bay is completed during late February or early March, the birds generally remain in the vicinity into May. By the end of May or the early part of June, however, they have all but disappeared from the region. Usually none are present in late summer or early fall, until the arrival of the breeding adults in October.

Most of the Spoonbills occurring in Florida at the present time belong to the third group, and studies that I made of them during April, May and August 1941 indicate that about 99% of this group are immature birds.

C. POSTNUPTIAL WANDERINGS

A. C. Bent (1926), in speaking of the summer dispersal of that notable wanderer, the Little Blue Heron, suggests that these journeys north of the breeding range "may be caused by overcrowding on their breeding grounds resulting in a desire to find new fields in which to search for food." He also mentions that "it is mainly the young birds, in the white plumage, that indulge in these erratic journeys." Gross (1940) states that young Herring Gulls "fly farther and exhibit a greater migratory instinct than shown by adults."

The experiments of Rowan (1929, 1932), and others, demonstrate that true migration is closely associated with the *adult* bird's gonadal development. The erratic dispersal of young birds at the close of the breeding season is evidently another type of movement altogether. What are its motivating forces?

The character of this form of dispersal has been discussed by Lincoln (1939), who writes:

These postnuptial movements of the herons and gulls are wanderings partly, no doubt, in search of food but are not to be compared with the great invasions of owls and other birds from the North. According to the banding records, while the northward travels of the young gulls and herons are conspicuous, not all birds banded at the same time and place make the same journeys. In fact, if the first season-recovery records are plotted on a map the result will have the appearance of a bursting bombshell, as the birds scatter in virtually all directions. It should be noted, however, that the postbreeding season vagrancy of these birds is later counteracted by a directive migratory impulse that carries the wanderers back to their proper winter quarters.

When there were many more Spoonbills throughout their breeding range than there are now, the wanderings of young birds at the close of the breeding season may have been influenced primarily by competition for food. It is hard to believe that such competition exists today and continues to be the direct motivating force causing these dispersals. Perhaps the current dispersals may be motivated by a form of hereditary learning or what is popularly called 'instinct.' This theory suggests that the habit has become innate and that the young disperse in response to an inborn urge that may never be fully explained or completely understood. One might paraphrase Landsborough Thomson and dispose of the matter by saying that to study the background of postnuptial wanderings of birds is "to investigate the nature of animal behavior, and to do this is to probe the inmost mysteries and to ask the very meaning of Life itself."

We can record current and recent evidence of these wanderings, however, and discuss their relation to certain known factors and influences.

Perhaps somewhere we may come upon some clues.

Take, for example, the possibility that Spoonbills are still forced to seek distant shores at the close of the breeding season as a result of competition for food. Is it conceivable that Spoonbills fledged in the Mexican colony at Isla de los Idolos west of Cape Rojo must journey northward along the Gulf coast from 250 to 350 miles in order to find enough food to sustain them? Or that Spoonbills in the Cuban colonies are so abundant that the extensive shores of that island do not provide enough food and that consequently large numbers must fly northward across the Florida Straits and up the southwest coast of the Florida mainland in order to find sufficient food? Both of these conjectures would seem to be entirely unreasonable.

It is not always possible to determine the age groups represented in a flock of wandering nonbreeders. In the case of herons I believe it is generally assumed that the bulk of such wanderers are birds of the year, in other words, juveniles only a couple of months old. It should be stated at once that this does not appear to be the case with the Roseate Spoonbill. I had opportunity for careful analysis of age groups in the summer flocks on the Florida west coast, a subject discussed in detail in the chapter on plumages. It will suffice here to say that only one individual was observed in these flocks in the first or juvenal plumage, which is recognizable only during the first five or six months of the bird's life. Other than this one example the youngest age group represented was made up of birds in the first winter plumage (averaging about one year old) which comprised 36% of the summer flocks. Birds in the second winter plumage (approaching two years of age) totaled 57%; immatures in the second postnuptial plumage (about two and one-half years old) totaled 6%, and adults totaled about two-thirds of 1%.

In general, the two extreme age groups, i.e. the newly fledged young and the adults, do not take part to any extent in the wanderings of Spoonbills that reach the Florida coast in spring. Furthermore, on a basis of data gathered in the summer of 1941, it seems that there is a stronger urge to wander in birds approximately two years old than in birds approximately one year of age.

Banding returns indicate a rather sharp distinction in the distribution of age groups of the Herring Gull. As this is also a species which does not breed until it has attained three years of age (i.e. its fourth year), its comparison with Spoonbills is of special interest. Although the initial dispersal of newly fledged Herring Gulls is characteristically in all directions, this is followed, in Atlantic coast gulls, by a general southward movement[32] of some regularity to wintering grounds along the Gulf coast and the east coast of Florida as far as Key West, Cuba and Jamaica. Very few second-winter birds are observed in this same region. The greatest concentrations of adults appear to winter in the New York City region, with many scattered out along the coast north and south of that point but in numbers that gradually decrease toward the two extremes. Second-winter birds occupy the zone between the adults and the first-year birds—from about Chesapeake Bay southward along the coast of the Carolinas. Banding also demonstrated that very few immature Herring Gulls wandered north in spring or summer to the natal colony during the second summer. More of them show up during the third summer when they are more than two years old. Incidentally, nearly all of those that do return to the natal colonies while they are still immature appear to find their way back to the exact colony in which they were fledged. Only gulls hatched on Kent Island returned to Kent Island to breed (see Eaton, 1933, 1934, and Gross, 1940).

D. 'SUMMER FLOCKS' IN TEXAS

We have not succeeded in banding enough Spoonbills to get such a clear-cut picture, but my studies of the age ratios suggest a pattern that is quite different from that of the Herring Gull. One of the first writers to mention the appearance of large flocks of nonbreeding Spoonbills on the Texas coast was Samuel N. Rhoads (1892). On the 28th of May, 1892, Rhoads observed a flock of 600 Spoonbills at the mouth of the Nueces River near Corpus Christi. At that time the Spoonbill was extirpated as a breeding species in

[32] Black-crowned Night Herons follow a similar pattern.

Texas. It was Rhoads' impression that these birds had bred "somewhere on the coast south of Brownsville." He noted further that they appeared in the Corpus Christi region as early as late April, obtaining maximum numbers in the latter part of May.

Bent (1926) quotes Rhoads and goes on to say that the Spoonbill spreads out over a wider territory after the breeding season is over and states that they occupy such territory "more or less regularly during the summer, fall, and early winter."

He also mentions that Spoonbills "breed on the East Coast of Mexico, in the lagoons south of Tampico, [and] migrate in the spring northward to the coast of Texas and perhaps beyond."

There are many references to the presence of Spoonbills in the spring and summer months in the vicinity of Point Isabel, just north of the mouth of the Rio Grande. Unquestionably these numbers have been increasing in recent years (since 1918), as has already been discussed in the chapter on abundance. For many years Spoonbills have been observed at Green Island in Laguna Madre some twenty miles due north of the town of Port Isabel. It is the habit of these birds to feed on the mud flats and sloughs of the mainland during the night and spend the day dozing on a partially exposed mud bank close to the northern shore of Green Island. They are present during the spring and summer only, but for the most part have always been immature birds and have therefore never shown any tendency to nest in that vicinity although Green Island is an egret and heron colony of considerable size.[33]

In the summer of 1930, John O. Larson of the Green Island Bird Sanctuary observed a flock of Spoonbills on the mainland some miles to the north, in Willacy County. He estimated that there were more than 1000 birds in this group. On June 20, 1931, Mr. Larson returned to this same area accompanied by Alden H. Hadley and Dr. Frank R. Oastler. The following account is contained in a report made at the time by Mr. Hadley (*unpublished*):

---

[33] More than 6000 nesting birds of all species.

On the morning of June 20, we took water and provisions aboard the sailboat and set out early on our quest. We sailed northwestward some 8 or 10 miles and then anchored more than a half mile off shore, on account of the extremely shallow water. After laboriously wading ashore over the mucky, slippery bottom, we reached an area of extensive mud flats which were baked and cracked by the sun's intense heat . . . . At length, beyond a series of shallow grass-rimmed lagoons, I detected a narrow ribbon of pink, which soon resolved itself into a large flock of Roseate Spoonbills . . . . We continued to approach cautiously, wading through the shoal water and across grassy flats until we succeeded in approaching within 200 yards. Careful estimates revealed the flock consisted of at least 500 birds . . . . About one half the birds took wing flying westward over an island and dropping out of sight. We then waded the remaining distance across the mud flats and crossed the island. Here a picture of wondrous beauty was unfolded before our gaze. Spread out in a line, perhaps one hundred yards in length was a group of about 275 Spoonbills, quietly and contentedly feeding in a shallow circular lagoon, while a short distance beyond, in another lagoon, a similar number was observed. We succeeded in crawling to within possibly 125 yards of the birds when with field glasses we watched them at our leisure . . . . One noticed many whitish or pale pinkish birds which would indicate that these were the young of the year.

Early in May 1934, the same region was again visited by Mr. Larson, this time in company with the writer and Jackson Larson. A total of 100 Spoonbills was observed on the mud flats, most of them immature birds.

On June 19, 1940, Mr. Larson and the writer made the same journey but found the lagoons dry and no Spoonbills present. On this same day, there were thirty-two Spoonbills resting on the mud bar at Green Island. They arrived between 7:30 and 8 A.M. and passed the entire day standing almost motionless on the reef. Shortly before 7 P.M. they started to move toward the feeding grounds, twenty-nine going toward the mouth of the Arroyo Colorado to the south and west and three flying east toward Padre Island. Following the flight of these three birds with binoculars, I watched them join a number of herons and egrets that were feeding on the vast shallows between Padre Island and Green Island.

In this flock of thirty-two Spoonbills there were only six that appeared to be in adult plumage or an advanced stage of the second postnuptial plumage. The remaining birds were in various degrees of immature plumage.

Warden Larson very kindly and efficiently kept a daily record of the Spoonbills at Green Island during the spring and summer months of 1940 and 1941. Because 1940 was a dry year and 1941 a wet year,[34] a comparison of these numbers is particularly interesting. There were nearly twice as many Spoonbills present at Green Island during the dry year as compared with the wet, possibly because the birds would tend to concentrate more during a drought and scatter over a wider area during a wet season when feeding grounds would be available over a more extensive territory. There is also a possibility that the rate or progress of migration (wanderings) may be affected by the amount of accumulated precipitation and therefore the location and availability of feeding grounds. Spoonbills reached a peak of abundance at Green Island earlier in the wet year than in the dry year, the delayed peak attained in the dry year not being reached until the drought had been somewhat relieved.

In general, the effect of climatic factors on the numerical fluctuations of these nonbreeding Spoonbills may be considered as negligible.

We know that the bulk of the summer flocks of nonbreeding Spoonbills on the Texas coast are immature birds, but no careful analysis has been made of the age groups. Hadley said that he noticed many whitish or pale pinkish birds "which would indicate that these were the young of the year." However, he does not mention other details of plumage, and we cannot be sure that the birds he described were actually in the first juvenal plumage. In 1940 the small flock that I observed on June 19 was 81% immature, perhaps more than that if some of the 'adults' were actually in the second postnuptial plumage.

In 1941 Mr. Larson noted the occasional appearance of birds that appeared to be in the adult plumage, i.e. they had a bright carmine 'drip' on the shoulders. They were as follows:

March 30......10	April 30.......36
April 14....... 5	May 1.........36
April 16.......12	May 2.........10
April 24.......12	May 6.........25
May 9..........18	

[34] Data from *Monthly Meteorological Summary*, Corpus Christi Weather Station.

As there were never more than thirty-six of these apparent adults and since it is uncertain whether any of them were actually in full breeding plumage, it is impossible to say whether or not their occurrence has any particular significance. Even if they were breeding adults, they might have wandered northward with the flocks of immature birds following the breeding season in Mexico, and their presence at Green Island does not necessarily indicate the possibility of the species nesting at that location.

A complete analysis of the age groups represented in wandering flocks of immature Spoonbill both in Texas and Florida, is discussed in the chapter on plumages and molts.

Warden Larson's records at Green Island suggest that the postbreeding-season flocks begin to arrive on the Texas coast late in March or early in April. Dr. Chapman (1914) found well-grown young "at least a month old and probably older" in the nests of the Pajaro Island colony south of Tampico on April 17 (1910). But I have found that summer flocks in Florida did not include birds-of-the-year under six months old, and there is no actual evidence that similar flocks on the Texas coast include this age group.

Warden Larson's data indicate that the summer Spoonbills may begin their return southward in July, occasionally delaying it into September. We know that the breeding colonies are occupied until sometime in August and that only small numbers of Spoonbills are observed on the coast after early October. It is not clear whether there is any distinction between the southward return of summering nonbreeders and the southward migration of the breeding population.

E. 'SUMMER FLOCKS' IN FLORIDA

The Texas coastal country is flat, with broad stretches of wet prairie that come down to meet the shallow lagoons and bays lying in back of the flat, barrier Gulf shore islands. Vegetation is low and sparse and one can see great distances in all directions. This is in sharp contrast to the southwest coast of Florida where vision is obscured by walls of mangrove that resist penetration, both physical and visual. In a general sense, perhaps, it is this contrast that has made

Plate 7.   The *Croc* was outfitted for a three months' survey of Spoonbill flocks inhabiting the southwest coast of Florida during the spring and summer.

Plate 8.   The ecology of the mangrove (*Rhizophora*) plays an important role in the life of the Spoonbill in Florida Bay.

Plate 9.   The Vingt'un Islands in Galveston Bay, Texas, where pirates once played cards, are hosts to Spoonbills and American and Snowy Egrets.

us so slow to distinguish the arrival and departure of summer flocks of Spoonbills to and from the Florida mainland. Once we have learned the habits of the Spoonbill and are able to anticipate its local comings and goings, its preferred roosting places, its times of feeding, it is relatively easy to distinguish a pattern that is quite similar to that of the summer flocks on the Texas coast.

Admittedly, there are still certain complications. The small group of nesting birds in Florida Bay generally have their young-of-the-year on the wing and pretty much shifting for themselves by the first of March. About this same time, *a very few* Spoonbills put in an appearance at some favorite location, such as Duck Rock or elsewhere on the mainland coast between Tampa Bay and East Cape Sable. Whether or not all of the Florida Bay birds ultimately move northward the short distance that separates them from the southwest coast is not known, but the sight recovery of an immature Spoonbill marked in the Florida Bay colony with a colored celluloid band and observed in Duck Rock Cove a year and a half later indicates that some of them may eventually make this journey.

In any event the relatively small numbers of birds comprising the Florida Bay population and the few breeding pairs encountered on the mainland cannot possibly account for the numbers that appear on the southwest coast by early May. In recent years these numbers have averaged 500 Spoonbills for the entire coast from Tampa Bay southward to the East Cape Canal. Throughout the summer months these numbers appear to be fairly constant but decreases may be noted locally during September and continue on a downward scale through October. By November most of the concentration areas on the coast are deserted except for the roost near East Cape Canal. Before Christmas, Spoonbills have left this area also, although on occasion a few stragglers may continue here or at nearby Alligator Lake as late as January. Not many years ago nests were built in the colony on this lake in January, but that appears to be a thing of the past.

Summering nonbreeders are found in definite areas which they habitually occupy. These

areas are not necessarily associated with the presence of other species in breeding groups and in no case are they concerned with locations at which Spoonbills have nested in modern times. I was able to study these summer flocks in some detail (April 18–May 23; July 27–August 11, 1941) and made careful notes on the plumage characteristics of 305 birds, which would seem to be a good representation of the entire group. From these notes on plumages I have constructed the following table in order to show the percentage of the various age groups represented.[35]

Plumage	Average Age	Number	% of Total
Juvenal	6 months	0	0
Second juvenal or first winter	13 months	109	36%
First postnuptial or second winter	19 months	174	57%
Second postnuptial	28 months	20	6%
Adult	35 months or more	2	0.006%
		——	
		305	

For a long time these Spoonbills that inhabited the southwest coast of Florida in spring and summer were thought of as resident birds. It was not appreciated that they were immature individuals incapable of breeding, and we were forever fretting about our inability to locate their breeding places! Ibises, herons and egrets that roost on the outer coast in the summer move inland along about October and scatter out in prenuptial roosts at the heads of the many rivers that empty into the Gulf of Mexico between Cape Romano and Cape Sable. When the Spoonbills disappeared in October and November, it was logical to suppose that they had merely retreated to some inland roost preparatory to beginning their nesting activities.

As we searched year after year on foot through the cypress country and by boat and airplane over the mangrove and glades areas, it became apparent that during certain months of the year there were no Spoonbills on the mainland of Florida. There were plenty of rumors but nothing ever came of them. On March 18, 1937, a

[35] Bent's description of plumages and molts has been used as the chief basis for estimating average ages (Bent, 1926).

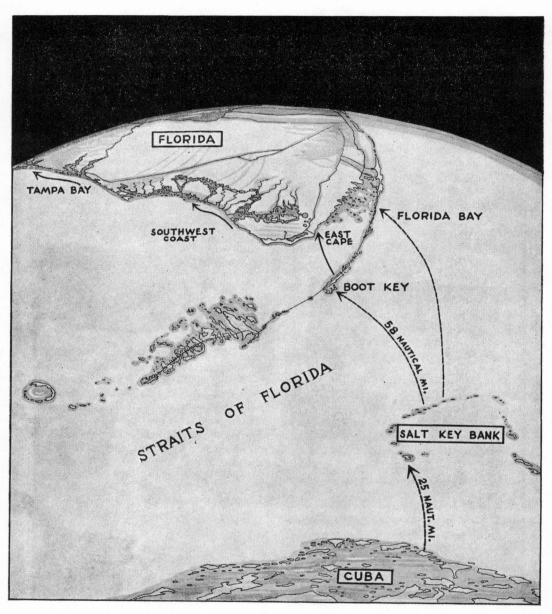

Figure 8.   Possible Routes Followed by Roseate Spoonbills between Cuba and the Florida Keys.
The Route from the Keys to the Mainland Has Been Established.

flight-weary Spoonbill sought refuge aboard the S.S. *Castilla*, a United Fruit Company boat heading north through the Florida Straits off Elliott Key (latitude 25° 23″ north, longitude 79° 57″ west). Captain W. A. Card, master of the *Castilla*, very kindly provided me with details of this occurrence. He stated that the bird came on board about 3 P.M. when the wind was southwest approximately fifteen miles per hour. He said that it seemed very tired.

There is no telling where the Spoonbill came from, although the nearest land is the Cat Key group south of Bimini. The important point is that a Spoonbill had been traveling across the Florida Straits between the Florida keys and the Bahamas.

Shortly afterward, Captain Cliff Carpenter of Tavernier, on Key Largo, was fishing in the Gulf Stream at a point somewhere between Alligator Reef and Molasses Reef. The date was late February or early March. He and his party saw a flock of about 150 Roseate Spoonbills on a course that carried them close to the boat and that was directed toward Florida Bay. The birds were near enough so that one of the party took several feet of motion picture film of them as they passed. The nearest land in the direction from which they had come is Muertos Keys at the north tip of Salt Key Bank, a little more than sixty nautical miles south-southwest of the lower tip of Key Largo.

On March 21, 1938, Commander C. C. von Paulsen, of the United States Coast Guard, was flying over Big Torch Key in the lower key group just west of Big Pine Key. Along the shore he saw twelve Roseate Spoonbills. At about this same time, John H. Baker advised me of the following Spoonbills at other points in Florida:

Date	Location	Number	Ages
March 17	Bottlepoint Key (Florida Bay)	61	Adults and immatures
March 15	Cuthbert Lake	6	. . . .
March 16	East Cape Canal and Alligator Lake	26	Adults (?) and immatures
March 19	Auger Hole (s.w. coast)	26	Immatures
March (?)	Pine Island Sound	2	Adults
		121	

On several occasions Claude Lowe of Tavernier reported to me the presence of a few Spoonbills on Boot Key, which lies on the ocean side of Key Vaca opposite the village of Marathon. Then on April 18, 1941, Mrs. E. F. Rivinus, a visitor from Chestnut Hill, Pennsylvania, observed six Spoonbills at Boot Key and was told by her guide that he had previously seen them in that same location.

There was no opportunity to investigate Boot Key at once, but a chance observation made early one morning the following July suddenly focused attention on this spot. On July 20, in company with L. L. Karcher, I was on board the Audubon patrol boat *Spoonbill*, at anchor off Sandy Key,[36] some six miles south and east of East Cape Sable. A group of nine Spoonbills appeared coming from the direction of the mainland and flying low over the water on a course that carried them in a southerly direction. Looking at our chart we saw that they were headed more or less in the direction of Key Vaca. We decided to investigate at once. Early the following morning we rowed a skiff out to Boot Key and managed to locate seven Spoonbills, all of them in immature plumage. Several people in the vicinity that we talked with said Spoonbills were seen there "every now and then." On August 1, we returned and investigated the area more thoroughly. My notes read:

One Spoonbill appeared. We explored interior of the key, finding marl flats that at low tide looked like Andros or another Bahaman scene. Deep tidal creeks wind through the key and there were many fish—snappers, barracuda, mullet, grouper and sharks—in them. On the flats well inside the key, I seined the never-failing *Cyprinodon*. Also small mojarra.

On the face of the above evidence plus its geographic location, it would appear that Boot Key may well be a regular stopping place for Spoonbills traveling between Florida and the north coast of Cuba by way of Salt Key Bank. From Boot Key to the Doubleheaded Shot Keys on Salt Key Bank is less than sixty nautical miles, and from Salt Key on that same bank it is only about twenty-five nautical miles due south to

[36] The same Sandy Key where Audubon observed Spoonbills in April 1832.

Nicolas Reef on the north coast of Cuba. This is obviously the shortest route from Cuba to the Florida keys with a stopping place en route. The straight-line distance from Nicolas Reef to Sombrero Light off Boot Key is about ninety-five nautical miles. Birds coming from Andros Island in the Bahama group could reach Salt Key Bank by crossing the shallow flats of the Great Bahama Bank and the deep water of Santaren Channel to the Anguila Isles at the lower end of the bank. This distance is nearly 100 nautical miles, but it is possible that stopping places on the Bahama Bank might be found en route. European Spoonbills cross the Mediterranean on regular migrations, both at Gibraltar and from Italy.

From Settlement Point on the western tip of Grand Bahama Island, it is only about sixty nautical miles to Palm Beach. The nearest point of all for a nonstop flight is Bimini, where there was once a Spoonbill colony, now reported as extinct (Bond, 1936). The distance from the eastern tip of South Bimini to Cape Florida just below Miami is about forty-six nautical miles.

It has not been possible for me to investigate the situation at Salt Key Bank or on the north coast of Cuba in the vicinity of Nicolas Reef (Bahia de Cadiz Key, Megano Key, etc.), but I do not hesitate to predict that movements of Spoonbills will be seen at these locations in November and December and in February and March.[37] April may also be a good month in view of the fact that the bulk of the summer flocks do not reach a peak on the southwest coast of Florida until early May.

There are occasional reports of Spoonbills from the Florida east coast as far north as Mosquito Lagoon and Merritt's Island. These are summer records and it seems likely that the birds are merely wanderers, although there have been unverified rumors of the finding of a nest or two. A few Spoonbills have been recorded within recent years near the southwest shore of Lake Okeechobee. One of these observations was made in the spring and the other two in the fall.

Fluctuations of the numbers of Spoonbills roosting at Duck Rock through the summer appear to be concerned chiefly with the time of low tide in relation to daylight hours (when counts could be made) and with the irregular presence of observers at this location.

F. OTHER EXTRALIMITAL RECORDS

There are some highly interesting extralimital records of Spoonbills, some of which carried the species amazing distances beyond their usual range. These have been plotted on the accompanying map so as to indicate the probable routes followed in reaching these distant points. The list is as follows:

1799—Mouth of Cape Fear River, North Carolina
1829—Natchez, Mississippi
1845—Janesville, Wisconsin
1849—San Francisco area, California
1856—Vincennes, Indiana
1865—Lancaster County, Pennsylvania
1865—'American Bottoms' below St. Louis, Illinois
1879—Charleston, South Carolina
1883—Gadsden, Florida
1884—Five miles below New Orleans, Louisiana
1885—Yemassee, South Carolina
1887—Gainesville, Florida
1887—Waverly Plantation, Louisiana
1888—Howardsville, Colorado
1889—Portland, Illinois
1890—Pueblo, Colorado
1897—Dauphin Island, Alabama
1899—Douglas, Kansas
1900—Sedgwick County, Kansas
1902—Riverside, California
1903—San Bernardino, California
1909—Imperial Valley, California
1911—Savannah, Georgia
1913—Okefenokee Swamp, Georgia
1918—Palo Verde, California
1919—Wendover, Utah
1927—Salton Sea, Imperial County, California
1928—Blountstown, Florida
1934—Lincoln County, Georgia
1935—Price's Creek, Sewee Bay, Christ Church Parish, South Carolina.

There seems to be nothing particularly significant or remarkable about the occurrence of those Spoonbills that were found along the Carolina and Georgia coasts as far as the mouth of the

---

[37] Since young of the year and adults are not included in the flocks arriving in Florida in the spring, there is not *necessarily* a correlation between these months and breeding dates in Cuba or elsewhere. Spoonbills are said to breed in Venezuela in May; in Cuba they are reported breeding in the fall or early winter, but data are incomplete.

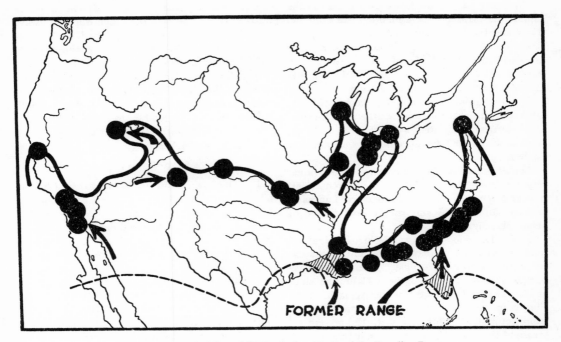

Figure 9.   Record of Spoonbill Wanderings North of the Breeding Range.

Cape Fear River.   There are both old and recent records for this route, from Barton's report of 1799 (Cape Fear River, North Carolina) to the bird seen on Price's Creek near Bull's Island, South Carolina, in 1935.   Three of these coastal flight records were made in the summer months, one in the spring and one in the fall.

The record for Lincoln County, Georgia (1935), indicates that this bird probably went inland along the Savannah River.

It seems logical to infer that most of the birds on this route originated somewhere in Florida, and there seems to be no correlation between these extralimital records and various periods of abundance of the species in Florida.

The midwestern records are all prior to 1901 and it seems apparent that the birds concerned moved north through the Mississippi valley by way of various tributaries to the points where they were observed or collected.   During the period represented, 1829 to 1900, there were Spoonbill colonies in Louisiana that are now extinct, such

as the one on Bayou Sara near Baton Rouge (Oberholser, 1938).   A lack of records for the Midwest since 1900 would seem to be due to the desertion of this and other colonies in Louisiana and the uncertain fortunes of the lone nesting group in the southwestern part of that state.

The Spoonbill collected near Pueblo probably followed the course of the Arkansas River.   In spite of the fact that the distance along this river from the Mississippi is considerable, it can be pointed out that Least Terns now nest along the North Platte River in Wyoming, which is an even greater distance from the Mississippi valley from whence these birds probably migrate.   Incidentally, this Spoonbill was taken in August.

The other Colorado record of a bird at Howardsville in the summer of 1888 suggests that this individual followed the course of the Colorado River and its tributary, the San Juan.   This would have carried it through the Grand Canyon —a rather amazing picture to contemplate!   The five birds that reached the vicinity of Wendover,

Utah, on the edge of the Great Salt Desert in the summer of 1919 may have followed the Colorado River and the Sevier, working north across Utah Lake and the Great Salt Lake to fresh-water marshes along that body of water. Why they would then cross the desert toward the Nevada line is beyond all possible explanation.

The Howardsville, Colorado, record and the Utah record, like those in southern California, are doubtless associated with Mexican colonies, such as that near Guaymas on the west coast of Sonora.

The Spoonbill in the Lancaster, Pennsylvania, museum is dated about 1865, and Warren (1890) indicates that it was collected in Lancaster County, an unusual and rather isolated record geographically.

Currently, Spoonbills wandering outside the normal range are seen on the Atlantic coast as far north as South Carolina. There are no reported occurrences for southern California since 1927. The bird seen west of the Apalachicola in Florida in June 1928 could have journeyed either from Louisiana or Florida. With the present increase of Spoonbills in Texas, we may expect new extralimital records from the interior of that state along some of the river valleys, and possibly from Louisiana and Arkansas. To date, no such occurrences have been reported.

Bent (1926) mentions three individual occurrences far south of the normal range in South America. He writes:

A greatly emaciated specimen was collected near Kidney Cove and the remains of a second were found at Whalebone Bay, Falkland Islands, in July, 1860, while Sclater and Hudson record a specimen from the Straits of Magellan.

Unfortunately the month or season in which birds were seen outside the range was not always recorded. Of those records for the United States in which the month was given, nine were made in summer, four in the spring and one in the fall.

The European species wanders to the Faroes, Norway, Sweden, Finland, Baltic States, Germany, Switzerland, Czechoslovakia, Poland, north Russia, and to the Azores, Madeira and Canary Islands in the Atlantic (1939, Witherby, Jourdain, Ticehurst and Tucker).

G. SUMMARY

1.   There is a well-marked migration of Spoonbills to the coastal country of Texas and Louisiana for the purpose of breeding in those two states. The fall migration is less well defined, being complicated by the presence of nonbreeding birds that wander into Texas after the nesting season is under way.

2.   There appear to be two distinct migrations of Spoonbills into Florida for the purpose of breeding, another that is more in the nature of a postnuptial wandering.

3.   Summer flocks in Texas generally arrive in May and June, remain until September or October. The age ratios of these flocks are not known.

4.   Summer flocks in Florida arrive in late March, dwindle in September. They may be composed 99% of immature birds.

5.   Extralimital records of the Spoonbill within the United States do not appear to be correlated with any particular periods of abundance or decline. River valleys or coast lines are the routes most frequently followed by these wanderers.

Part IV. Limiting Factors

IT IS obvious that a bird or other animal cannot exist under natural conditions, from day to day and year to year, without meeting many dangers and difficulties. In their struggle for existence, animals are preyed upon by other animals; their offspring are destroyed by storms; they contract lethal diseases, or meet with an untoward accident (like the Spoonbill that was run over by a truck on a highway in eastern Florida!).

An examination of factors limiting the abundance and distribution of an animal indicates that some of them may be of a favorable nature. These are the welfare factors and have to do with types of suitable nesting cover, availability of an adequate food supply, and so on. There are likewise decimating factors, which exact a toll of young and adults alike. Man is sometimes a direct decimating factor when, for example, he puts a shotgun to his shoulder and shoots an animal; he may be an influence that indirectly affects the welfare of certain forms of wildlife through his activities in clearing land for cultivation or in draining marshes. Weather is an important influence, but it, too, may be direct in its action upon a species.

Sometimes the operations of these factors and their influences are quite complicated, and it is necessary to examine the subject in considerable detail in attempting to decide what forces are at work. What may appear to be a perfectly obvious factor may turn out to be only a single contributor in a whole combination of conditions and circumstances acting together to produce the true limiting factor. Elton (1927) points out that the humidity of the air, for example, cannot be considered by itself because it depends upon such things as temperature, wind and rainfall, while these, in turn, may be controlled by the type of vegetation or the degree of exposure.

What factors and influences limit the distribution and abundance of the Roseate Spoonbill? I began my field work on this species with certain preconceived notions on this subject, nearly all of which I have since had to throw overboard. Even now, I have by no means discovered all of these factors, and my interpretation of those suggested by intensive field work is probably not always correct and should best be regarded as tentative. We are dealing here with some of the fundamental properties of animal existence and should mistrust even what appears to be logical. It is encouraging to know that there seems to be a general appreciation of this state of affairs. Elton writes:

> In field work there is not usually time or opportunity for studying the real limiting factors of species; and so description of habitats resolves itself into an attempt to record any condition with which a particular species appears to be constantly associated, even if it is a condition which is only correlated with the real limiting factor or factors and has no significance in the life of the animal. If this is done it is possible for other ecologists to get at least a clear idea of the exact type of habitat frequented by the animal, and perhaps carry the work still further.

A. WELFARE FACTORS

Roseate Spoonbills do not build their nests just anywhere. The nesting site apparently measures up to certain more or less inflexible requirements which combine to provide a habitat in which the Spoonbill can successfully initiate and carry through with its complicated reproductive cycle. Up to this point, my study suggests that if so much as a single item in this combination is lacking, is deficient in any way, the area is no longer suitable as a nesting place for the species and may be deserted immediately or by slow degrees, according to circumstances.

The welfare factors that combine to create the reproductive environment of the Roseate Spoonbill are concerned with both land and water areas, with food and its abundance and availability, with protection from enemies, and with climate. There are certain definite characters and qualities to each of these that make up the essential ingredients—not singly, not by two's and three's, but as a unified, correlated interdependent totality: the Roseate Spoonbill's nesting site.

Each of these essential requirements is discussed separately in order that we may have a general understanding of its role in the Spoonbill's life, and especially its indispensable place in the whole structure.

49

1. Nesting and Roosting Space

Quite obviously, there must be an adequate space that will support or contain the nests. Inseparable from this area is additional space for roosting. Let us consider the characteristics of these two spaces by themselves and devoid of their inescapable relationship to other requirements. We find that Roseate Spoonbills nest on the ground or in any one of at least nine different shrubs and plants,[38] varying from ground-clinging plants like the morning glory to cypress trees seventy-five or eighty feet in height. Thus, the nesting site does not necessarily have to be provided with any particular type of vegetation and may require little or no protecting or supporting plants or shrubs. Spoonbills may nest in a thick growth of fragile panic grass; in this respect they are similar to the genus *Platalea*, which nests very often in marsh grasses or reeds.

If the nest can be placed almost anywhere within reason, according to local conditions and circumstances, it would seem that the physical character of the nesting space is of no consequence. There is a discernible average, though, and in our species the preference seems to be for low shrubs and trees, with ground nests being rather exceptional. However, I am unacquainted with details of the Roseate Spoonbill's nesting habits in South America, so no positive statement can be made applying to the species as a whole.

Abel Chapman in 1909 found the European Spoonbill nesting in beds of glasswort in southern Spain (Cano de la Junqueria) (Kirkman, 1913). If they attempted to build in similar vegetation on the mainland of south Florida, they would quickly be preyed upon by raccoons and other ground predators and in certain cases the nests would be washed out by spring tides.

In short, the nature or composition of the nesting space may be of no great importance in itself; but it becomes useful and adequate when it is related favorably to certain other conditions and qualities in the whole environment.

I believe that the roosting space is inseparable from the nesting space because of its constant use

[38] Red mangrove, desert hackberry, marsh elder, a species of panic grass, bald cypress, southern elder, hackberry, morning glory, and willow oak.

by one member of the pair during the period of incubation and while the young are still in the nest; by the inevitable fringe of nonbreeders that clings to the environs of every Spoonbill colony; by advanced young-of-the-year that are on the wing while other nests in the colony are still occupied; or by other species associated with the colony. Since each individual nest site is a territory defended by its claimants, considerable friction and even disaster may result if this territory is invaded again and again by strange birds. Although the roosting space is essential and must be immediately adjacent to the area occupied by the nests, it does not necessarily have to have a specific character. Usually roosting Spoonbills on the edge of a nesting colony occupy the larger trees and shrubs, which give them a vantage point from which they can detect the approach of enemies. A colony of Spoonbills in southern Spain (Kirkman, 1913) was located on an almost bare mud bank, the nests being constructed on top of dead and broken reeds and mud. Here the roosting birds virtually perched upon the ground, but it was evidently an insular site and vision doubtless was unobstructed in all directions. The same would apply to the colony of *Platalea alba* found by Governor Ussher on a small rocky island off the coast of Sierra Leone (Bannerman, 1930).

Thus, with all Spoonbills the nesting and roosting spaces may run the gamut of variety; there appears to be nothing *essential* about them except the nature of their environmental associates.

2. Adjacent Shallows

Perhaps the outstanding requirement of a Spoonbill habitat is the presence of shallow water areas in immediate proximity to nesting and roosting sites. Because of the structural peculiarities of its mandibles, the Spoonbill must feed in extremely shallow water, i.e. (generally) water no deeper than the length of its lower leg. Thus, depth of water is directly concerned with food availability. It is also important and apparently essential that the young have access to shallow water upon leaving the nest. At this time and for weeks thereafter, the young learn to forage in the shallows for themselves, and they remain close to the nest where they are under the watchful eyes of the parent birds. The proximity of shallows, therefore, has a twofold survival value.

3. Minimum Tidal Range

If the rise and fall of tides in the Spoonbill habitat is excessive, food will not be available at all times. While this situation does not present a serious difficulty for nonbreeding Spoonbills (which feed on the low tide and roost on the high), it may offer grave problems to Spoonbills that are engaged in providing the growing young in the nest with food. An abundance of food must be available at all times throughout the breeding cycle. It is conceivable that a colony of Spoonbills may be located on a coast or island where the tidal fluctuation is several feet and still obtain food from adjacent nontidal marshes or ponds without too arduous or too lengthy a trip, except perhaps during storms. But this suggestion overlooks the fact that young Spoonbills require shallow water areas at the nest where they can forage for themselves. My observations indicate that young Spoonbills at the time of fledging do not continue to be fed by the parent birds as is apparently the case with herons, egrets and possibly ibises.[39] The parent Spoonbills resist begging at this time, and the young soon learn to find their own food. Most of the Spoonbill colonies with which I am personally acquainted are located on waters that have no periodic tide. In cases where colonies are on tidal waters, the fluctuations are relatively small in range, and the average range of spring or extreme tides for those colonies studied is but slightly more than one foot.

4. Suitable Water Environment

From every point of view, this requirement is of the utmost importance. Spoonbills sometimes nest in fresh-water habitats; since in such instances they depend in the main on these same habitats for their food, the water must be in a normal, healthy condition with a proper balance

---

[39] Possibly because the bill, which is relatively narrow and almost like that of a young ibis at hatching, has acquired the broad 'spoon' at the tip by the time the young is fledged. This spoon may render feeding from the adult's throat a difficult procedure.

of plant and animal life and free from any form of pollution. There are colonies in Texas located on islands surrounded by brackish water, but most of the adult birds appear to feed on the borders of fresh-water ponds located on the mainland two or three miles away. In such cases, both these fresh-water ponds and the brackish water of the bay must have a water environment that supports a normal, healthy population of marine life. If water increases in salinity beyond the density of ordinary sea water (as it sometimes does due to evaporation, lack of precipitation and the influence of winds from certain directions), the animal life may become limited. However, I have learned that certain important forms, which are nearly always associated with Spoonbill habitats, can withstand excessive and frequently fluctuating salinity. On the other hand, the density of salt water may become so excessive that practically no animal life can exist.

Up to this point, I have considered welfare factors concerned directly with the habitat itself. Although I have touched upon the marine environment, which is a part of this habitat—in fact, the more important part—I haven't considered the possible importance of the animal content. The place occupied by food animals essential to Spoonbill existence is discussed under the next three subheadings.

5. Constant Availability of Food

In the chapter on 'Food and Feeding Habits' the connection between shallow water, tide range, water chemistry, temperature and the numbers, kinds and availability of various marine animals will be discussed at length. I wish to mention here, at the risk of being repetitious, that all of these related characteristics of the environment have a great deal to do with the constant availability of food.

The shallow waters, whether they are fresh or brackish, polluted or healthy, tidal or nontidal, contain characteristic animal populations. Whether or not certain of the more abundant forms are present at all times in depths that make them available to nesting Spoonbills, depends on the existence of a proper combination of these environmental characteristics and factors.

6. Abundance of Food

Food animals may be available at all times but lack an abundance sufficient to meet the needs of a Spoonbill colony. Once again this abundance is a result of a combination of certain environmental factors.

7. Nutritional Value of Food

Aldo Leopold (1933), in discussing welfare factors, suggests that there is reason to believe that each species requires minute quantities of certain minerals or certain protein vitamins. He writes:

These are not "food" in the gross or quantitative sense. The quantities required may be so small that the amount transmitted from the parent to the egg seems in some cases to sustain the resulting progeny for a considerable period. Nevertheless they are so necessary that the exhaustion of the reserve supply in the tissues often results in malformation, impaired reproduction, or even death . . . It is not unthinkable that the presence or absence of these substances helps determine the geographic distribution of species.

He also points out that deficiency of food is commonly believed to decrease the size or numbers of litters, although actual proof of this is lacking.

It seems possible that Spoonbills in captivity may lose their color and certain functional abilities—for example, the urge to breed—partly as a result of an improper balance in their diet. Other factors, such as temperature, light and humidity, may also be important, but the need for certain food values may be of primary importance.[40] Spoonbills in the St. Louis Zoo that had lost most of their color regained it after being given a diet that included cottage cheese (Kennon, in litt.), a milk product that is evidently rich in vitamins of the so-called B-G complex. Domestic poultry breeders consider that the water-soluble vitamins of milk are an essential part of the diet of domestic fowls because of their effect on growth, egg production and what they term

---

[40] See article by W. A. Watts (1941, *National Geographic Magazine*, **79** (1): 56–65) describing the American Flamingoes that have retained their color and bred in captivity in Hialeah Park, Florida. Mr. Watts writes that "a diet rich in certain vitamins was needed to maintain physical vigor and retain the glorious color of the plumage." Cooked shrimp, cooked fine rice, special mash and cod liver oil (vitamin D) is fed these birds.

'hatchability' (Owen, Borden Company, *in litt.*).

As yet we don't know enough about the vitamin content of Spoonbill food items or the direct physiological relationships of the different vitamins, but it seems likely that Spoonbills must obtain certain of these values in proportions that are conducive to general health. This suggests variety, and further discussion of Spoonbill food will demonstrate the variety that is obtained under natural conditions.

8. Freedom from Predators

It is not through mere chance that most Spoonbill colonies are located on islands. These islands are usually quite small; and since they are occupied by nesting birds for a part of the year only, they may not offer a favorable habitat for raccoons, bobcats, armadillos, skunks and other ground predators. There are areas on the Florida mainland that seem to provide all of the essentials for a Spoonbill nesting place but are literally overrun with raccoons. When Spoonbills nest on the mainland, they either occupy an island, as in Alligator Lake, Cuthbert Lake and Lake Okeechobee, or they build their nests seventy-five or eighty feet from the ground—on aerial islands as it were—as in the Big Cypress colony. When the young take leave of such lofty nests and work their way from branch to branch to the ground, their vulnerability, so far as ground predators is concerned, may depend on the amount of precipitation; during a drought, they may be more vulnerable, i.e. more accessible, than at other times.

Certain regions may have an overabundance of Fish Crows or grackles. Whether or not these areas are rendered unfavorable to the successful nesting of Spoonbills would seem to depend on the stability of such predator populations from season to season and also, in the case of the grackles at least, on the relative abundance of grain crops on adjacent farmlands.

Thus, the nesting place must be located so as to minimize the chances of ground predators reaching the eggs and young. It is possible, however, that factors other than physical isolation may create a vulnerability in an ideally situated colony under certain conditions.

9. *Freedom from Disturbance by Man*

We are told that, in India, Spoonbills sometimes nest on the edge of a village or even in the midst of the village itself (Butler, 1896–98). It would be interesting to know how long they must be conditioned to man's presence to accomplish this immunity to fear. Our Spoonbills have been subjected to a far different type of conditioning! They seek the most remote places in which to nest, and well they might. We are forced to conclude that the ideal nesting site in our hemisphere is located away from travel routes. The last surviving colonies on the Florida mainland (Alligator Lake and Cuthbert Lake) were in areas that were among the last in that state to be reached by roads or made accessible to boats. Some of the current colonies are within sight of boat channels but are well protected by barriers of nearly impassible oyster bars or mud flats.

In analyzing the habitat 'essentials' thus far discussed, I note that all of them can be duplicated in regions with which I am acquainted outside of the normal breeding range of the Spoonbill. Such areas may be located in southern Indiana, in Arkansas, or in South Carolina. What is it, then, that must be present in addition to these requirements? What is it that limits the northward extension of the Spoonbill's breeding range?

10. *The Climatic Factor*

The northernmost breeding colony of Roseate Spoonbills (extinct since the 1890's) was located on Bayou Sara in West Feliciana Parish, Louisiana. This is just short of 31°N. latitude and, so far as we know, the species has never nested north of this site. Most of the United States breeding colonies have been south of 29°N. latitude.

Although the limits of a species' range may be dictated by a number of considerations, a combination of climatic conditions is usually the underlying factor in making unoccupied range adverse. These climatic factors are difficult to pin down, and the case of the Roseate Spoonbill is no exception. There are certain obvious temperature differences between Florida and South Carolina, for example; but these are nicely balanced during the summer months. Furthermore, this period of warm days and nights in many regions north of the Spoonbill's breeding range appears to be prolonged enough in summer to permit the successful nesting of these birds. But they do not breed north of 30° (currently), and we must admit that temperature differences do not appear to be the reason.

The fact is that we cannot explain the limits of the Spoonbill's range because the real key to its distribution is still unknown to us. This key may be an intangible that will be very difficult to discover, but it is just as likely to be a perfectly obvious factor that is not yet apparent. Perhaps we can't see the forest because of the trees! Meanwhile, I must be content to say simply that the Roseate Spoonbill is a tropical and subtropical species that has not been known to nest beyond the tropical and subtropical regions.

11. *Size of Colony as a Factor*

Perhaps the actual numbers of breeding birds in a colony are, under certain conditions, an important factor operating favorably or unfavorably upon breeding success. There may be a population mean beyond which the normal rates of reproduction and mortality result in a stable population, and a colony whose breeding population has fallen below this mean may not be able to maintain its population level or even combat a gradual decline in its numbers.[41] This is an intriguing problem but one which cannot be understood or evaluated until we have secured much more detailed information on the relative nesting success of different Spoonbill colonies, both large and small, and until we know considerably more about their migrations and the mortality rate from hatching to breeding age.

B. DECIMATING FACTORS

Decimating factors kill directly. Some of them exact a toll that may be termed 'natural'; others have to do with man and the works of man and are, in this sense, unnatural. I have found that the major decimating factors in the life of the Spoonbill are evidently disturbance by man (which appears in a variety of forms), predation,

---

[41] See discussion: Darling, 1938.

disease and parasites. Each of these factors, however, must be considered in its relation to the behavior pattern of the Spoonbill itself. This is a complicated relationship and gets us into quagmires of speculation. What is the apparent importance of each of these factors and how do they seem to affect the current status of the Spoonbill in different parts of its range?

1. Disturbance by Man

There appears to be a direct connection between the tolerance that a species exhibits for the presence of man at the nesting time and the relative abundance of that species. Of course this does not hold good for all of our native breeding species, but we cannot fail to be impressed by the 'tameness' of Robins, English Sparrows, Starlings and other birds that are extremely abundant. These birds have successfully adapted themselves to a world dominated by man. They build their nests in the midst of his habitations and search for food on his lawn or in his fields.

Compare the characteristics of the English Sparrow, for instance, with those of the Roseate Spoonbill. The one is a street gamin, pugnacious and resourceful; the other a shy, retiring and secretive creature. The one can build its nest almost anywhere and obtain food under conditions that would mean starvation for most birds. The other is greatly limited in its choice of nesting and feeding environments. The one can withstand excessive cold and heat; the other appears to be conditioned by heredity to a life in tropical or subtropical climates. The sparrow raises several broods each year and appears to reach breeding maturity at one year of age. The Spoonbill raises only one brood a year and does not appear to reach breeding maturity before three years of age.

Added to these things, we find that the Roseate Spoonbill is shyer and less tolerant of man's presence, particularly at the nesting time, than most other birds. From the day when the first flock arrives on the nesting site until the young birds are ready to fly—a period that may last for more than four months—it is possible for the mildest sort of human interference to break up the entire breeding cycle.

a. Unintentional Destruction

On this subject I have received the following comment from Mr. Ernesto Runnacles who has observed the Spoonbill in the breeding colony at *Los Yngleses* in Argentina. He writes:

> I found my first breeding colony of Roseate Spoonbills in 1932, and in subsequent years the species has tried to return to breed at the same spot, but has not always succeeded for it is very shy until properly established. I have found that to arrive before eggs are laid is just about equivalent to destroying the nests . . . I calculated on the ninth of October that there were . . . 200 Roseate Spoonbill nests . . . next Sunday all the Spoonbill nests being built were deserted. On my first visit my guide fired a few shots with his revolver while we were approaching the colony and this might have caused the Spoonbills to make their decision.

It should be mentioned that in this same colony in 1932 there were also forty nests of the Cocoi Heron and 100 nests of the American Egret. These birds did not desert after Mr. Runnacles' initial visit.

In my detailed study of the Spoonbill's breeding-cycle behavior in Texas during the spring of 1940, I found that this species is a great deal shyer than any of the herons and egrets nesting in the same area. When the colony is approached, Spoonbills are among the first birds to fly and the last to return. They get up *en masse* and leave the vicinity as a flock, going off and standing in a compact group along the shore of a separate island some distance away. Herons and egrets, on the other hand, are more likely to flush with some reluctance and drop back again as soon as one has passed that section of the colony in which their nests are located. This last form of behavior is especially true of American Egrets, and perhaps equally so of Reddish Egrets. Snowy Egrets are more annoyed than frightened by one's presence and are quite vociferous in their protestations. Ward's Herons occupy the highest nests in these Texas colonies and consequently are the first to sight the intruder. They also appear to flush from the nest with some reluctance, as well as annoyance, which may be voiced by the emission of dismal croaks. Usually they fly as far off as do the Spoonbills, but it is a scattered flight, not a concerted one, and the birds will return as soon as one's boat begins to pull away from the island.

Quite naturally, these forms of behavior vary with the progress of the breeding cycle, and this emotional fluctuation as it relates to the Spoonbill is discussed in the chapter on 'Breeding-Cycle Behavior.'

The mass hysteria that appears on occasion to overcome a nesting group of Spoonbills during the breeding cycle is not only in sharp contrast with the reactions of allied species but also with the behavior of Spoonbills discovered at some distance from the breeding colony. Even during the breeding cycle, Spoonbills on the feeding grounds may be quite tame, at least when observed individually or in very small groups. In early July 1940, I found adult Spoonbills feeding singly in cattle ponds on the Hawkins Ranch in Matagorda County, Texas. These ponds were only a mile or two distant from the Spoonbill colony in that region, where on that date the young were still in the nests. It was assumed that these adults were obtaining food for the young, but their behavior was strikingly different from what it would have been in the colony. They allowed us to approach within fifty feet without showing undue alarm and continued to feed in and out among the gigantic Brahma steers that were cooling themselves by partial emersion in the shallow waters of the pond. When one of the birds did flush, it flew only a short distance and then alighted and resumed its feeding.

A fairly large flock of Spoonbills on the feeding ground is more readily frightened (less tame, if you will) than a single bird or a small group. It seems as if the fear reaction increases or is multiplied according to the number of Spoonbills present. Perhaps fear varies with the individual bird so that the larger the flock the more chance there is that it will include easily frightened individuals.

The Spoonbill's habit of reacting in concert is a serious factor. Mr. Runnacles' evidence on this score is of interest, and a small colony that was preyed upon by raccoons in Florida Bay early in 1940 deserted the area entirely, although not all of the eggs had been destroyed by the raccoons. This is all the more alarming when we consider that these birds are apparently incapable of picking up the threads, as it were, of an interrupted

behavior pattern and continuing their reproductive activities with ultimate success. All the evidence that I could obtain indicates that a deserted nest of the Roseate Spoonbill is deserted for good and all.

This is not only in direct contrast with the usual behavior of herons and egrets but of the European Spoonbill as well. Although most authors state that the European species raises only one brood, there is evidence that it will lay a second clutch if the first is destroyed. R. B. Lodge, who observed the species in the Maarden Meer in Holland, found that when Spoonbill nests were robbed they not only laid a second time but these second clutches were larger than the first, one containing six eggs and another seven, the average number being between three and four (Kirkman, 1913).

Rev. F. C. R. Jourdain considers that the European Spoonbill is wary and shy because it has been so frequently shot at; where they are protected they are not especially shy, though always rather nervous and easily alarmed. He adds: "Owing to the difficulty of making continuous observations in the localities where they live, most of the life history of this species is still imperfectly known" (Kirkman, 1913).

From all this it would be correct to infer that well-meaning visits to a Spoonbill colony for purposes of detailed observations or the taking of photographs at close range should be rigidly avoided from the time of the flock's arrival in the vicinity of the nesting site until the young are well grown. Otherwise, there is grave danger of mass desertion of the colony or, at the very least, a considerable loss of young and eggs through partial desertion. This does not mean that Spoonbill nesting colonies must forever be shut off from the public gaze. According to local circumstances, it is quite possible to anchor a boat within a reasonable distance of a Spoonbill colony and from the deck or cockpit observe the birds' activities with the aid of a telescope or pair of binoculars. This 'reasonable distance' will vary with conditions and probably should never be less than 100 yards, usually more; the exact point that the birds are in the cycle is an important consideration.

b. Deliberate Destruction

Deliberate destruction by man requires little explanation. It is of more than passing interest, however, to contemplate the probable results of a raid on a mixed colony of herons, egrets and Spoonbills by agents of the feather trade. The reconstruction of such a scene is not a pleasant pastime, but it emphasizes the rapidity with which whole colonies of Spoonbills may have deserted their hereditary nesting areas. Associating at breeding time, as they undoubtedly did, with both American and Snowy Egrets, the Spoonbills must have been driven from their nests in the very midst of the breeding cycle. One can imagine the hysterical flight of the entire colony, the widespread loss through mass desertion of nests containing eggs and small young, and the fatal results of the parents' inability to 'pick up the threads.'

Although Spoonbills are not directly protected by Federal law, their plumage under the Tariff Act and the Lacey Act may not be legally possessed, bought or sold or transported from one state to another *if the birds were illegally killed.*[42] In states where this bird is found, it is protected by law and it is illegal to sell its feathers. There is a commendable reluctance on the part of state officials to issue permits to scientific collectors for the purpose of obtaining specimens of the Spoonbill or of its eggs. As a result, there are few instances of Spoonbills being shot in this country. In Texas, where they are most numerous, I came across isolated cases of such shooting; the motive seemed to be curiosity for the most part and ignorance both of birds in general and of the law. In 1940 there was one such report from the Corpus Christi vicinity and another from Scott's Bay near Houston. In the last instance the 'curiosity' of the gunner must have been considerable because his bag included one Roseate Spoonbill, two im-

mature Snowy Egrets and four adult Snowy Egrets.

In connection with this Scott's Bay case, Captain E. T. Dawson of the Texas Game, Fish and Oyster Commission made the following statement in a letter to William J. Tucker, Executive Secretary of the Commission (August 1, 1940):

It is my opinion, in the light of our findings, that very few Roseate Spoonbills have been killed along the Texas coast the last two years. No doubt, some thoughtless persons have shot at these birds sometimes. This specimen is the only one reported to us this year.

In Florida the Spoonbill is observed by the general public less frequently than on the Texas coast. Most of these observations occur during the summer months when there are more Spoonbills in that state than at other seasons. Yet the Spoonbill is far better known in Florida than in Texas, probably because of its more or less recent return to Texas. The normal reaction of people who come across a group of Spoonbills in Florida is one of pleasure. I believe that most persons would also be inclined to take a protective attitude toward the birds and would resent any attempt to kill them. There is a sort of group psychology to be found in this attitude, a conditioned result, perhaps, of the millions of words that have been ground out by real estate and resort promoters who have described the tropical beauties of Florida in such justly glowing terms. The tourists gaze in wonder and delight at rows of coconut and royal palms, at golden sands and wide, palm-studded prairies. If a small group of Spoonbills is encountered, they drink in this exotic sight in the same spirit. They are enchanted and appreciative.

Actually, a very small percentage of either residents or tourists in Florida make their way into the relatively remote and relatively uninviting regions where Spoonbills congregate. An item in the Fort Myers *News Press* for August 6, 1940, under the heading "Rare Spoonbills Found at Beach" told of a party of fisherman trolling in Ostego Bay that "forgot all about fish when they discovered a flock of 14 Roseate Spoonbills." The item went on to say that "these birds have become rare in Florida" and concluded with the statement that the party spent thirty minutes

---

[42] Unfortunately a loophole in the Tariff Act permits legally obtained Spoonbill feathers to enter this country if affidavits are filed to the effect that they are to be used for tying fish flies. One American dealer (Herter in Waseca, Minn.), in a current price list, quotes "Roseate Spoonbill Quills" at 10 cents each, 20 cents per pair. "Roseate Spoonbill Body Feathers" are offered at 10 cents for $1\frac{1}{2}$ dozen.

watching the birds feed before resuming their sport. Fortunately, this reaction is typical.

I have talked with innumerable natives in Florida who know the Spoonbill intimately; most of them are commercial fishermen. Their attitude toward the 'Pink Curlew' is adequately summarized by the individual who said to me, "I wouldn't kill one of them birds; they're too purty and there're too few of 'em. I killed one once't a long time ago just outa curiosity, but I sure wouldn't do it again and I wouldn't want to see no one else do it neither."

If Roseate Spoonbills are killed deliberately in Florida today, the chances are that the guilty party will be a respectable business man, probably from the North, who has chartered a guide boat and found the fishing dull. He will probably regret his action afterward, but at the moment he will respond to the intoxication of the vast and uninhibited wilderness.

Not long ago rumors came to our attention to the effect that northern tourists, sport fishing on the west coast of Florida, had offered as much as $25 per bird to guide-boat captains if they would secure Spoonbills for them so that they might take the feathers home as rare souvenirs of their brief sojourn in the lush tropics. While these rumors have not been positively authenticated, owing to the natural reluctance of the boat captains to mention names, it is quite possible that there have been a few instances of this sort. However, the conservation work of the National Audubon Society on that coast has created, in general, a feeling of coöperation among the guide-boat captains and a realization that these birds are an outstanding ingredient of the local color that is an essential drawing card to tourists and sport fishermen. This attitude reduces to a minimum the possibility of such deliberate decimating activities.

Spoonbills have been killed for food over a considerable period of time. In England Spoonbills were a food item until about the middle of the Seventeenth Century, when, as a result of raids on the nesting colonies, they ceased to breed in the British Isles. Apparently these raids were chiefly for the purpose of securing Spoonbill meat for the table. An early record is contained in the 'Calendar of Patent Rolls of Edward I' which is dated 1300 A.D. This tells of a commission to inquire as to who had carried off "eyries" of Shovelards[43] in several locations in Norfolk (Beetham, 1927). During the reign of Henry VIII, the Spoonbill was considered a great delicacy, and the Bishop of London, Cuthbert Tunstall, had a colony of them in his park at Fulham. In the Year Book of Henry VIII for the fourteenth year of his reign is an account of a court action for trespass made against a tenant in 1523 by the Bishop of London for taking herons and Spoonbills from his park. Bills for Henry VIII's household expenses include a notation of the payment of sums for the delivery of Shovelards (Spoonbills) from Cobham Hall ("Shoveland to the King's grace"). About this same time the Earl of Northumberland paid sixpence each for Spoonbills "to be hadde of my Lord's own mess at Pryncipale Feestes."

Apparently there was some reduction in numbers to be noticed early in the Sixteenth Century for, under an Act of Parliament of 1534, the taking of the eggs of certain wild fowl, including Shovelards, was prohibited by law. For every egg of the Spoonbill that was taken there was a fine of eightpence. The bird was still a breeding species in Queen Elizabeth's time, and an old manuscript dated about 1570, describing some of the manor houses, tells of a breeding colony on one of these old manors in Essex. They had evidentally disappeared as breeding birds by about 1662, when Sir Thomas Browne, in his manuscript account of birds found at Norfolk, states that they were shot by fowlers not for their meat "but for their handsomeness."

There is an early story of their being taken for food in Holland (Willoughby, 1678), and in his account of the "Brazilian Spoon-bill" Willoughby says, "its flesh is edible," which suggests that they may have been used as food in Brazil. As late as

---

[43] The old English name for the Spoonbill was Shoveland or sometimes Sholarde, Shoveler or Popeler. At this same time Shoveller Ducks were usually called 'Spoonbills'; later these names were exactly reversed. It is certain, however, that down to at least the late Seventeenth Century the English name for *Platalea* was generally Shovelard or the above variations.

about 1939, Dr. George B. Saunders of the United States Fish and Wildlife Service found a Spoonbill hanging in the markets at Tampico, Mexico, where it was being offered for sale as food. There have also been reports from the Florida keys as recently as 1935 telling of the taking of young Spoonbills, presumably nestlings, which were cooked in a kind of stew. Fortunately, however, I have found this to be only an occasional practice.

I have not come across any records of their use as food in either Texas or Louisiana; but since the Cajun French have always found Night Herons (Gros-becs) a table delicacy, there is no telling how far their experiments may have ventured in the gastronomic field. There are definite statements that the Spoonbill is not a food item in Spain and Italy. The Italians, who feast upon thrushes and Skylarks, apparently scorn the Spoonbill and say that its flesh is not edible (*Le carni sono immangiabili*) (Arrigoni degli Oddi, 1929). To the Spaniards it is *nada buena* as meat for the table (Beetham, 1927).

When a species shows signs of becoming rare, it is sought after by collectors. This type of collector has no valid claim to inclusion within the ranks of the legitimate scientific fraternity who take specimens of birds or other animals in order to describe the plumage or the anatomy or to study the food habits in detail. The collector of rare and vanishing species does not add to our scientific knowledge; because he has been responsible for the final extinction or extirpation of species, he has been on occasion a source of annoyance (!) to scientists and conservationists alike.

In the chapter on abundance I have already related how collectors eagerly killed as many Roseate Spoonbills as they could obtain during the early days of its decline in Florida. In England the Spoonbill had become so rare by 1889 that one which was shot on the Kentish coast of that year was sold to a collector for seven pounds (Gardiner, 1923). Apparently, any chance of the Spoonbill's return as a breeding bird to the British Isles has been in the past minimized, if not actually destroyed in large part, by the activities of collectors. A companion group that may well bear an equal responsibility is made up of ignorant gunners who kill without reason.

2. *Predation*

The outstanding work that has been done on the predator-prey relationship has been concerned for the most part with game birds, particularly quail, pheasants and grouse. There are certain fundamental principles in such matters, but it is difficult to apply theories and hypothetical equations to the Roseate Spoonbill when they have been devised for gallinaceous birds. According to Errington (1936), "the interrelationships of predation are exceedingly complex and variable, and how much they will ever be understood is problematical." It is Errington's belief that most prey species produce a surplus population that is "frittered away" generation after generation. In other words, the surplus is always temporary. Predation, according to this general hypothesis, is incidental.

There may be nothing wrong with these ideas as generalizations, but when we relate predation to a bird like the Roseate Spoonbill, we must seek our own explanations. In considering this subject, we must divide the Spoonbills of this country into two separate categories: (1) the Texas population, which is still increasing, but which apparently has not yet reached a level of stability; and (2) the Florida population, made up of breeding birds of uncertain status, and of nonbreeding birds that are present during a portion of the year only. Predation does not affect the adult Spoonbill in Florida, but it does directly involve its eggs and young.

What do we know about 'annual surplus,' 'carrying capacity of the range,' and 'stable population' as these terms apply to the Spoonbill? We have already said that the Texas birds have not yet reached a population level that can be considered as stable; in Florida the numbers are so small that we can be sure any resemblance to stability is a false one. Carrying capacity of range infers maximum density, which is presumably unattainable at the periphery of the range, although this point can obviously be argued. A discussion of the annual surplus of a species that

Plate 10.　June scene on the shore of Carroll Island in the Second Chain-of-Islands, San Antonio Bay, Texas—Spoonbills, Reddish Egrets and Louisiana Herons.

Plate 11. In flight the Spoonbill stuns the observer with its flashing colors and a loud swishing of the large, stiff flight feathers. The voice, rarely heard, is low and undeniably weird.

Plate 12. The sheltered south shore of Bottlepoint Key, Florida, is a favored feeding ground.

does not breed until it is in its fourth year can be rather complicated. I have mentioned elsewhere that a study of the recoveries of banded Herring Gulls (which do not ordinarily breed until the fourth year) indicates that 80% of the young that fledge and leave the natal colony may perish before they reach maturity (Gross, 1940). Dr. Gross found that the expected life span of a Herring Gull is about eight years, or five years of life as a breeding adult. In a colony of 1,000 birds there must be 200 new individuals added each year to maintain the population level. Dr. Gross adds:

Hence the great mortality of the young that we have noted need not be alarming, indeed it is well that many of them perish otherwise we would witness an over population of the species which already prevails in many of our colonies calling for measures of control.

Such a theory can only be applied to a large population that is literally bursting at the bounds of its range's maximum carrying density. Furthermore, from the viewpoint of our present discussion, predation was only one of the factors concerned in the high mortality of immature Herring Gulls. Dr. Gross also mentions accidents, lack of an adequate food supply, adverse weather conditions, and lowered resistance during the postjuvenal molt which might cause death from exposure and from disease and parasites. He also considered that the inexperience of the young gulls might be a factor, since they are "less wary and are more apt to meet with disaster than are the adults." These data are interesting as a comparison, but we haven't banded enough Spoonbills to know if that species and the Herring Gull are alike in any respect but that of initial breeding age.

Predation, then, may be incidental in its relation to a large population but of monumental gravity to a small population, especially one that is continuing to decrease. Let us examine this generality in the light of actual field experience.

a. Grackle Predation

I had an opportunity to study the effect of grackle predation during several seasons in Spoonbill colonies on the Texas coast. The grackle of that region is almost as large as a crow and is known as the Great-tailed Grackle. This species has evidently been increasing in parts of Texas and possibly spreading into new range, although Dr. Walter P. Taylor (*in litt.*) does not know as yet whether this apparent spread represents normal ebb and flow or a permanent increase in distributional area and in numbers. At several points along the coast these birds nest and roost on the coastal islands, invariably on the islands occupied by colonies of wading birds. There is always some predation in the form of egg destruction, but there seems to be considerable fluctuation in this habit from season to season. This fluctuation may be correlated with the relative availability of other food, i.e. grain crops, etc.

At the Second Chain-of-Islands in San Antonio Bay, grackle predation has been noted in the Spoonbill colony ever since it was established in 1928. Yet the breeding population of this colony has increased with an amazing rapidity,[44] although in one season (1940) grackle predation was responsible for a large part of the nest-mortality losses, which reached 98%. Apparently the other principal cause of loss involved in 1940 was an ectoparasite (see discussion of disease and parasites in this chapter). The loss occasioned in 1940 should be first evident in 1943 or 1944 when the young of that year would have matured. The great increase at this colony in 1941, for instance, would seem to be a reflection of the highly successful seasons of 1937 and 1938.

On the whole, colonial-nesting birds appear to have an irregular pattern of successes and failures. There are good years and there are bad. So far as grackle predation in the Second Chain colony is concerned, it did not prevent the birds from returning to nest with marked success in the same location the following year. Fluctuations in the amount or intensity of predation from year to year have an important bearing on this subject and should be more thoroughly studied. The 1940 season on the Texas coast was poor with unseasonable weather at the outset and a long delay in the initiation of reproductive activities. Not as many Spoonbills nested as the previous year, nor as many herons and egrets. We are dealing

---

[44] As mentioned elsewhere, from 50 nests in 1934 to 600 nests in 1941.

with intangibles here, but it seems barely possible that the Spoonbills may have started their nesting activities at a psychological disadvantage. The simultaneous infestation of ectoparasites among the young may be considered as an accident, but it couldn't have helped the situation. Perhaps the grackles were simply opportunists and certainly the stage was all set for a field day on their part. The Spoonbills not only failed to resist their depredations, but many of them appeared to respond to the general hysteria and deserted their nests although the eggs had not been destroyed.

So I am still unable to state whether this grackle predation may be pigeon-holed as *incidental* or not. Indeed, can such items be pigeon-holed at all? Perhaps we will know more about its importance in another two or three years; but chances are that we will never be able to make an absolutely pat statement. There may be certain immutable laws in nature, but their language will have to be extremely general or quite vague if they are to remain intact indefinitely. As we continue our minute examination of the workings of nature season after season, we are bound to have an increasing conviction that above all else nature is dynamic; it is changeable and frequently capricious. Predation, as it relates to the Roseate Spoonbill, may have one meaning today and an altogether different meaning tomorrow. Whether or not we will learn enough as we go along to permit us to guess what we will find day after tomorrow, remains to be seen. Planning for the future will require careful study, and we should not fail to benefit from all that has been learned to date.

b. Raccoon Predation

In December 1939, a nesting colony of Spoonbills was established on one of the Manatee Keys in Florida Bay. This site is a few miles west of the long-established nesting location on Bottlepoint Key, and it is known to be the habit of Florida Bay Spoonbills (an inconsistency that I cannot explain) to breed in certain seasons on keys adjacent to Bottlepoint as well as on that principal nesting key. Old nests on Manatee indicated that they had built in that location prior to

1940, and we had also found some of them nesting on nearby Stake Key for two or three years previous to 1940.

The Manatee group comprised only twelve nests, but this small number is of some consequence in Florida Bay where the average number of breeding pairs during the last five seasons has been between fifteen and sixteen. Incubation had scarcely begun when the nests were discovered by raccoons. These animals destroyed nearly all of the eggs, and all Spoonbills deserted the area. There was absolutely no attempt made to lay a second clutch.

As the Manatee Keys are located in Florida Bay some five nautical miles in a straight line from the Florida mainland and an equal distance from the nearest point on Key Largo, the presence of coons was totally unexpected. My first reaction, quite naturally, was to think that we had found *the* limiting factor in Florida Bay, but a host of questions arose which required a lot of field work and study to answer. Where did these raccoons come from? How long had they been on these keys? Why had they come there? How did they live in that environment?

If I was to understand the significance of the relationship of the raccoon (predator) and the Roseate Spoonbill (prey), I would have to find the answer to these and many other questions. For some weeks thereafter, I diligently forgot about Spoonbills and studied raccoons. It was soon apparent that the existence of the raccoon in that environment is quite obviously limited by certain definite factors.

An initial exploration of Manatee Key disclosed the presence of not more than two or three coons. Their tracks were plainly to be seen in soft mud along the edge of the mangrove roots near the site of the Spoonbill colony. I also found trails along other shore lines of the key and evidence that these resourceful mammals had been digging out the large burrowing crabs that live on the higher ground of these keys. After consulting a chart of the region, it seemed most likely that they had reached Manatee by following the natural bridge or chain of keys leading northward to the mainland near Madeira Point. The first job was to examine this chain of keys

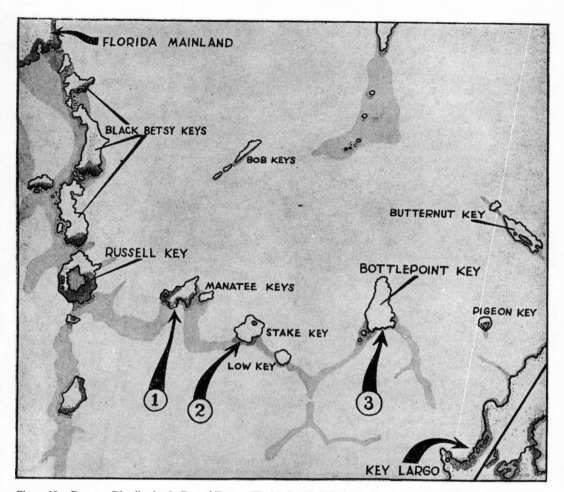

Figure 10. Raccoon Distribution in Part of Eastern Florida Bay in Relation to Spoonbill Nesting Groups:

1. Nesting Site Occupied in Winter 1939–40; All Eggs Destroyed by Raccoons.
2. Occasional Nesting Site; Raccoons May Occur Here Infrequently.
3. Regular Nesting Site; No Record of Raccoons (Raccoon Density Indicated by Stippling and Shading.

and see what we could learn about their raccoon populations, if any.

The next key to the north is a large one named Russell Key. It has a sizable land-locked pond in the center and around the western and southeastern rim of this pond we found an abundance of coon sign. To the north of Russell, on various segments of the Black Betsy Keys, were additional signs and on the mainland well-traveled trails.

This chain of keys lies along a curving line some eight nautical miles in length (see accompanying map). The keys themselves are a typical combination of pioneer and mature red mangrove. Between various segments of the chain, pioneer red mangroves are rapidly building land that will eventually make this chain a long narrow peninsula. It seemed plainly evident that raccoons would have no particular difficulty in traveling from key to key over the entire distance from the mainland to Manatee.

My observations indicated that there was a reasonably large population of coons on the mainland in that vicinity, large enough possibly to create an overflow which had established itself on the outlying keys. I found that there were possible precedents for such dispersals. In February and March of 1930, Dr. E. W. Nelson (1930) collected and studied raccoons among the Ten Thousand Islands of the southwest coast of Florida, an environment with many similarities to that of the vicinity of Madeira Point and adjacent Florida Bay. He relates that single trappers in that region "sometimes took the skins of more than 800 raccoons on the keys in a season, but that, owing to this severe trapping, it is difficult now for a man to get even one-third of that number. Similar accounts of the former abundance of raccoons on other keys off the coast were given me by trappers elsewhere . . . The total catch of raccoons for southern Florida and the keys must be very large." This statement was made more than a decade ago. Since then, demand for the skins of raccoons has sharply declined and these animals appear to have greatly increased throughout southern Florida.

Dr. Nelson also studied the raccoons that are found on the main line of Florida keys from Key Largo south and west to Key West. As in the Ten Thousand Islands many of these keys are separated from each other by deep tidal channels, and these mammalian inhabitants have been isolated long enough to form subspecific characters. Dr. Nelson described four new raccoons, all differing from the Florida raccoon of the mainland. These four groups are distributed as follows:

Subspecies	Distribution
Procyon lotor marinus	The Ten Thousand Islands, a broad compact belt of mangrove keys lying for about 100 miles along the southwestern coast of the peninsula from a little south of Naples to Shark River
Procyon lotor inesperatus	The Key Largo group found along the southeastern border of the peninsula on Virginia and Biscayne Keys, Elliott Key, Key Largo, Plantation Key and Upper and Lower Matecumbe Keys
Procyon lotor auspicatus	The Key Vaca group, including Long Key, Duck, Grassy and Fat Deer Keys, Key Vaca and Knights Key
Procyon lotor incautus	The Big Pine Key group, including No Name, Big and Little Pine Keys, Torch Keys, Ramrod, Cudjoe, Summerland, Saddlebunch, Boca Chica Keys and Key West

Dr. Nelson found that these new forms tended to be smaller in size than the mainland raccoons and also duller and paler as to color. He pointed out that raccoons isolated on islands on the Atlantic coast side of the continent[45] from Cozumel Island off Yucatan to the Bahamas and the coast of southern Florida were all smaller than animals on the adjacent mainland. On the Pacific side of the continent, however, raccoons of the Tres Marias Islands, which are high, wooded and supplied with fresh water, are about the same size as the animals of the neighboring Mexican mainland.

In the Florida keys, as on other Atlantic coast islands, raccoons have no access to fresh water, as Dr. Nelson puts it, beyond "the fortuitous opportunities that may occur during a heavy rain." It seems possible that this is the chief factor contributing to their small size. In further comment on this interesting point Dr. Nelson writes:

Previously I had always thought of raccoons as animals dependent on available fresh water and it surprised me to find them living in great numbers among the mangrove islands, both in the Ten Thousand Islands and on other Florida keys, without any possible source of such water.

In Florida Bay the local center of abundance appeared to be Russell Key, particularly the shores of the pond already mentioned. Salinity tests

---

45 There are no raccoons in Cuba, where Spoonbills continue to breed in several colonies. S. C. Bruner (*in litt.*) suggests that the only mammalian predator (other than man) that might attack Spoonbills in Cuba is the introduced mongoose, which, however, does not climb trees.

indicate that the water in this pond may, on occasion, have a much greater density than ordinary sea water. In February 1940, for example, the salinity of the water in Russell Key pond was slightly in excess of 42.8.[46] In spite of this high density, the pond seems to maintain a numerous population of fish, including killifishes which are eaten by Spoonbills as well as by raccoons.

Another factor mentioned by Dr. Nelson is this all-important one of food supply, and he felt that "the abundance of crabs, shell fish and other food provided by the sea for the raccoons would appear to remove the possible factor of food shortage from the list of possible causes for the smaller size among these animals." His interest is in the size of the key raccoon as compared with the mainland animal, a point that does not enter our discussion; but his remarks on the food of these raccoons has an important bearing on both distribution and abundance. He speaks further of their feeding on "an abundant supply of fish, crustaceans and the shell fish left exposed on the mud at each low tide." In Florida Bay there is no periodic tide and the occasional fluctuations in water levels result from amount and accumulation of precipitation and the direction and force of the wind over extended periods. If the water level is not too high, the coons in this region can resort to extensive shallow flats where fish, crustaceans and certain edible forms of molluscs are available. However, their distribution may be radically affected by excessive precipitation. During September 1940, there were unusually heavy rains over eastern Florida Bay. Recorded precipitation for September alone, as measured at the Tavernier weather bureau station, was 20.1 inches, a departure of 12.43 inches plus from the normal rainfall for that month. There was also an excessive amount of rainfall during the following December. Water levels on Russell Key in the fall and early winter

of 1940–41 were high enough to bring about a drastic shift in the raccoon population, which extended along the Black Betsy Keys toward the mainland. Evidently the animals had been forced to retreat to such higher portions of these outlying keys as could be found or to the more elevated ground of the mainland. Possibly the higher water levels made it difficult to secure food readily, and in a region where there are no periodic low tides, this would be quite a serious situation. I estimated that only one-third of the raccoons present on Russell Key one year before were still there in late January 1941. Two or three animals were still present, however, on the Manatee Keys.

A possible reason for raccoon abundance and a practical explanation for their presence on these keys is the relative absence of natural enemies. Dr. Nelson suggested that the "absence of natural enemies evidently gives favorable conditions for their increase and the accounts given me of the amazing numbers of them trapped on the keys, when the high prices of furs gave incentive, makes it apparent that they must have been excessively numerous for an animal of their size." I found evidence of a fairly large bobcat population on the mainland at Madeira Point but no indications that these animals crossed to outlying keys. In the bay proper the only animals large enough to prey upon raccoons would seem to be crocodiles, which, however, are not too abundant and which may feed exclusively on fish. There are several pairs of Bald Eagles nesting on keys in the bay, but these birds would only be able to capture young coons and the chances would not be very great that such predation would occur often. Thus, so far as natural enemies are concerned, the raccoon would appear to be a rather free agent on these outlying keys.

The causes behind a dispersal of raccoons over keys in the bay would appear, therefore, to be a response to the combination of a normal pressure of numbers in an abundant population on the mainland, a certain desirability in the outer key environment, plus the aquatic propensities of the raccoon itself. The presence of coons as far from the mainland as the Manatee Keys suggests that the

---

[46] Salinity in parts per one thousand. An average 1000 grams of sea water contain 35 grams of sodium chloride, magnesium salts and calcium. Sodium chloride by itself amounts to approximately three-fourths of the total or a little more than 27 grams. However, sea water is usually said to contain on the average 35 grams of salts of various kinds; salinity is grams of salts per 1000 grams.

Russell Key population may have been numerous enough to have built up a pressure of numbers of its own. As Elton (1927) points out, dispersals are concerned "with the movements of animals in search of food, of shelter, or of their mates." But we can only theorize. Dispersal has to do not only with the biological side of the picture but also with psychology or even chemistry, meteorology or oceanography!

There is no question, however, about the presence of raccoons on these keys far from the mainland; regardless of how they get there or why, two factors concerned with apparent fluctuation in their numbers can be easily recognized. One of these is the land-building role of mangroves, which has reached a stage in that particular region where it is possible for raccoons to travel almost dry-shod back and forth to and from the mainland at will. This is an extremely important fact, because (1) it would appear to accomplish the gradual destruction of any distinct race of raccoons that may have evolved on these outlying keys in former times, and (2) because there is no telling when conditions may result in several peak years for the coons, the impetus of which would carry them along the entire chain of keys as far as the main Spoonbill nesting site on Bottlepoint. They have been reported already from Stake Key (see map).

In connection with this study of the Roseate Spoonbill, I have no particular interest in whether the Florida Bay raccoons are another new race or not, unless this would also mean that these insular raccoons are by habit more aquatic than their fellows on the mainland. The insular races described by Dr. Nelson had developed certain habits that were a result of necessity. He writes of the Ten Thousand Islands, for example: "Most of these islets are completely covered by the sea to a depth of from about one to three feet at each high tide, and are totally devoid of fresh water. As most of these islands have no large trees to afford hollows and no dry land the raccoons must make their homes on top of the mangrove roots where they are forced to retreat by the incoming tide." However, similar conditions do not prevail throughout the range of races occurring in the Florida keys, where for the most part there

would be higher ground to which the animals could retreat during high tide. Furthermore, periodic tide is negligible on the Gulf side of the range of *Procyon lotor inesperatus*, and in Florida Bay proper there is no lunar tide.

A special adaptability to life on Florida Bay keys would seem to mean that 'Florida Bay raccoons' would be more likely to disperse as far as Bottlepoint Key than would mainland raccoons.

The mangrove factor has another aspect that is of special interest: for how long a time have these keys been joined so as to form a natural highway? Davis (1940) writes:

> The land-building role of mangroves is influenced by many marine factors of a complex nature, and certain studies of oceanography and geology were necessary to understand these factors. Such things as tidal and other marine currents, turbulence of the water, and changes in sea level were difficult to measure or estimate. Sedimentation and accumulation of organic materials could be calculated only in the roughest fashion in so short a time. All these factors can be partly understood, although the observations and data are not of much quantitative value.

In his extensive studies of the ecology and the geologic role of mangroves in Florida, Davis did considerable field work in Florida Bay. He found that land building was more evident in Florida Bay than elsewhere, one important reason being that this region is not subject to a daily rise and fall of tide. By contrast, he found areas on the coast of the peninsula where the mangrove is exposed to both tide and surf and where there is little or no land building. In his summary, he states that "numerous instances of new and enlarged islands and some instances of extended mainland coasts were found . . . if new, mature swamp areas are considered land, then there are more than a thousand acres of recently formed land in the Florida Bay to Biscayne Bay region." He even suggests the possibility of using mangrove plantings to extend the coast and form new islands.

The additional acreage mentioned by Davis has been added, in his opinion, within the past thirty or forty years. A study of topographic maps of the United States Coast and Geodetic Survey compiled from air photographs taken in January 1935 and supplemented by surveys to May 1937, indicates that considerable growth of

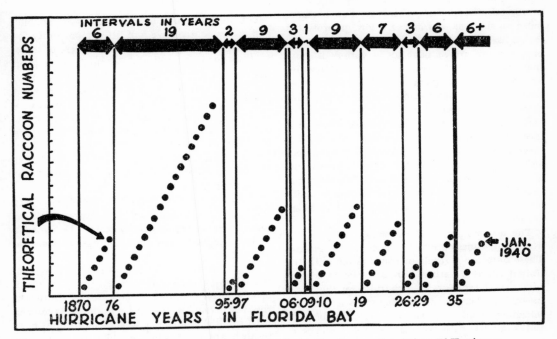

Figure 11.   Theoretical Relationship between the Florida Bay Raccoon Population and Hurricanes.

pioneer mangrove occurred on the southern tips of the line of keys from Russell Key northward to the mainland between those years and 1940. Unquestionably the progress of this pioneer growth and the actual land building that follows is more rapid in the later stages.   Very likely it has been a matter of only a relatively few years since raccoons have been able to travel this route without actually swimming.[47]   If this is true, then it is possible that the raccoon factor in the life of Florida Bay Spoonbills is a recent development.   On the other hand, if raccoons occur in numbers along the main line of keys to Key West, what was there to prevent them from

occupying keys in Florida Bay regardless of 'land' bridges?   I have only one available answer: my surveys in Florida Bay resulted in the discovery of raccoons only on keys connected with the mainland by shoals covered in part with pioneer mangrove.   There were no raccoons, for example, on the Bob Keys to the north of Manatee, or on Pigeon Key east of Bottlepoint, or on Butternut Key northeast of Bottlepoint.   None of these keys are connected with the mainland or with nearby Key Largo, and to reach them coons would have to swim or be carried there by wreckage or driftwood.

It is interesting to note, too, that there is no record of the presence of raccoons on Bottlepoint Key, which is at the extreme end of the chain of keys that we have been discussing.

Great fluctuations in the coon population of this region result from the periodic occurrence of hurricanes, with their direct effect upon increase or decrease of shoals or land bridges between the

[47] Don McKay (in letter dated 1-18-41) states that raccoons reached Bird Island in Orange Lake (Florida) during the 1940 nesting season, with considerable damage resulting to the eggs of nesting birds, particularly Louisiana Herons.   Many nests were deserted.   He believed the recent slaughter of some thirty-six alligators in the lake was responsible for the ability of the coons to reach the island, where they had not previously occurred.

keys. These storms vary in intensity; but when a tropical disturbance of seventy-five or more miles an hour sweeps across a low, unprotected region like Florida Bay, the mangrove keys in the bay, none of which have an elevation of more than approximately two or three feet, are inundated by a driving mass of water that is sometimes of tidal wave proportions. Since 1870 there have been twelve such storms in the eastern part of Florida Bay. It seems very doubtful if raccoons living on keys in the bay could survive these hurricanes. This suggests that a repopulation must take place following such storms; if this repopulation must await normal dispersal from the mainland, hurricanes become a major factor in limiting the distribution and numbers of raccoons in this area.

The accompanying figure shows the years in which hurricanes occurred in eastern Florida Bay. These data are a result of consultation with the United States Weather Bureau office in Miami and several residents of Tavernier on the lower tip of Key Largo, one of whom has a vivid recollection of all these storms since that of 1895 and is familiar with records going as far back as 1870.

Of chief interest is the interval between storms which, it will be seen, varies from a few weeks to one span of nineteen years. Theoretical increase in the raccoon population has been plotted for the entire period from 1870 to date, although the evidence indicates that raccoons in any numbers may not have been present on outlying keys in Florida Bay during this entire period. The assumption is that the raccoon population curve will be ascending until the next hurricane in that region (although a temporary retreat toward the mainland may be a result of abnormally heavy rainfall over a period of time).

I have given so much attention to the subject of raccoons because it seems obvious that when this animal comes in direct contact with nesting Spoonbills in Florida Bay the resulting predation can scarcely be termed *incidental*. Furthermore, there is the possibility that raccoons, as a decimating factor, may appear upon the scene again and again and may even reach the main colony on Bottlepoint Key.

3. Disease and Parasites

For the most part I have studied live Spoonbills and consequently have had little opportunity for any original investigation of the present topic. In June 1940, a number of Spoonbill nestlings in the Second Chain colony in San Antonio Bay, Texas, were deserted by their parents. I thought at first that these young birds, which died in a very short space of time, were killed by Great-tailed Grackles, or else starved to death following their desertion. These were obvious conclusions, but a post-mortem conducted by Dr. C. Brooke Worth of Swarthmore College indicates that neither was correct.

I also assumed that mass desertion of the colony was caused primarily by the depredations of grackles on the eggs of nearby nests. Dr. Worth's findings suggest that this assumption was also at fault.

Of the specimens of young sent to Dr. Worth, the following post-mortem is typical. Although no conclusive diagnosis of the cause of the deaths could be given, Dr. Worth found the birds covered with small ectoparasites in sufficient numbers to result in abnormal behavior which may have been the chief cause for desertion. It is fairly well known that parent birds will not offer food to young in the nest except in reaction to the stimulus produced by the hunger crys and posturings of the young, and in some cases to the special color at the gape of the young bird's mouth, such as is present in many species. If these young Spoonbills were so weakened that they were unable to lift their heads or beg, it is fairly certain that they would not be fed and their desertion would simply be a matter of time.

I visited this same colony the following year (1941) but found no evidence of mortality among nestlings. The causes of the infestation of parasites remain unknown.

The complete post-mortem contributed by Dr. Worth is included herewith.

Roseate Spoonbill   Age: four days   Sex: ?

History

Found dead in nest in colony at Second Chain-of-Islands, San Antonio Bay, Texas, June 12, 1940. Alcoholic specimen. Desertion of nest by parents ascribed tentatively to depredations of Great-tailed Grackles. Four specimens sent to me, of which this is the first examined.

General

A newly hatched fledgling. No outward signs of gross injury, such as pecking by grackles. Bird covered with small red ectoparasites which are either 'seed ticks' or large mites. These occur in clusters, such as in the region of the upper neck and in the folds of the thigh, but also less commonly as individuals scattered over the entire body surface. There are about fifty ectoparasites, their heads buried in the skin of the bird.

Visceral examination

Heart and lungs grossly normal.
Trachea clear.
Oesophagus and mouth empty, clean.
Stomach divided into well-recognizable proventriculus and gizzard.
Proventriculus empty.
Gizzard contains a small quantity of material resembling mud. Under the dissecting microscope this is seen to be made up of about 50% mineral matter and 50% organic matter. Of the organic material, the only recognizable objects are about a dozen small fish scales.
Intestines contain a small quantity of muddy material. Yolk sac still very prominent, containing about 7 or 8 cc of yolk still unabsorbed.

Cloaca contains a large fragment of stone, shaped like one-half of a longitudinally split oval pebble. This object measures about 5 × 10 mm. in its axes.
Kidneys grossly normal. Gonads not seen.
Liver and pancreas grossly normal. Spleen not seen.
No internal parasites observed.

Gross diagnosis

As to immediate cause of death, no conclusive diagnosis. As to cause of desertion by parents, the large number of ectoparasites may well have been an important factor. Had the parents remained attentive, it is also possible that the ectoparasites might have become a direct cause of the nestlings' death.

Comment

Treating of nests with insect powder by the warden might be tried. Ectoparasites sent to Dr. C. M. Herman for identification.

C. INFLUENCES

Environmental conditions that affect wildlife indirectly rather than directly have been termed influences. These may be both favorable and unfavorable, depending on the circumstances. The most obvious of these influences is weather; others that affect the fortunes of the Roseate Spoonbill are drainage, cultivation, oil drilling and other human activities which have no direct interest in the Roseate Spoonbill or its way of life, but which touch it, for good or bad.[48] When a new road is built across a swamp that was previously unpenetrable, the taxpayers are concerned with the road as a route that will permit them to carry their produce to markets. A gasoline station is located somewhere on this new road and in time a little community grows around this beginning. None of these people even heard of a Spoonbill, or a Louisiana Heron or an American Egret. But the little 'rookery' a few miles away is soon visited by boys from the new community and its comparative isolation suddenly disintegrates. In time, so do the birds. The roads and the gasoline station, the community and its inhabitants are all perfectly legitimate (and inevitable), but they are the 'influences,' the indirect factors, that result in desertion of another site.

1. Weather

We are so familiar with weather that its operations seem fairly obvious. It is good, bad or indifferent; and it seems like an easy matter to correlate its condition with bird behavior and point dramatically to cause and effect. This is not the case. Except when weather indulges in violent excesses—prolonged and severe droughts, gales and hurricanes, record freezes or cloudbursts —the lives of most birds proceed with little apparent concern as to minor climatic fluctuations.

The storms that destroyed eggs and young in Texas in 1936 and in Florida Bay in 1940 are the only direct evidence I have found of the actual loss of Spoonbills as the result of weather conditions. The wind and driving rain of a storm and the resulting high tides act as decimating factors rather than influences. Storms can be influences when they alter the habitat, as in Cuthbert and Alligator Lakes where hurricanes killed the mangrove trees and apparently rendered

---

[48] Another item that appears to be more of an influence than a factor is the geographic location of a Spoonbill colony with relation to optimum range for the species. This point is mentioned here but not discussed. We know too little of the qualifications of optimum.

them unsuitable for nesting sites. I am not at all sure, though, that Spoonbills wouldn't return to breed in these two places regardless of the condition of the cover, if there were a sufficient number of adults still alive that had formerly bred in this vicinity. Beecher (1942) has described the encroachment of civilization on a small slough in Illinois; although a general exodus of birds from this area took place as the marsh grew smaller, some Red-wings exhibited so great an apparent attachment to this home area that they ultimately accepted sand-bar willows in place of the cattails in which they had formerly nested.

Bayard Christy (1928) found four Spoonbill nests in Alligator Lake in February 1927. At that time the red mangrove in which the birds nested was in good condition. John B. Semple (*in litt.*) visited the same colony a year later and found it abandoned except for a few Wood Ibises. The red mangrove was still unharmed. In January 1929, Pike (1931) discovered twelve Spoonbill nests in this same location. It was in the following September that a tropical hurricane killed large areas of mangrove and other trees in that region. Bent (*in litt.*) wrote: "I visited this lake in 1930 and found that recent hurricanes had killed all the large trees and there were no Spoonbills there, only a few Wood Ibises and Cormorants."

Such has been the situation ever since so far as Alligator Lake is concerned. At Cuthbert Lake, where damage to vegetation was not so great as in Alligator Lake, although many old mangroves were destroyed, Spoonbills have nested only once in recent years, in 1937. On this occasion, according to Audubon Warden Earle Moore, they built their nests in a large fern-like plant which grows in profusion on the island.

Only a very small percentage of Spoonbills present on the Florida peninsula in spring are adult birds. Is it, then, a lack of nesting cover, a lack of adult Spoonbills, or some other deficiency that prevents the species from returning to nest in these hereditary sites?

Weather may be an influence in other ways. Temperature has sometimes been closely correlated with the start of laying in certain species

(Starling, Kluijver, 1933; Prairie Horned Lark, Pickwell, 1931). Mrs. Nice (1937) found that the start of laying with the Song Sparrows at Columbus, Ohio, was closely correlated with the mean temperature. She points out, though, that some birds appear to be unaffected by temperature in the matter of nesting: European Cranes, ducks, various marsh birds, Hooded Crows. In the spring of 1940 Spoonbills, herons and egrets on the Texas coast were approximately a month later than usual in beginning their nesting activities (see chapter on 'Breeding-Cycle Behavior').

Because the delay in nesting occurred in both the Spoonbill colony on San Antonio Bay and in the Galveston Bay colony nearly 200 miles away, it would appear that the critical influence may have been of a general climatic nature. Possibly there was some connection between this situation and the record 'freeze' of the previous January, when great numbers of fish and many crustaceans, including shrimp, were killed by the low water temperatures (Gunter, 1941). It was estimated that on the Texas coast alone at least a million pounds of fish succumbed during that period of low temperatures.

In addition to the delay that was noted in the start of nesting activities the following March and April among fish-eating species on the Texas coast, there was a general falling off in the numbers of nesting pairs in all colonies. At the Second Chain colony American Egrets fed lizards (*Cnemidophorus* sp.) to their young, the first season that this was observed.

The following table shows the number of nests built by Spoonbills on the Second Chain during eight years. The gradual upward trend has been interrupted on only two occasions: 1936 and 1940. In 1936 gale winds and high tides occurred just after the start of incubation.

Year	Number of Nests
1934	50
1935	53
1936	23
1937	109
1938	141
1939	157
1940	87
1941	600

One inference with regard to the falling off in 1940 is that the January freeze of that year had a serious effect on the abundance and possibly on the distribution of the normal food supply of these birds, but there is no actual proof that this was the cause. Millions of shrimp may have succumbed on the Texas coast, but they may have been eaten by gulls and other birds before investigators arrived. Gunter found no subsequent decrease in the shrimp catch.

At the Vingt'un colony in Galveston Bay, there was a general reduction in the number of nesting pairs, but the two ibises showed increases and Black-crowned Night Herons were unaffected.

Species	Number of Nests		
	1939	1940	1941
Roseate Spoonbill	140	32	234
Snowy Egret	250	10	*
Louisiana Heron	200	0	*
American Egret	12	0	210
Ward's Heron	12	4	5
Black-crowned Night Heron	25	24	?
White Ibis	16	30	41
White-faced Glossy Ibis	6	29	75
Wood Ibis	0	0	3
	661	129	568*

* "Too many to count" (warden's report).

In addition to the possible effect of this period of cold weather upon the food supply, a number of large trees, chiefly hackberries, were killed by the cold on the Vingt'un Islands. Evidently as a result of the loss of these trees, which had been used as nest sites, most of the birds shifted to an adjacent island, where they nested in 1940.

The two ibises, which showed an increase in 1940, I observed feeding that season on crayfish along the levee banks of rice fields as far inland as Anáhuac. These creatures probably survived the freeze. Night Herons, which did not decrease, have been found to be extremely adaptable in their food habits, as was demonstrated by studies on Long Island, New York (Allen, 1938).

2. Drainage and Cultivation

Because the Roseate Spoonbill is popularly thought of as a marsh bird, many persons have suggested that drainage of the Everglades may be the chief factor in its decline in Florida. In com-menting on the disappearance of the Spoonbill as a nesting species in England, Henry Ogg Forbes (Butler, 1896–98) stated that marshes and fens, in which the birds nested, were gradually drained in parts of England.

Spoonbills, including the European, will nest in areas that are not marshes. Various English colonies were located in trees in the parks of manor houses as well as in marshes and fens. A Spanish colony occupied a growth of glasswort (Kirkman, 1913) and, off the coast of Sierra Leone, Spoonbills constructed their nests on a rocky island (Bannerman, 1930). In Texas, nests in the two most successful colonies are on rather well-elevated and perfectly dry coastal islands.

Of course, Spoonbills must be close to shallow water in order to secure their food supply, but there are many examples and types of shallow-water areas in addition to marshes. So far as the situation in Florida is concerned, there does not appear to be any obvious connection between desertion of Spoonbill colonies and drainage of the Everglades. In Florida the Spoonbill has always been, so far as we know, an inhabitant of the littoral—a species whose niche is quite definitely maritime. It is true that there were nesting colonies in fresh-water lakes and swamps in that state, but there is no indication that these inland colonies were ever very large.

Certainly from the viewpoint of the food habits of our species, drainage of marshes has had no effect on littoral fishes, crustaceans, water insects, etc., which are able to adapt themselves to all sorts of changes in water density and which appear to be extremely abundant in all shallow-water regions of the Gulf coast.

3. Oil Drilling

The dangers that confront the Roseate Spoonbill are real enough without enlarging them, without making mountains out of mole hills. Oil fields and Spoonbills are something of an anomaly as a picture for placid contemplation, but they are not entirely incompatible.

When Dr. Frank M. Chapman (1933) went ashore on Pajaro Island on the Mexican Gulf coast in April 1910, he noted that the rim of the island was thick with a black, tarry scum of oil.

A well on the mainland had blown out and, catching fire, had burned for three months, consuming an estimated 10,000,000 barrels of oil. Yet in the midst of this, a Spoonbill colony of some 200 nests was completing a successful season.

When oil was discovered in the coastal marshes of Louisiana, it was only a question of time until wells were drilled in the vicinity of the Louisiana Spoonbill colony. In June 1919, Alfred Bailey and E. G. Wright (1931) found fourteen Spoonbills in the Black Bayou breeding site, but no nests. They commented: "The Black Bayou colony was broken up by the discovery of oil; greasy derricks and rattling machinery now are found where the Roseates once held forth." In early July 1940, I visited this same oil field, which in the meantime has produced millions of barrels of oil and is still in operation. The man who took me to the Spoonbill colony (which is also flourishing) is a patrolman for the oil company and appeared to be as proud of the Spoonbills as he was of the producing wells.

Oil drilling in open coastal waters, however, may be quite a different matter. In June 1941, I visited an oil rig in San Antonio Bay not far from the Second Chain colony. Crude oil had been pumped from barges lying alongside this rig and had produced a slick several miles long. Young Spoonbills at the Second Chain were fledging at this time, and most of them were to be found feeding along the rim of the nesting islands. If the wind and tide had been from an easterly quarter and this film of heavy oil had reached the shores of the Second Chain, the results might have been quite serious. By great good fortune, the residue was carried to the mainland shore two miles north and east of the colony. These open water drilling rigs are a real threat to wildlife. A blowout (which may occur as a result of a failure of the human equation, and despite careful mechanical checks) can pollute vast areas of normally healthy water environments. Birds of many kinds and in great numbers may die as a result of direct contact with floating oil.

D. SUMMARY

1. Welfare factors are concerned with the type and character of the environment in which the Spoonbill lives. These habitat characteristics must satisfy certain requirements as to

a.   Nesting and roosting space, which is found in many kinds of vegetation but which must have certain important relationships, the most vital being

   (1)   Adjacent shallows, which have a twofold survival value in providing available food and harboring the young when they are learning to fend for themselves;

b.   Minimum tidal range, also of importance because of its relation to

   (1) Food availability

   (2) A suitable water environment, i.e. 'clean' water that will support an abundant animal community, since food animals must be

     (a) Constantly available

     (b) Abundant

     (c) Nutritious;

c.   Security from predators and disturbance by man;

d.   Geographic location, of importance because of the climatic factor;

e.   Size of the colony, a less tangible factor but one which may be very essential.

2.   Decimating factors kill directly.

a.   Man, long the most serious enemy of the Spoonbill, both on this continent and abroad, kills deliberately and through ignorance or carelessness. He is now of negligible importance as a decimating factor in the U. S. portion of the range.

b.   Predators (especially raccoons and Great-tailed Grackles) may only be important when a population is much reduced. Otherwise, their effect is evidently temporary.

c.   Thus far, the record indicates that parasites and disease may be only temporary and local in their effect.

3.   Various influences affect the environment, and may be favorable or unfavorable according to the circumstances. Those that concern the Spoonbill's welfare are climatic conditions, drainage, cultivation, oil drilling.

Part V.   Breeding-Cycle Behavior

MY studies of the reproductive cycle of the Roseate Spoonbill have been reassuring. The unusual features of the bird may remind us of the Pleistocene but nothing could be more unsound or more unscientific than to link this *appearance* of antiquity with the physiology or psychology of the bird itself. *Ajaia ajaja* is a vigorous race. Within the natural limitations that encompass the lives and attributes of all animals the Spoonbill's existence is successful and well balanced. It is perfectly attuned to its environment.

Man, though, has come upon the scene in the last three-quarters of a century and wrought changes that have been permanently disastrous in some areas, temporarily so in others. These changes affected the habitat in some regions it is true, but the outstanding result was almost total annihilation and dispersal of the birds themselves. Those that were not killed were widely scattered, their lives repeatedly harassed by gunners of the plumage trade. The breeding Spoonbill population of the Florida mainland has never recovered from the uninhibited destruction of the half century from 1850 to 1900; but their failure to recover has not been due to any deficiency in the species. Florida is at the outermost edge of the Spoonbill's range; it is at the northern rim or periphery. The birds were destroyed, driven out, shamefully persecuted for two generations. Is there any wonder they dwindled and all but disappeared? Is there any wonder they do not readily return and prosper anew under a more hospitable aegis? Where are they to come from? Cuba? South America? This is one of our problems, and we will do well to examine it cautiously and thoroughly if we are to hope and plan for a reestablishment of breeding Roseate Spoonbills in peninsular Florida.

In the present account of breeding-cycle behavior, my treatment of the many vital activities in the life of the species must be as scientific and authentic as material and subject require, but I have also kept the general reader in mind. It is a far cry from the quaint mythology that surrounded early bird studies to the scientific investigations of today. As late as the Seventeenth Century, Willoughby[49] (who was probably the most accurate writer on the subject up to that time) still thought that Black Storks were kind to their parents and fed, nourished and otherwise maintained them during their old age. To his credit he branded as false the current belief that these storks lived only in "Republics and free-States." He had seen them "in the Territories of some Princes in Germany!" Willoughby's descriptions of Roseate Spoonbills collected by explorers and voyagers in distant Brazil and Mexico are accurate enough, although the drawing of a European Spoonbill that accompanies his text (see figure) is somewhat wanting.

Today we even seek to penetrate the bird mind and interpret bird emotion, which, as Julian Huxley (1916) has said, is "not yet complicated by reason." For birds are unable to *think* as men do. Their acts result from the stimulation of some movement or display, some posture or sound in another bird that 'releases' certain behavior in the recipient. The 'mind' of a bird is like a chart of patterns, some innate, others acquired. All of them are capable of definite responses, which are released by a visual or auditory stimulus. In turn, these releasers may appear only at a certain season, and are evidently dependent on the development of the gonadal cycle in the individual.

I will not, therefore, speak of 'Mr. and Mrs. Spoonbill' or refer to their 'love' for each other. It is much more complicated than that and, as I think will be agreed, much more interesting.

A.   PREPAIRING PHASE

This period in the breeding cycle considers the behavior of the birds from the time of their arrival in the vicinity of the breeding colony until the pairs are formed. In some species that are highly territorial the males arrive before the females, and in such cases the male birds are the first to occupy the territories. (The female Northern Phalarope takes up territory ahead of the male bird and therefore is the first to arrive on the breeding

---

[49] 1676, Francisci Willughbei ornithologiae. . . .

71

Figure 12.   Francis Willoughby's Spoonbill.

to be correlated with a considerable drop in the mean temperature curve, but during November 1941, the usual pairing time in Florida Bay, the mean temperature was three degrees above the normal for that month.   Mean temperature appears to be the only climatic factor that has been consistently correlated with the gonadal cycle in birds (Nice, 1937; Blanchard, 1941).   There are also factors other than external ones.[51]

In 1940 some 300 Spoonbills were first observed near the San Antonio Bay colony at the Second Chain-of-Islands on February 25 (J. G. Fuller, *in litt.*).   This flock approximated the full size of the breeding group in the colony at that time.   At the Vingt'un colony on Galveston Bay, some 180 miles farther east, adults usually arrive about March 5, according to Warden W. T. Friddell. In 1940 the first group of arrivals came in on that date to the number of twenty-five individuals. Pairing commenced about April 23, which Friddell considered to be a month later than the usual date.

1.   Prepairing Behavior

The length of the pairing bond varies with different groups of birds, a subject that has been discussed by Heinroth (1928)[52] and Lack (1940). A few birds are believed to pair for life, but there is little positive evidence of this.   Some species,

place.[50])   Apparently the arriving Spoonbill flocks are made up of both males and females, although the sexes are alike in appearance and there is no actual proof of this.

On the Texas coast adults reached the vicinity of the nesting colony on San Antonio Bay late in February 1940, as much as two months before pairing.   I believe that pairing was delayed in that particular season, however, and it may be more usual for the birds to arrive approximately a month ahead of the pairing date.   At the Florida Bay colony during two seasons (1939 and 1940) the adults appeared in early October and pairs were formed about one month later.   In 1941 pairing was delayed at this colony until mid-December.

The delay in the Texas colony in 1940 appeared

[50] 1935, Tinbergen.

[51] Correlations have been indicated between the mean temperature curve and migration.   Nice (1937) suggested a formula for the temperature threshold for spring arrival of male Song Sparrows at Columbus, Ohio.   This threshold was set at 53° F. (11.6° C.) on February 23, and decreased about $^3/_4$ of a degree F. each day for a month.   Increasing day-length was also a conditioning factor.   Mrs. Nice further points out that the migration of some early species is strongly influenced by weather (*Wettervögel*) and other late migrants (*Instinktvögel*) are less affected.

Spoonbills migrating within the tropics may not be greatly influenced by temperatures.   They probably migrate chiefly in response to hereditary rhythms in the gonadal cycle (see Blanchard, 1941).   This is an interesting speculation with regard to the Florida Spoonbills, some of which arrive in October to breed in Florida Bay and others in March to breed on the mainland.   The origin of these separate sexual rhythms is most certainly a remote one, and we can hardly expect to find the explanation in current environmental conditions.

[52] Ehigkeit oder Keinehigkeit.   *Beitr. z. Fortpfl.-biol. Vögel*, **4**: 1–3.

notably members of the grouse family, have meet-ings between the sexes solely for copulation while in many species of ducks the male leaves the fe-male soon after she has laid the eggs. In a great majority of birds the sexes remain together until the brood is raised and in this category we find the Roseate Spoonbill.

In general, individuals in the Spoonbill flock during this prepairing phase do not appear to have any interest in each other, and there is no apparent evidence of individual recognition such as can be observed between mated birds following pair formation. It seems possible that the same male and female might remate in successive years through mere chance, but there is little reason to believe that such rematings would ever be delib-erate. The chance is further reduced by the fact that Spoonbills construct a new nest each year, so there is no tendency for the pair to return to the same nest, as has been noted by Schuz in the case of White Storks (Lack, 1940).

For the most part, the Spoonbills that I watched in Texas from April 8 until the first pairs were formed on April 25 and 26 divided their time be-tween utter inaction (dozing with heads under the feathers of their backs) and curious forms of behavior that I labeled respectively 'up-flights' and 'sky-gazing.' The up-flights took me com-pletely by surprise; although they were at first rather disconcerting (I thought the flock was de-serting the area), they were also one of the most spectacular of behaviorisms. Owing to the ex-treme shyness of the Spoonbills I had to place my blind on a small island of the Second Chain group (San Antonio Bay) some seventy-five yards from the island on which the birds were performing. On April 9 I was in my blind, and there were only four Spoonbills in view, although I had apertures cut in the blind on all four sides. I had just writ-ten in my notes that the main flock must be out of sight behind the next island to the north when there was a roar of many wings; an instant later some 300 Spoonbills swept over the island next to me, came around in a half circle, and suddenly settled among the shallow oyster bars 100 yards away. I had just time enough to note that only one or two among them were in immature plum-age when they rose again, circled the neighboring

Figure 13. An Up-Flight's Advance Guard.

island, and returned once more to the shallows off to the north.

As this great flock swept in front of me their vivid colors were strikingly contrasted with the coffee-brown color of the bay. Their line of flight was across the wind at this point so that they flew against a backdrop of dull brown, and at right angles to the gray streaks of the shallow surf.

Between that date and June 10, I counted twen-ty-four of these up-flights, and I did not see them all. They continued through the first part of the breeding cycle, ceasing abruptly with the begin-ning of the incubation phase but reappearing when the first large-scale hatchings began. D. S. Lehrman (in litt.) suggests that there may be a seasonal variation in the flight reaction so that in certain phases of the cycle the reaction will be more readily elicited than in others. If an in-stinctive act is not produced for a long period, the threshold becomes so low that the act may go off of its own accord. Thus, early in the cycle when the flock has been established on the breeding grounds for only a short time, the flight reaction threshold may be so low that it will go off by it-self. It seemed to me that the flights were cor-related with a kind of nervous excitement.

The so-called sky-gazing behavior has been

noted under many different circumstances and is performed by birds of all ages. It was especially prevalent among the adult birds that I watched in Texas during this phase of the cycle and was seen only occasionally after the pairs had been formed. A group of twenty or twenty-five adults would be observed standing placidly on an oyster bar facing into the wind. When another Spoonbill flew over them, most of these birds extended their necks full length and pointed their bills skyward. There was no accompanying sound or additional display. After a few seconds the heads were lowered and that appeared to be the end of it. On several occasions I saw this same performance among immature birds, including a rather inept performance by a young Spoonbill in captivity, an individual that had no association with adults of the same species. In conversation, Mr. Lehrman suggested that sky-gazing must be an innate form of *releaser*. An inept performance by an immature bird would be explained by the fact that instinctive behavior is related to a high threshold and poor coordination during immaturity. Maturity brings a lowered threshold and good coordination.

I was unable to correlate this sky-gazing behavior with any particular phase of activity except that it was most pronounced in the period just preceding formation of the pairs. On the other hand, it cannot be overlooked that it was observed among both immatures and among adults that were not associated even remotely with a breeding group (Duck Rock, Florida, in late July).

When I began my observations in the Second Chain colony in April 1940, I was quite naturally pleased that pairing had not yet taken place. As the days lengthened into a period of more than two weeks, however, I began to wonder if the birds were ever going to pair. Nevertheless it was an amazing and interesting experience to observe the flock throughout this phase of the cycle. There was little suggestion that anything was going to happen more exciting than occasional preening, wing-stretching or a dilatory search for food, although the up-flights were a considerable diversion.

As I watched, I realized that the flock was probably made up more or less evenly of males and females and that sooner or later, by means of some ancient bond that must exist between the two sexes, the pairs would be formed, nest constructed, eggs fertilized and laid, and the whole cycle of reproduction carried through to completion before my eyes. I saw birds that, whether male or female, were alike to me and that at this time showed no special behavior even so much as hinting at their respective sexes. They dozed in the hot sun, most of them on one leg, their heads turned around backward so as to lie hidden between their shoulders. As the minutes and hours passed and nothing happened I dozed myself, waking an hour later to glance hastily from the aperture in the blind and to find every bird in its place and the sum total of activity still an exasperating nothing.

There is certainly no time in the life of the bird that is more intriguing to us than these days just prior to the actual beginning of the sexual cycle. We understand, of course, that during the progress of this preliminary period the individual birds are approaching a physiological status that we speak of as breeding condition. Adult birds make their finest appearance at this time—their plumage at its very best and the soft parts exhibiting their most resplendent hues. Birds that are given to song now indulge in their most extravagant melodies. From the point of view of human enjoyment, it is this phase of the cycle that

Figure 14.   The Sky-Gazing Posture.

Plate 13.   Spoonbills do not breed except in this completely adult plumage.

Plate 14.   Texas boasts some of our most populous and successful bird-nesting colonies.   A scene (Spoonbills, American Egrets, Reddish Egrets and Louisiana Herons) at the Vingt'un Islands.

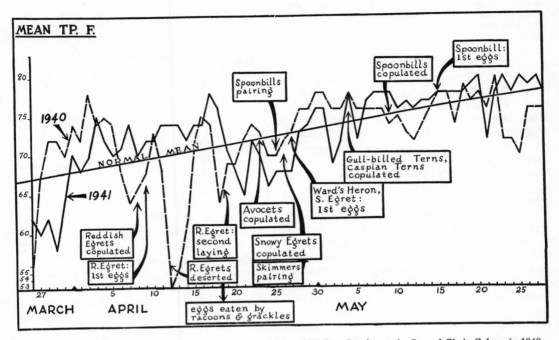

Figure 15. Mean Temperature and Reproductive Activities of Various Species at the Second Chain Colony in 1940.

gives us the greatest pleasure, both visually and audibly, although the birds themselves may be concerned only with defending territory or obtaining a mate.

Actually, this phase of the bird's life represents an advanced stage in the gonadal cycle. Blanchard (1941), working with small passerines (*Zonotrichia leucophrys* subsp.), learned that gonadal development in the males could be divided into seven histologic stages, ranging from inactive to breeding condition. Variations occurred in the dates at which males entered the period of rapid development just prior to breeding (stage 5). Naturally, meteorological correlations were looked for and, although mean temperature showed the highest correlation, the combination of temperature with precipitation or sunshine or both "might explain, better than temperature alone, the yearly differences in the time of attainment of stage 5 and in the dates for first copulation and first eggs."

The accompanying graph shows the mean temperature curve as recorded at the Corpus Christi Weather Station during portions of March, April and May, 1940 and 1941. There would appear to be a possible correlation between the delayed pairing of Spoonbills in 1940 and the low mean temperatures encountered in early April of that year. In 1941, when pairing did take place the first week of April,

the mean temperatures had then risen above the normal mean. It will also be seen that most sexual activities took place on a rising temperature curve.

Nice (1937) found a correlation between the mean temperature curve and migration, start of singing and start of laying in the Song Sparrow. There may be many exceptions, but Mrs. Nice mentions eight species whose spring migration appears to be conditioned by the mean temperature curve. The same factor has been correlated with singing in the Mockingbird and with egg laying in the Starling and the Prairie Horned Lark.

Experiments of Rowan (1929; 1932) and of Bissonnette (1930; 1937) showed that *light* has an important effect on gonadal development. In 1940, however, when the Spoonbills were delayed in pairing on the Texas coast, the daily percentage of possible sunshine[53] during the four months, February through May, averaged 69% compared with 56.25% for the same period in 1941 when pairing was not delayed.

Possibly, as Blanchard suggests, physiological changes may be "fundamentally dependent upon an inherent annual rhythm" rather than on external factors. In other words, although the environment may be responsible for

[53] From records compiled by Corpus Christi Weather Station.

variations in the rate and duration of early gonadal development, these may be within limits that are set by what Blanchard terms "the hereditary clockwork of the population."

B. PRENUPTIAL PHASE

On April 25 I watched Spoonbills on the Second Chain from a location on the mainland a mile distant. With a telescope I counted 289 individuals along the shores of the islands and saw no activity that suggested any further developments. Early the next morning, however, there were signs of great activity among many of the species that nest on these same islands, although the Spoonbills appeared to be immune to whatever influences were abroad.

Some few of the herons had already paired and were even now well along with nest construction, but on this particular morning the zeal for pairing, copulation and nest building appeared general. The most active species were Ward's Herons, Snowy Egrets and Reddish Egrets. On exposed shell reefs nearby Black Skimmers were making *scrapes* and were extremely noisy about it. Laughing Gulls and Willets were more vocal than usual. Late in the morning there were two up-flights among the Spoonbills, one at 11 o'clock and one at 11:56. At about this same time I observed two Spoonbills that quite evidently had paired, probably the day before or earlier that same morning.

1. Pair Formation

In Florida Bay in November 1939, I witnessed a curious form of behavior among the Spoonbills on Bottlepoint Key that I now believe is the beginning of pair formation in this species. After days of inactivity the birds were seen one morning (November 6) flying in and out of the red mangroves, some establishing themselves conspicuously on the tops of the trees and other individuals flying directly at these first birds, both flapping their wings vigorously. Often one or both birds would take off and fly in a short circle that ended in a return to the original positions, although occasionally one of the birds would drop into the shallow water nearby. The culmination of this behavior was obscured by heavy mangrove foliage. Similar activities were observed under slightly

Figure 16.   The Beginning of Pair Formation.

more favorable conditions in Texas (April and May 1940). The first pair observed (pair V-1) had already been formed when my notes on their behavior began on April 26. Their reactions to each other and to the birds around them and the behavior of other individuals and pairs in the vicinity during the month that followed[54] are the basis for the following tentative description of sex recognition and pair formation in the Roseate Spoonbill.

Individual birds were not marked so it was necessary to observe very closely any behavior that appeared to be indulged in exclusively by either the male or the female. Male birds (known as such from their positions in repeated copulations) were the only ones that defended the territory around the nest, gathered nest material and showed aggressiveness toward other Spoonbills, engaging in threat displays (antaposematic displays [Huxley, 1938]) after they had paired. Only females remained passively at the nest or nest site throughout this phase (until incubation began) and actively took part in actual construction of the nest. Only females were approached by other Spoonbills with what semed to be a form of *gamosematic* display (i.e. a display which assists the pair to find each other[55]), and then only when the female was perched at the nest site, where she

---

[54] Actually a period of twenty-eight days during which pair V-1 was watched for a total of fifty-one hours.
[55] 1940, Lack.

responded to the approach of any Spoonbill by the agitated shaking of a twig or loose stick with her bill.

From these facts, plus the sum total of my observations, I believe that pair formation is accomplished as follows:

Initially the female isolates herself in a tree or bush that may or may not be used later on as a nest site[56] (known males were never observed consistently or for any length of time in this relatively passive role). Apparently the female Spoonbill advertises her desire to pair by occupying this site and by simultaneously shaking convenient twigs or branches with her bill, especially when approached by another Spoonbill.

Lack (1940) states that the ♀ British Robin "normally takes the initiative in pair-formation." However, ♂ Robins have already established territories so that the situation is not similar to that of the Spoonbill, but reversed. The ♂ Spoonbill seeks out the ♀ ; the ♀ Robin seeks out the ♂. In Black-crowned Night Herons the ♀ seeks out the ♂ (Allen and Mangels, 1940). In most birds it is the ♂ that *first takes up a territory*. I saw no evidence of this in the case of the Roseate Spoonbill. Of course, this species is a colonial nesting bird and *territory* is not of the 'permanent' character of that selected and defended by territorial passerine birds.

The ♀ Northern Phalarope is the first to occupy the territory (Tinbergen, 1935), pairing therein with the ♂ after attracting him with gamosematic displays. In territory defense by the ♀ and in other characteristics, however, this species differs greatly from the Roseate Spoonbill.

The ♀ Tinamous are also the isolated displaying sex (Lack, 1940). Lack states that although Levick thought the ♀ Gentoo Penguin was normally the isolated sex, Brian Roberts subsequently related to him that at the beginning of the season "both sexes have similar behavior (♀'s as well as ♂'s may defend stations), but gradually the birds sort themselves out." Both sexes of the Common Tern also show similar behavior at the beginning of the cycle and the same may be true of Cormorants and Shags, some writers describing the ♂ as the isolated displaying sex, others the ♀.

In the Roseate Spoonbill the gamosematic display of the female is simple but would seem to be sufficiently 'improbable' (Lorenz, 1937) to release the desired male reaction at the proper time. In other words, it would be improbable at any other time of year to find a female Spoonbill perched conspicuously and consistently in a bush

[56] In Texas this was usually the actual nest site, but I believe it was not always so in Florida Bay.

or tree nervously agitating a nearby branch or twig.

The accompanying display of the male at this time appears to be confined chiefly to the manner of his approach to the female (i.e. male behavior). He flies at her, wings beating as he attempts to gain a perch next to her. There is nothing threatening about his behavior; he jerks his head up and down in short nodding movements, and it seems quite possible that he may utter the low clucking sounds that I heard later on after the pair had been formed. I did not hear such sounds at this time, owing perhaps to the distance from which these pairing activities were observed.

If the male Spoonbill were to approach another member of the same species during this phase, his behavior would fall into one of two categories: (1) he would threaten, striking at the other bird with lunges of the head and bill, his head lowered and wings raised slightly (*antaposematic display*), or (2) he would simply bob his head up and down a few times and walk on. So male behavior toward recognized females at this particular time in the cycle is likewise improvable, released only by another Spoonbill occupying a tree or bush and at the same time grasping and shaking twigs.

The next step is acceptance of the male by the female. From what I was able to observe of this behavior it appears that the female repulses the initial advances of the male. The exact manner and the criteria by which she ultimately accepts the male I cannot describe. I could not detect

Figure 17. The Female Ultimately Accepts the Male.

areas of brightly colored plumage or of soft parts that were limited in extent, degree of color or in any other way to the male Spoonbill, so that it is not apparent that sex discrimination in this species is based on a difference in outward appearance. Rather it would seem that the basis for sexual selection in pair formation is simply 'male behavior' in response to 'female behavior.' The one behaves like a male, the other like a female.

Lorenz (1935) was the first to attempt the classification of the main types of pair formation among birds, but in a later paper Tinbergen (1939) revised the groupings into three main types as follows:

(1) Only the ♂'s have *releasers*[57]; nondisplaying males are treated like females.
(2) Only ♀'s have releasers and all individuals not showing the ♀ releasers are attacked, i.e. treated like males.
(3) Releasers are present in both sexes.

Evidently the Roseate Spoonbill belongs to group three and indeed most birds fall into this category, which corresponds to the *cichlid-fish type* of Lorenz (display by both sexes and no dominance order).

The possibility that the male Spoonbill emits a low clucking sound when performing his initial display is of interest, and in this connection it can be mentioned that the female Song Sparrow has a special call note by which the male may be able to differentiate sex. Mrs. Nice (1937) found "no evidence that the female pays the slightest attention to the appearance, character, or singing ability of her mate, or even to the number of legs he possesses." Noble (1936) found that a similar note is given by the female Flicker. In his studies of the British Robin, Lack (1939, 1940) found that sexual discrimination requires some

time and is apparently difficult. In general an unmated male treats males and mated females alike "but reacts differently to a potential mate." The factors concerned are unknown.

After Roseate Spoonbills are paired it is possible (and there is even some proof) that the two birds recognize each other on sight. Pair V-1 demonstrated this possibility during their long betrothal. When both members of the pair were absent from the nest site, other Spoonbills would gather in the vicinity. If male V-1 returned first he immediately drove off all other Spoonbills, but as soon as female V-1 appeared he exhibited signs of recognition, that is, he bobbed his head and moved toward her as if wanting to be near her. Doubtless her *manner* was noticeably different from that of the other Spoonbills, although I could never detect this difference myself. Lack (1940) says that individual recognition has been proved for many species. Some birds can distinguish their mates at considerable distances by sight and in some cases by sound.

When female V-1 was present at the nest site and male V-1 absent, she was repeatedly approached by strange birds that I believed were unmated males. Their interest in her appeared to be sexual, but it seemed to me that they were not only aware from her behavior that she was a female but also that she was already mated. Their approach was hesitant rather than impulsive and headlong (as would be the case with a male attempting to pair with an unmated female), and they were easily cowed by the returning male who was the rightful mate.

Figure 18.   Interlopers Are Easily Cowed by the Rightful Male.

[57] "The doctrine of 'releasers,' herein set forth—or devices for the production of stimuli, which serve as the 'keys' to 'unlock' or release those 'innate perceptory patterns,' characteristic of the species and the individual, and which result in instinctive reactions—seems at last to offer a sound and satisfying explanation of that riddle so long embodied in 'the secondary sexual characters of birds,' and one which I believe that Darwin, when struggling with his 'Theory of Sexual Selection,' would have welcomed with open arms."—Francis H. Herrick (1937, *The Auk*, **54** (3): 245).

It was interesting to note that when female V-1 hopped to the ground and mingled with these strange birds they failed to court her and, in fact, more or less ignored her as they did each other, although I saw her on several occasions involuntarily involved in the squabbles that took place between these birds and that I interpreted as the threatening displays of rival males. I do not believe that they were able to recognize her as a female except when she assumed her special role at the nest site. However, I believe that her mate eventually learned to distinguish her individually even when she was on the ground, possibly as a result of experience.

2. Betrothal Period

In the case of pair V-1 the betrothal period extended from April 26 through May 8, or thirteen days. From evidence accumulated on other species, it seems possible that the gonadal cycle of the male is well advanced when pairing takes place but has not yet reached the final stage (Blanchard, 1941, stage 7: mature sperms free in the lumen; breeding condition).

In many respects this was the most interesting period in the cycle. As I mentioned earlier, April 26 was a day of considerable sexual activity among a number of species, but I was able to find only one pair of Spoonbills that had been formed. When first seen, one of them was perched in a low bush, and the other was approaching with a stick in its bill. There was visual evidence of their attachment to each other—little head nods and crossing and rubbing of bills. That first stick was never actually presented to the bird on the bush but simply dropped in the course of events and apparently forgotten. After this brief display the birds stood side by side, both with heads in the feathers of the back.

One of these paired birds was constantly hopping to the ground to run off other adult Spoonbills, and during these first days would not permit other Spoonbills to come within ten feet of the nest site. This bird paid no attention to other species, although Snowy Egrets and Reddish Egrets were constantly invading the territory.

At one time this member of the pair hopped to the ground and defended the territory three times

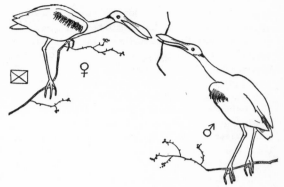

Figure 19. One of the Pair Approaches with a Stick.

in ten minutes, each time returning to a perch beside the other member. The more active bird, I decided later, was the male.

The display indulged in by the male in driving off other adult Spoonbills involved the same threatening posture that I sometimes saw among seemingly unattached birds that wandered about on the beach and on the ground near the nesting bushes (*antaposematic display*). The head is lowered and thrust forward in a threatening manner and the wings are raised so that the patches of carmine appear to be more than usually prominent. This raising of the wings also reveals the brilliant color of the tail coverts.

On this first day, most of the Spoonbill flock was still inactive, and of 138 individuals that I was able to count from my blind, all except six were adults.

The second day the V-1 pair was relatively quiet. Occasionally both were absent from the nest site and once they returned together, walking daintily toward the location where I had first seen them. One of them threatened and chased a third bird (this, I believe, was the male), and then reached down and picked up a short weed stalk, shaking it in his bill, as he turned in the direction of the female. Both birds then hopped to the nest site, the male again offering the stick to the female. She took it in her bill, shook her head vigorously, and attempted to lay the stick among the branches at her feet.

This was the beginning of nest construction which proceeded from this point on in what appeared to me an aimless sort of way without the apparent enthusiasm that was to be seen later.

Throughout this phase there was considerable variation in the intensity of emotion displayed by these two birds, and I took this to be typical of that part of the cycle as it applied to the whole species. For example, the vigor with which male V-1 defended his territory was sometimes quite marked and on other occasions he showed little or no interest in the invasions of other Spoonbills. On the second day that I watched them, pair V-1, after brief stick ceremonies, stood quietly for a time and then both of them hopped to the ground and mingled peacefully with a group of Spoonbills along the beach. A few minutes later one of them went back to the nest site and began pulling at sticks and branches, shaking them with considerable excitement. Those on the shore watched this performance like an audience watching the card tricks of a professional magician. After a while this group began moving around again and, as they walked past each other, they would nod and bow. This interlude came to a sudden end for no apparent reason when every adult in sight joined in an up-flight. An immature bird (whose feathers were considerably splattered by mud) was the only Spoonbill that did not fly from the portion of the colony that I was watching. When the adults got up, he didn't even raise his head.

This muddy youngster finally perched close to

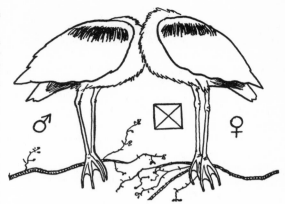

Figure 21. For Hours the Pair Does Nothing at All.

nest site V-1. When the adults returned to the area, male V-1 immediately cleared his territory of all other Spoonbills except the youngster. The birds that were driven off were probably unmated males. They seemed quite irritable and every now and then would threaten each other, occasionally two of them flying at each other with furiously beating wings so that they rose two or three feet off the ground. This performance gave them the appearance of fighting cocks, but I am sure that it was merely a sham battle and that no damage was done.

When female V-1 returned, the male drove off the muddy youngster and the pair settled at the nest site. A few minutes later every Spoonbill in sight was again on the alert, necks outstretched, heads held high, a sure sign that an up-flight was about to take place. When they were in the air, I saw that this alarm had been caused by a Duck Hawk,[58] which was heading into the wind toward Matagorda Island.

There was no behavior of special note between April 27 and May 2. On the latter date, I recorded in my notes (9:30 A.M.) that forty-five Spoonbills were present on island No. 5. Of these, thirty-six were standing on one leg with their heads in the feathers of their backs; three were standing idly in the water along shore; six (three pairs) were perched near nest sites.

Figure 20. They Had the Appearance of Fighting Cocks.

[58] Several times a soaring Black Vulture had the same effect.

The V-1 pair appeared to have grown quite lethargic; as I watched, the male bird moved slowly to the beach, walked leisurely into the water and poked around with his bill. He then stood and preened. Another adult, apparently from another pair, dropped into the water and picked up a short floating stick. With this in his bill, he walked slowly into the nearby bushes and disappeared.

At this time all of the other wading birds had laid their eggs and were getting started with incubation. The whole Spoonbill flock was gradually pairing, and the flock that had occupied the oyster reefs and shore lines dwindled in size with the formation of each pair.

On May 3, at a nearby pond on the mainland late in the day, I watched the copulatory activities of several other species, including Gull-billed Terns, Least Terns, and Caspian Terns.

The V-1 pair showed signs of progress on May 4, when I saw the male attempt copulation. At 6:30 A.M., a strange Spoonbill was perched near the nest site and the V-1 pair was on the ground nearby (I was able to identify these individuals by events that transpired immediately afterward). Male V-1 hopped up beside the stranger, who began nodding his head; male V-1 nodded back. A moment later male V-1 threatened the stranger and drove him off. This little exchange seemed to excite him considerably, and he grew even more excited when female V-1 joined him at the nest site.

At the appearance of the female, the male took hold of a branch with his bill and shook it vigorously. As she stood on the rim of the now partially formed nest, he picked up a loose stick, shook it several times, and then presented it to her; both birds nodded in short, jerky fashion. Suddenly the male was standing on her back, but obviously off balance. Surprised and unready, she began flapping her wings and in the process changed her position slightly. The male toppled off quite ignominiously.

Unperturbed, he maneuvered for a second attempt. This time she deliberately repulsed him, turning ever so slightly as he approached, so that she was always facing him. Giving up, he turned away and hopped to the ground.

Figure 22. Surprised. . . She Began Flapping Her Wings.

During these events several Spoonbills stood just below the nest on the ground, watching intently. When male V-1 hopped to the ground he at once moved straight toward these *kibitzers* in a threatening attitude; but they stood their ground. Female V-1 remained on the nest rim, where she preened her feathers. Male V-1 disappeared.

On this date there were many Spoonbill pairs being formed, and those that had already achieved this initial state were busily starting their nest-building activities. Spoonbills that were evidently still unmated continued to stalk about in small groups, fighting among themselves now and again. I noticed that the paired birds did not tend to join the up-flights that still occurred. It seemed that one result of these up-flights was the scattering and dispersal of these unpaired individuals.

3. The Role of Territory

Toward the end of the betrothal period (May 7–8) and during the copulation phase (May 9–15), male V-1 spent more and more time defending the territory around the nest. At the same time this territory definitely dwindled in size. Males of other species defend a much larger territory than is at first needed. Tinbergen (1939) found that territories occupied by male Snow Buntings were without exception larger at first than later on.   As new males arrived in the vicinity, the size of the territory grew smaller, and Tinbergen concluded (in agreement with Huxley, 1934) that there is an increase in the fighting intensity of the male as the diameter of the territory decreases.   Eventually a limit is reached when the fighting intensity is so great that it keeps all new males from further establishments within the original area.[59]

As for the Roseate Spoonbill, the territory may at first be as large as in the case of the V-1 pair, in which the male drove off all Spoonbills from within a radius of about twenty feet of the nest site.[60]   In the end, it is usually reduced to include little more than the nest itself.   During incubation the setting bird did not appear to be interested in defending beyond the distance to which it could extend its neck.   There may be exceptions to this, depending on the physical surroundings, i.e. demand for nest space.

During one of ♂ V-1's excursions (May 7) I noticed an immature Spoonbill standing nearby with a stick in its bill. It juggled the stick for a while and then dropped it. At that moment, ♂ V-1 came along carrying a stick. The immature bird immediately behaved like a ♀, leaning forward and begging for the stick, just as I had seen ♀ V-1 do on numerous occasions. Pausing momentarily, ♂ V-1 shook the stick in his bill with some vigor, but at length dropped it and went off in search of another, which he eventually presented to ♀ V-1. When a stick is dropped, the bird will often ignore it and go some distance in search of another.

Later male V-1 came slowly toward the nest carrying a stick.   The female was on the nest site watching intently.   He perched near her but turned his back, holding the stick away from her. She came toward him, head lowered and bill open in a begging attitude.   After a moment he turned around and gave her the stick, which she enthusiastically worked into the nest.   The male again turned his back, as if not interested in what she was doing.

Although the male Spoonbill defended his territory with a varied *intensity*, he never failed to de-

Figure 23.   The Male Never Failed to Defend the Territory against Adult Spoonbills.

fend it against adult Spoonbills and only occasionally drove off immature Spoonbills.   He made no attempt to fight off invasions of other species.   As early as April 30, when the intensity of his defense was not so great as a week later, I watched a Reddish Egret drive V-1 from his own nest site. Twice V-1 (sex ?) tried to return to the site but was driven off.   Eventually the Reddish Egret, which was busily constructing a nest adjacent to the V-1 site, went off in search of nest material, and V-1 immediately occupied the nest site again. When the egret reappeared with the feathers of his head and neck erected in threatening display, V-1 retreated even before the egret had come close.   The egret then turned and scattered a whole group of Spoonbills that were standing some ten feet away.

Once the Reddish Egret came flying in with some nesting material in its bill.   After this had been deposited on the nest, it turned and attacked all Spoonbills within a considerable radius.   This kind of behavior continued until the egret had finished nest construction, after which it ceased to bother the Spoonbills.

On May 12 (after the V-1 pair had copulated but before any eggs were laid) a Snowy Egret that was beginning incubation near V-1's nest succeeded very easily in driving male V-1 from his own territory.   Shortly thereafter, V-1 assumed the defensive role and ran off several Spoonbills from the vicinity of the nest.   By that date, how-

[59] Similar behavior has been noted in the Reed Bunting, Song Sparrow, House Wren, Red-wing and in at least one fish, the stickle-back.

[60] Spoonbills that were late in pairing may not have the opportunity to defend such an extensive territory.

ever, it was apparent that V-1 male was defending a much smaller territory than in the beginning.

The day before eggs were laid (May 14), male V-1 tolerated both immature and adult Spoonbills within a few feet of the nest. He only chased them when they perched on a branch immediately adjacent to the nest. Although in general the intensity of territorial defense had increased from the time of copulation until egg laying, there was still a fluctuation even in the later phase. On May 14 the V-1 pair showed very little inclination to drive off other Spoonbills.

In the Roseate Spoonbill it would appear that, while the female selects the nest site, it is the male that establishes limits of the territory and is its chief defender (I was never able to see evidence of the female defending the territory, although she may defend the nest itself). Territorial defense by the male begins very soon after pair formation and continues until the young are partially grown, or possibly until they leave the nest. It should be born in mind, of course, that by the time eggs are laid the size of the territory has diminished until it includes only the immediate vicinity of the nest itself. It does not seem possible to compare territory in a colonial species like the Spoonbill with the definitions of Mayr (1935) and Tinbergen (1936). The fact that the Spoonbill territory is larger at first than is needed may be correlated with the necessity for preserving the bond between the pair early in their attachment when this bond is not so strong as it is later, and when there are large numbers of unmated males in the colony looking for mates. If the male Spoonbill failed to drive off other Spoonbills from a large space around the nest site early in the cycle, it seems possible that the female might respond to the advances of another male, with resulting promiscuity and confusion in general. Thus, this larger territory would appear to have important survival value.

C. COPULATION AND NEST BUILDING

May 9 was cloudy and warm with a threat of rain. As I rowed my skiff the mile from the mainland to where my blind was placed, I saw a number of Spoonbills flying singly and by two's and three's toward Mustang Lake, which is a feeding place.

These were the first regular flights that I had noticed and suggested at once that incubation might be under way in some of the nests.

I followed a route by which I could get into my blind without disturbing any of the Spoonbills on the neighboring island. On that particular morning, my first glance showed that the V-1 pair was perched quietly at the nest, and seven minutes later (6:50 A.M.) for the first time I saw them copulate.

Female V-1 was standing on the nest, leaning slightly forward and shaking a loose twig in her bill. The male stood to one side watching her. Slowly he moved to a branch that placed him directly behind her. As she continued to shake the twig in her bill, he reached across her back so as to grasp the same twig with his mandibles. At this she turned her head toward him so as to give him a good grip on the twig. Both birds were now grasping the same twig which they continued to shake with short, rapid movements of their heads.

Unhurriedly the male mounted the female, reaching forward as she shook her head and bill so as to grasp firmly the slender middle portion of her mandibles between his own. In the meantime the female flattened herself on the nest and, still holding her bill, the male shook his head nervously and then released her bill and hopped off. Both birds shook their feathers and preened, and the female began working on the nest. The male

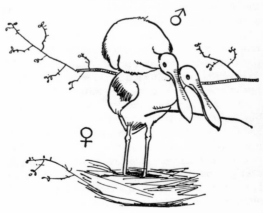

Figure 24. He Reached across Her Back so as to Grasp the Same Twig.

hopped to the ground and moved off, as if searching for another stick. The whole procedure from the first movement of the male toward the female until the completion of the act was quite leisurely and consumed about seven minutes. The male was on the female's back a matter of only twenty or twenty-five seconds.

Male V-1 did not reappear for about an hour, but between 8:05 and 9 A.M. (when it began to rain quite hard) he made eleven trips carrying nesting material, and the pair copulated a second time at 8:35. During one five-minute interval he brought three sticks to the female. Each time she ruffled her plumage, raised her wings slightly and, thrusting her head forward with the bill slightly open, appeared to beg. He always gave the stick to her immediately.

Sometimes the male helped the female work the stick into the nest, but for the most part the real job of nest construction was left entirely to the female.

Male V-1's trips for material seemed to take him to the same source of supply each time: a patch of brush at the north end of the island. On this date his trips were quite definitely hurried, and when the stick was very large he would hold his head high and mince along at a peculiar gait in order to keep the stick off the ground. He never flew on these journeys but always walked both coming and going. Once he returned with a stick about three feet long which the female accepted and which she worked into the nest with what appeared to be more than usual excitement, the male watching her and nervously shaking a nearby branch which he grasped with his bill.

All activity appeared to cease during a heavy rain, although terns and Skimmers left the oyster reefs and flew about noisily. Laughing Gulls, which had been calling loudly, grew quiet. Many Spoonbills waded into the water where they bathed and preened themselves. One bathing bird submerged itself almost entirely, crouching low in the water. After shaking itself for a minute or two, it remained in the crouching position but did not move. Another Spoonbill standing nearby moved toward it and attempted to copulate. I do not know if the crouching bird was a male or a female, but the reaction was an interest-

Figure 25. The Male Grasps the Female's Bill.

ing one and is in accord with Lack's statement (1940) that the major stimulus for copulation in most species is simply that "the female keeps still." The crouching posture has additional releaser value for some species.

A third copulation was observed (V-1 pair) a half hour after the rain had ceased.

I have not heard of other male birds holding the bill of the female during copulation. Probably many species grasp the feathers on the back of the female's head; Vogt (1938) noticed this behavior in the Eastern Willet. It is plainly evident that nest building and copulation in the Spoonbill are closely associated, and the nest is not actually finished until copulation begins and the male starts to bring nesting material very rapidly.

Apparently V-1 pair first copulated on May 9, although the initial act may have occurred the previous day after I had left the blind. On May 12 I examined nest V-1 but there were no eggs. Spoonbill nests in this Texas colony were well constructed and not only contained more material than nests examined in Florida in the mangrove habitat, but were more substantial in their construction.

The first egg appeared in V-1 nest on May 15 approximately the sixth day after the first observed copulation. Nice (1937) states that the development of the Song Sparrow egg takes about five days. Blanchard (1941), speaking of the Nuttall's Sparrow, says that the average time between first copulation and first eggs is 5.9 days. According to Tinbergen (1939) the interval between first-observed copulation and first egg for the Snow Bunting was thirteen days in one instance, eight in another.

On May 18 I found eggs in forty-nine nests as follows:

4 eggs in 3 nests	(12)
3 eggs in 24 nests	(72)
2 eggs in 15 nests	(30)
1 egg in 7 nests	(7)
49 nests	121 eggs

These counts were made on island No. 5 (where V-1 pair was located) and on nearby Carroll Island. On island No. 5 it was the fourth day of egg laying. The three nests containing clutches of four eggs were on Carroll and suggested that, unless eggs had been laid on four successive days, pairing was accomplished on Carroll Island ahead of Spoonbills on island No. 5. V-1 nest contained two eggs on this date (May 18). On May 24 there were three eggs in V-1 nest, and this appeared to be the full clutch. On that same date, there were sixty-nine nests on Carroll Island containing a total of 194 eggs, or an average of 2.8 eggs per nest. By May 27 the final total was reached for the entire colony: eighty-seven nests and 230 eggs, an average of 2.6.[61]

D. INCUBATION PHASE

When incubation was well under way (May 30) I decided that it would be well to move a blind

---

[61] This was less than the total number of nests counted during three previous seasons, and there may have been a correlation between the freeze of the preceding January and this falling off in the number of nesting adults, as discussed elsewhere in this report. The average number of nests in this colony during the three previous seasons (1937–1939) was 135.6. At the Vingt'un colony, 180 miles farther east, there was a similar drop in the number of breeding adults in 1940.

The over-all average for eggs per clutch in the Roseate Spoonbill (Florida and Texas colonies) is 2.7. This is the same as the average given for the West African species, and less than the average given for European and Australian Spoonbills.

Figure 26. Incubation Was in Progress.

nearer to some of the nests in order to observe details of this phase of the cycle. Accordingly, I had to terminate my acquaintance with the V-1 pair (there being no vegetation in which my blind could be concealed on island No. 5) and move to Carroll Island. There I set up a small blind thirty-five feet from nest No. 23 and from which I could also see activities at nests 1 to 25 inclusive. To facilitate my note taking, nests had been marked by placing a numbered lath in the ground in front of each.

On this date (May 30) incubation was in progress to the exclusion of all else. From the blind I had an unobstructed view of nest No. 23 which was three feet off the ground and in the open. All other nests from 1 to 25 were partially obscured by vegetation. I had entered the blind shortly after sunrise (5:55 A.M.); although the Spoonbills in that part of the colony left the nests at my approach, they were on them again less than two minutes later. Incubating herons and egrets stood up but only a very few of them flew.

At 6:11 there was a brief up-flight among the Spoonbills, but not all of them participated. No. 25, for example, merely got off the nest and, with neck extended in the *alert* posture, gave the usual alarm notes which may be written—*huh-huh-huh-huh-huh-huh-huh*,[62] repeated in a low and rapid tone, the bill held partly open.

---

[62] Referring to the European Spoonbill, Herr Szikla (Kirkman, 1913) says that during the breeding season they utter a noise that may be interpreted as *huh, huh, huh, hurum, huk, huk, huk, huk, hur, hur, hum, hum*. Jourdain in the same account, expresses a doubt as to whether or not this is the true song of the species. In the Roseate Spoonbill I heard the similar sound (*huh-huh-huh*) given as an alarm note and never in connection with the usual displays, regardless of their purpose. Jourdain himself

Figure 27.   Shading the Eggs.

At 6:35 the bird on nest 23 stood up, preened briefly, grasped a twig from the rim of the nest in its bill and then settled down again. Aside from the incubating Spoonbills there were two or three adults visible on the tops of the bushes, apparently the free members of incubating pairs. In the next half hour No. 23 moved twice, once shaking a twig in its bill, preening the feathers of the lower breast and touching the eggs with the tip of the bill. The second time it turned so as to face away from the sun.

1. Nest Relief

There was a general nest relief throughout the colony between 7:06 and 7:38 A.M. (May 30). The first relieving bird to appear went directly to nest No. 14, which contained four eggs. Both birds of the pair crouched, thrusting heads and necks forward and both emitted low, cackling and clucking sounds. The relieving bird appeared very broody and the incubating bird was not at all loath to leave. They rattled their bills together, both heads shaking rapidly from side to side. The relieving bird seemed to prod the other lightly under the side, and the one on the nest rose and walked off with head low and neck outthrust. The relieving bird settled on the eggs, feeling them daintily with the tip of the bill. The departing bird stood nearby and shook and

noted that, in the Naarder Meer colony in Holland, Spoonbills uttered a grunt or "note of anxiety" which might be written as *ur* or *urd*. The only grunt that I heard from the Roseate Spoonbill was given when the birds were busily feeding. A low, clucking or 'chicken sound' sometimes accompanied the threat display used during territory defense or between rival males; this is similar (to my ears!) to the sound given during the greeting ceremony and in other displays between members of a pair.

preened its feathers for some five minutes. As other nest reliefs occurred at adjacent nests, the relieved birds began to get up and fly off, apparently toward feeding grounds on the mainland.

No. 23 was relieved at 7:38. This time the bird on the nest made the first sounds, the same clucking notes, but very throaty, with the bill partially open. While making these sounds, it rose and walked from the nest. The relieving bird then stood on the nest rim and gave similar notes as the other bird flew off toward the mainland. The new arrival placed its feet very carefully on each side of the eggs, sat down on the tarsi, and then cautiously settled its body on the eggs. When the two birds were together, I got the impression that the new arrival was slightly larger and perhaps the male of the pair.

After nearly an hour on the eggs, No. 23 stood up and preened several times, picked up sticks and juggled them briefly in its bill or reached out and grasped a twig in its bill and shook it nervously. Vogt (1938) describes this tendency to pick at objects as typical of the incubating Willet and also mentions the Marsh Hawk playing with bits of dried grass while incubating. Vogt says: "If this was not boredom and play-relief, what was it?" It was my impression that incubating birds get tired and that this play is a sort of compensating behavior.

This was approximately the fifteenth day of incubation for some of the Spoonbills (V-1 pair), and for a few on Carroll Island it may have been the seventeenth or eighteenth day. It was hot and clear, with light air stirring, and high cumulus clouds over the distant horizon. The entire colony was quiet, the only sounds being the shrill whistled notes of the Great-tailed Grackles and the liquid gurgles of the Snowy Egrets. Now and then the quiet would be disturbed by the activities of nest relief, which is quite a noisy procedure in the case of some of the herons and egrets. Many of these other birds, being more advanced in incubation than the Spoonbills, were adding sticks to their nests—usually a sign that hatching is about to occur.

I was much interested in the activities at nest No. 23 and kept a careful record of the behavior of the incubating bird on this nest. Between 9:48

and 10 A.M. there was nest relief at many of the
Spoonbill nests, but the other member of the pair
did not appear at No. 23. I noted that setting
birds seemed less willing to leave on this occasion
than those had that were relieved between 7:06
and 7:38 A.M. Perhaps the increased temperature
of this later hour had a tendency to increase
broodiness.

Following is a concise report of the behavior of
No. 23:

7:39 a.m.   No. 23 (♂?) settled on eggs.

10 a.m.   No. 23 in full sunlight; temperature in sun
approaching 100°F. Bird restless, standing
frequently and preening, bill slightly open,
throat pouch vibrating (incubating American
Egrets stand and preen more frequently than
Spoonbills; Ward's Herons seldom move during incubation).

10:39 a.m.   No. 23 has now been on eggs three hours.
Much of the time its eyes are closed.

11 a.m.   No. 23 stands and droops wings to shade eggs.
Preens and nervously tugs at twigs in nest.
Stretches right leg back to full length.

11:39 a.m.   Temperature in shade now 100°F., nearly
120°F. in sun. No. 23 has been on nest four
hours. Vibration of throat and throat pouch
accelerated. Head nods rapidly up and
down. Eyes are closed most of time but bird
does not seem actually asleep.

11:40 a.m.   An adult Spoonbill flew over and No. 23 rose
and *gave nest relief call*, i.e. low clucking sound
with head raised and bill open. Settles back
on eggs; head bobs up and down as with
palsy.

11:56 a.m.   No. 23 stood up and, reaching down in front,
touched eggs with tip of bill. Male grackle
came near and 23 stabbed at it with bill, raising wings slightly in usual display.

Grackle only species other than Spoonbill
toward which this threatening display was

Figure 28.   Bill Open, Throat Pouch Vibrating.

Figure 29.   The Nest Relief Call Was Given Nine Times.

used. When herons or egrets came near nest,
No. 23 would lean to one side to avoid contact
with them. It seemed clear that it was at
the bottom of a peck order in which those
species occupied various positions that I was
unable to study at any length.

12:40 p.m.   Nest relief ceremony at nest No. 20. No. 23
rose and *gave nest relief call*.

12:50 p.m.   No. 23 *gave nest relief call*. Has been on eggs
five hours and twelve minutes.

1:39 p.m.   No. 23 has been incubating for six hours and
in this time has changed position nineteen
times. By comparison, Spoonbills in shade
appear to stir very little.

1:50 p.m.   No. 23 *gave nest relief call*. Five additional
times through the afternoon it gave this call,
at the following times:

1:59
2:45
3:14
3:25
3:53

At 4 P.M., having been in the blind for ten
and three-quarter hours, I was suffering considerably from the heat and the effects of my cramped
position and so decided to leave. My departure
frightened No. 23, who flew from the nest, having
occupied it for eight hours and twenty-one minutes. From No. 23's behavior I feel sure that
such a long stretch without relief must be unusual. The other member of the pair had not met
with an accident, and later both birds were observed at the nest.

Steady incubation of the eggs does not appear
to begin until the clutch is laid and may not be
very regular for the first few days even then. On
May 24, nest V-1 had contained the first egg for

nearly ten days, and I estimated that the full clutch of three had been deposited about May 19 or 20, or four or five days previously.   On the 24th the adults spent very little time on the eggs, except possibly to shade them from the sun during the extreme heat of the day.   Later on in the incubation period, all birds seemed to brood the eggs throughout the day.

In a previous study that I made of Black-crowned Night Herons (Allen and Mangels, 1940) I experimented with marking adult birds individually by smearing the nest rim with red paint thinned with linseed oil.   There was little hesitation on the part of Night Herons in settling on a nest treated in this manner.   Because of the obvious value of securing observations of marked birds whose sex was known and in order to compare the reaction of a Spoonbill to that of the Night Herons, I smeared thin blue paint on the rim of nest No. 23.   The pair returned to the nest together, and the one that appeared to be the male because of his slightly larger size and more aggressive behavior began almost at once to remove each individual stick that had been treated with paint.   This operation required nearly half an hour, but by the end of that time he had removed all of the treated sticks and resumed incubation. In taking the sticks from the nest he picked them up with considerable care, leaned forward, and dropped them to the ground.   The other member of the pair (♀ ?) paid very little attention to these activities.

E.   HATCHING AND CARE OF YOUNG

From my observations of various nests in the colony, I estimated that the incubation period was twenty-three to twenty-four days. One difficulty I encountered in making this estimate was the possibility that incubation did not begin with the first egg.   However, by comparing events at the Second Chain colony with similar activities on Bottlepoint Key in Florida Bay I believe that this is the correct incubation period for the species.

At the Second Chain colony in 1940 the first eggs hatched on June 7.   In three nests I examined on Carroll Island on that date, there were newly hatched young with the inside of the broken

egg shells still damp; other eggs in these nests were just pipping.

During this hatching period the birds were extremely excitable and once more up-flights were frequent.   For this reason I spent a minimum of time near the colony and then only in the very early morning.   Hatching continued through the next five days.   I noticed that Spoonbills added nesting material just before eggs hatched.   It was interesting to speculate by what means the parent birds could anticipate hatching.   Obviously, such reactions must have been stimulated by the appearance of a new set of releasers: perhaps the pipping and hatching of Spoonbill eggs in neighboring nests, the small cries of young Spoonbills or the initial feeding activities of other parent birds.   In their studies with the Gray Goose, Lorenz and Tinbergen (1938) described the reaction of that species to any object within or without the nest that had a broken outline, for example, any egg of which the shell had been broken.   The reaction was for the goose to break up and eat such an object.   However, the sight of a pipped shell did not bring about the same reaction, since it was inhibited by the cries of the young.   Tinbergen (*in litt.*) relates that Herring Gulls continued to turn their eggs throughout incubation but ceased to do so once the egg had pipped.

Many of the young, soon after hatching, became infested with a form of seed tick (as described in the chapter on 'Limiting Factors'). Apparently the behavior of young that were heavily infested was so abnormal, i.e. responses were lacking or deficient, that as a result many of them were deserted by the parent birds (June 12). These circumstances resulted in heavy predation by Great-tailed Grackles, chiefly of eggs that still remained unhatched.   Owing to these circumstances, I terminated observations at the colony in order to give the surviving birds every chance to raise young that were not infested and hatch eggs that had not been destroyed by grackles. A later check (June 21) indicated, however, that the loss of young and eggs was at least 98%, and I believe that the chief cause was the tick infestation, the grackles having been merely opportunists.   Oddly enough there was no evidence that other nesting species on the islands had been similarly infested.

I was able to substantiate one interesting point with regard to feeding of the young. Young Spoonbills invariably secure their food from the adult by reaching into the *side* of the adults' open bill at the base. The stomachs of young birds examined contained fish scales, and I found a small prawn on the rim of a nest containing young three to four days old.

From start to finish, the 1940 season at this colony had been a disastrous one and some concern was felt as to the possible psychological effect the following year. However, in 1941 the colony not only began its nesting activities at the usual time but a spectacular increase in the number of breeding adults was recorded, the most conservative estimates placing the total number of Spoonbill nests at 600 for the entire colony. I inspected the area late in June 1941, when many young were already on the wing, and could find no evidence that even a single young Spoonbill had been lost.

F. SUMMARY

1. Spoonbills usually arrive on the breeding grounds about one month before pairing. However, pair formation may be delayed as much as another month, possibly when the mean temperature is below normal.

2. There is no evidence that Spoonbills remate year after year; on the contrary, such rematings would appear unlikely. Prepairing behavior includes innate forms of communal ceremonies termed 'up-flights' and 'sky-gazing,' which vary in their intensity according to the stage of the cycle.

3. A tentative description of pair formation indicates that the ♀ is the isolated displaying sex. Her '♀ behavior' stimulates '♂ behavior,' but her exact criteria in selecting a mate are not understood. *Releasers* are present in both sexes.

4. During the 'betrothal period,' the ♂ defends a wide territory around the nest site against the invasions of other Spoonbills, brings nest material to the ♀, who constructs the nest and otherwise assumes a passive role at the nest. Only the ♂ undertakes defensive displays, only the ♀ is 'courted' by individuals that show ♂ behavior.

Paired birds may learn through experience to recognize each other individually.

The ♂ may unsuccessfully attempt copulation during the betrothal period.

During this period there is a recurrent fluctuation in the intensity of mutual displays between the sexes and of defensive displays by the ♂.

5. The territory may be larger at first than needed in order to protect the bond between the pair, which at first is not as strong as it will be later on. When incubation begins, the dimensions of the territory shrink to the immediate vicinity of the nest.

6. The Spoonbill is at the bottom of a peck order in a mixed breeding colony, herons or egrets readily driving it from its own territory even when the intensity of the defending ♂ is at peak.

7. In one pair the first successful copulation observed occurred on the fourteenth day after pair formation. The ♀ leans forward over the nest and shakes a stick with her bill. The ♂ moves slowly behind her, reaches over her back to grasp the stick in his bill. He then mounts her, grasping the narrow portion of her closed mandibles in his bill. During copulation the ♀ crouches on the nest.

In one pair three copulations were observed in two hours and forty minutes, during which time the ♂ brought the ♀ eleven sticks.

8. One pair laid the first egg on the sixth day after the first observed copulation. Possibly the remainder of the clutch is laid at a rate of one egg every other day, but evidence is incomplete. The average clutch (Texas and Florida) is 2.7 eggs per nest.

9. The incubation period is approximately twenty-three to twenty-four days in duration. During this phase, nest-relief displays occur and involve behavior that is superficially like that of defensive or fighting displays (head outthrust, wings raised, low clucking notes). Even the human observer can detect the difference in the *manner* in which these displays are exhibited. This performance is indulged in by both sexes; only the ♂ was seen in threat displays.

Nest relief usually takes place at least two or three times during the daylight hours, but in one instance a bird went unrelieved for more than eight hours. This individual stood on the nest and gave the nest-relief call nine times during the last four hours of that period.

Incubation does not appear to be regular until the full clutch is deposited.

Spoonbills add nest material just prior to hatching.

Plate 15.   Delicate pink against a blue sky—here is reason enough for the existence of the Roseate Spoonbill.

Plate 16.   Spoonbill and American Egret occupying adjacent nests.   Snowy Egrets nested in the
dense vegetation directly below.

Part VI.   Food and Feeding Habits

MANY persons have asked if the Roseate Spoonbill might not have become depleted in Florida because it is unable to find enough to eat! There is a vague feeling that a bird with such an unusual bill must have an unusual diet as well. It is true that the physical equipment of the Spoonbill limits its choice of food, but that can be said of any animal. There is nothing particularly remarkable about the various kinds of food that the Spoonbill eats, and these items are not especially limited in abundance or in availability. In Florida, where Spoonbills have grown scarce, there are a host of shallow-water areas abounding in the small animal life on which this bird feeds. The fact is there are far more such areas than there are Spoonbills.

Although food is not the basic reason for shortage of Spoonbills in Florida, it is just as vital to the Spoonbill as to any other animal, even more so in some respects. The form of its bill quite definitely restricts the species to shallow-water habitats; while there are many kinds of shallow waters, only some of them provide Spoonbill food in sufficient quantities to make them acceptable feeding places. Thus, the question of food is linked directly with distribution; since quantity of food is important, it is also linked with abundance. The key to the presence or absence of Spoonbills in any given area can very often be found by analyzing the food situation. If we are to understand this relation of the Spoonbill to its environment, we must investigate thoroughly its food and manner of feeding.

A.   Feeding Equipment and Its Use

The neophyte bird student learns to group birds and find out something as to their food habits at the same time, by observing the character of their bills. A thick heavy bill on a small passerine bird identifies it as a seed eater; a thin narrow bill on a similar bird indicates that it is chiefly insectivorous. The long, sharply pointed beak of the heron can impale a fish as readily as the slender decurved bill of the ibis can probe the cave-like retreat of a fiddler crab. Few beaks are as specialized as the Spoonbill's. Its spatulate-shaped mandibles are remarkably different in shape and in function from those of any other bird. Although, in a sense, the word 'spoon' is descriptive of the shape of the mandibles, it is somewhat misleading as to their function. The bird does not use its mandibles as a scoop, in the manner of the Shoveller or 'Spoonbill' Duck. Although the mandibles of both species appear to be well supplied with sensitive nerve ends, those of the Spoonbill do not have the rows of comb-like teeth through which food can be sifted (see drawing).

The upper mandible of the Roseate Spoonbill may be over six inches in length and has a lateral groove running from base to tip, which is probably a conduit for the main stem of the nervous system of this mandible. The breadth of the upper mandible varies from a little more than an inch at the base to less than an inch toward the middle, widening to two inches across the broadest part near the tip. At the tip there is a small process or 'nail' (Audubon: "claw"), which corresponds to a similar process of lesser size on the tip of the lower mandible. Evidently the system of nerves extends to the tip, and these processes, besides being sensitive as to touch, serve a mechanical purpose by assisting the bird to take hold of an object.

Selection of an item can be accomplished while that object is still held in the forcep-like grip of the mandibles. (Audubon spoke of the "elegance" of their manner of feeding.) It is necessary for

Figure 30.   Mandibles of Spoonbill and Shoveller.

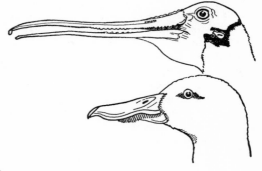

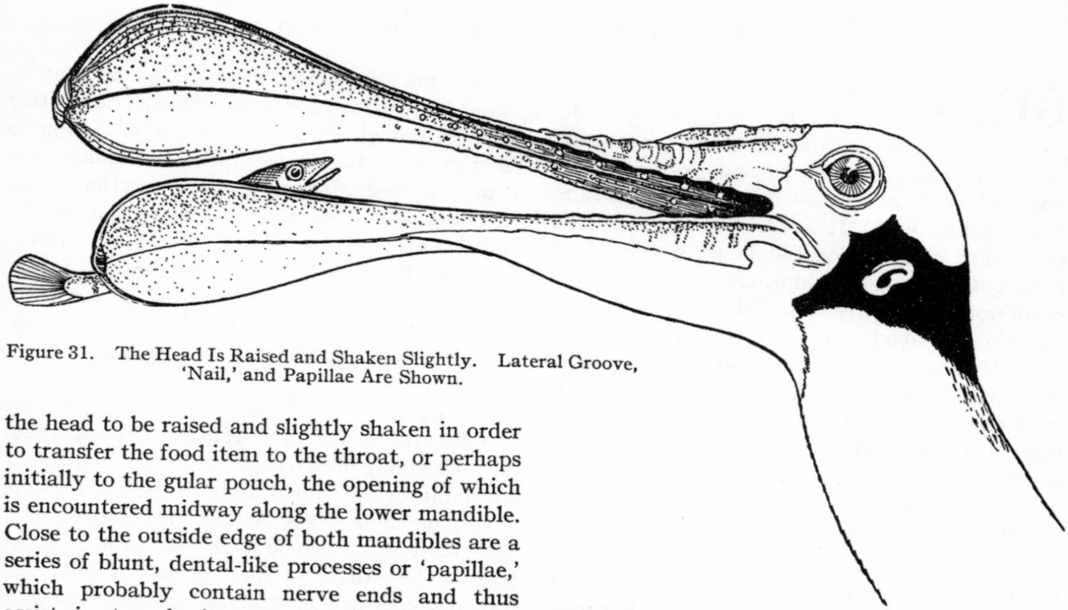

Figure 31.   The Head Is Raised and Shaken Slightly.   Lateral Groove,
              'Nail,' and Papillae Are Shown.

the head to be raised and slightly shaken in order to transfer the food item to the throat, or perhaps initially to the gular pouch, the opening of which is encountered midway along the lower mandible. Close to the outside edge of both mandibles are a series of blunt, dental-like processes or 'papillae,' which probably contain nerve ends and thus assist in transferring the food to the throat. These are not 'teeth' in the sense that they are large enough or strong enough to be used in chewing; their function seems to be more that of holding and directing.   For example, I have seen a Spoonbill pick up a small fiddler crab and start to swallow it.   When the crab was midway along the bill, it was held firmly while the bird's head was shaken vigorously from side to side, apparently in an effort to get rid of the larger claw of the crab.   Sometimes the claw is shaken off without difficulty, at others the crab must be transferred once more to the tip of the mandibles so that it can be beaten against a hard surface and the claw loosened in this manner.   There are rows of processes on each side of the groove in the roof of the mouth; these would likewise seem to be used for handling food objects rather than masticating them.   Snipes and sandpipers have similar rows of papillae.

It is well known that the Roseate Spoonbill (and other species of Spoonbills, for that matter) secure their food by swinging the bill from side to side.   Audubon wrote: "They move their partially open mandibles laterally to and fro." Lt.-Commander J. G. Millais compared the swinging motion of the bills to the rhythmic swinging of mowers in a hayfield.   Bently Beetham's observation (1927) of the European Spoonbill is very much to the point: "It seemed not to be searching for any particular prey, but rather to be promiscuously screening the mud and flimsy vegetation for whatever it might contain."   All Spoonbills are thoroughly omnivorous in the sense that they will eat anything, a fact that should be amply demonstrated in this discussion.

Evidently the side-to-side motion of the mandibles is an instinctive act, coordinated with the central nervous system so that the form (i.e. the side-to-side motion) remains relatively unchanged, regardless of the nature of outside stimuli.   In other words, this side-to-side motion is a form fixed or determined in the animal itself. Captive Spoonbills exhibited a hunger response by swinging the head and bill from side to side although no food was visible.   Other captives, approaching a tray in which cut up fish had been placed, swung their bills exactly as if searching through muddy water for natural prey.   Upon reaching the tray of fish, these motions ceased and the pieces of fish were picked up and swallowed in the only manner in which this could be accomplished. This picking-up motion would seem to be a reflex, or taxis, directed toward a visible stimulus while it is being performed. In other words, the fish in the tray were the stimulus and the oriented reaction was the forward and downward motion of the head and neck employed in picking up the fish in order to swallow.

Audubon (1838) speaks of Spoonbills "munching the fry, insects, or small shell fish, which they secure, before swallowing them." It would seem that this munching is chiefly a selective and preparatory process rather than a predigestive one, although the armor of crustaceans may be cracked to facilitate swallowing. However, the manner of feeding unquestionably varies with the prey. Fishermen on the coast of Texas told me that they knew when Spoonbills were feeding on killifishes or small fry from the manner in which the birds moved through the water. At such times, depending on the relative abundance of prey, the pace will be quite rapid; they will sometimes run from side to side and flap their wings, leaping ahead in order to intercept a school of minnows. Along a shore line which is thick with marine grasses and in which there are small prawns (*Palaemonetes carolinus* Stimpson) and very small examples of silversides, the birds feed more leisurely. Then, when a school of fry escapes into an open pool, the birds will suddenly leap into action, running with long strides and flapping their wings simultaneously in order to head off the escaping meal.

It seems clear that, although the broad mandibles are not used as a scoop, their width is of importance in trapping small marine animals that would escape a more slender-billed bird. Of equal importance is the sensitiveness of the bill, for the shallow water in which the Spoonbills feed is often opaque, and the prey must be literally *felt* out of it. Then, too, some forms of marine life on which the Spoonbill feeds are lifted out of the mud itself, a mud that the Spoonbill is unable to probe in the manner of many birds but through which it feels as one might with the fingers of the hand, although the Spoonbill's instrument is far more efficient. Usually the tips of the mandibles are swung through the surface mud, and an area in which Spoonbills have been feeding

is a maze of little semicircular tracks, some of them describing the full 180° that a really hungry and energetic Spoonbill will cover.

To return for a moment to Audubon's term of 'munching,' it would seem that, in addition to type of prey as a variable, we must consider relative availability, tidal conditions and status of the individual bird. On a marly flat in Florida Bay I watched several Spoonbills feed leisurely from shortly past noon until 4:30 P.M. The most abundant and therefore the most available food animal in those shallow waters were small schools of killifishes, chiefly the sheepshead minnow and the sail-finned killifish. The former were most numerous in shady spots along the edge of the mangrove, where they sometimes burrowed into the soft mud or fed on microorganisms that were attached to the scanty marine vegetation. The sail-fins were most numerous in little beds of turtle grass in which they found shade and protection as well as food in the form of minute protozoans and other organisms. Neither of these fish were very abundant in this particular location; as I watched quietly from a narrow dock close by, it was quite evident that the Spoonbills were occupied with their feeding for such a long time because they weren't securing very many fish.

I decided that these birds, which were adults, had no immediate responsibility in the breeding colony a mile away. The nests in the colony contained eggs on this date; after these eggs had hatched, adult Spoonbills seldom returned to that location to feed. Instead, they secured most of their food in the shallows immediately adjacent to the nests, where it was not only closer to the young but also more abundant. I can't explain why they didn't always confine their feeding activities to the more productive shallows of the nesting key; perhaps birds, too, have an occasional and purely psychological impulse to 'get away from it all.'

In a tidal area the major feeding is done on the low tide and hunger is satisfied very quickly. Instead of several hours, it is more usual for the birds to feed for a period of only ten or fifteen minutes.

On one occasion I watched an adult Spoonbill

feeding in a cattle pond on a ranch in Texas. Relatively speaking, food animals in this pond were more numerous than in the Florida Bay area where the birds fed for several hours. This Texas bird was feeding rapidly, but the great difference lay in the fact that the young in the nearby colony were hatched and partially grown. The bird moved about quickly and paused at frequent intervals to swallow. Its prey was chiefly small aquatic insects (water boatmen, and back-swimmers) and tiny, immature top minnows. After this bird (an adult male) had fed for some ten minutes, it was collected. The stomach contained only 7 cc. of material, yet 100 individual animals were counted.

The lower mandible is constructed so as to permit ready access to a throat pouch, which Audubon described as "very dilatable and of the same general nature of that of the Cormorant's and Pelican's." The esophagus appears to be quite slender but can be greatly enlarged. It leads directly into the proventriculus, the glandular part of the stomach secreting the peptic fluids. The main portion of the stomach is the muscular or grinding part. According to Audubon, the esophagus and proventriculus of the Roseate Spoonbill are similar to those of the curlews; but the stomach proper is like that of the herons in the arrangement of its muscular fibers and the softness of its lining. However, it is said to differ from the heron's stomach in being larger and more muscular, possibly because the Spoonbill feeds in part on molluscs. The stomach of a Flamingo described by Audubon (1839) was very muscular, with the lateral muscles extremely well developed, the lining thick and tough and marked with longitudinal coarse grooves. The Flamingo feeds on molluscs.

I have already mentioned the absence of comb-like teeth on the mandibles of the Spoonbill, although they are to be found on the upper mandible of the Shoveller Duck and other surface-feeding waterfowl. According to Audubon, the upper mandible in the Flamingo is furnished with "about 150 oblique lemellae," which serve as strainers.

B.   THE SPOONBILL'S FOOD NICHE

What do we mean by *niche?* Aldo Leopold (1933) speaks of it as "a habitable position."

Elton (1927) says that it is an animal's place "in the biotic environment, its relations to food and enemies." In the case of the Roseate Spoonbill, this niche is more closely associated with food than with anything else. In general, it must be an area of shallow water, but even this requisite has to be further broken down. Perhaps the most convenient way of describing the Spoonbill's niche will be to discuss several typical habitats occupied by Spoonbills—habitats that are fundamentally alike but that differ in detail. A composite of these various environments will be the best possible picture that one can secure of the Spoonbill's food niche.

1.   Florida Bay

The *ideal* in this region is typified by shallow mangrove pools within the southern interior of Bottlepoint Key. This part of the bay is nontidal, that is, there is no periodic tide but only an occasional change in the water level brought about by the force of the wind blowing continuously from a given direction. The waters of the bay have access to these interior pools through a narrow creek that winds into the key from its southern edge. Usually the water depth is only three or four inches, but a period of prolonged winds from a southerly quarter or a series of heavy rains will infrequently raise this depth to a foot or more.

The pools are hidden from the view of anyone approaching the key, regardless of direction, and are also well screened from the weather by a heavy growth of red mangrove that completely encloses them. There are a series of these ponds connected by narrow openings through intervening walls of mangrove. In extent, the open area of the pools averages about fifty feet in length by thirty feet in width.

The mangroves on either side are no less than fifteen feet in height and afford excellent nesting sites for the Spoonbills. Other birds that nest in these same mangroves, although at a later season, include Louisiana Herons, Green Herons, White-crowned Pigeons and possibly a few others. Maynard's Cuckoos are observed there and Mangrove Clapper Rails tread among their roots.

There are no mammalian inhabitants on this key (an important point!), but the immediate

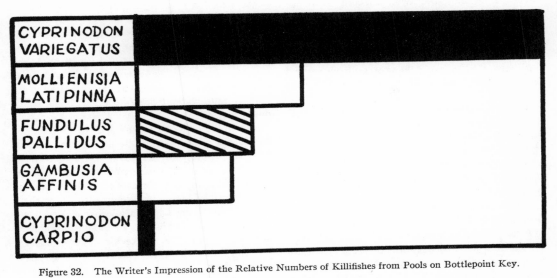

Figure 32. The Writer's Impression of the Relative Numbers of Killifishes from Pools on Bottlepoint Key.

neighborhood of the pools is populated by at least three reptiles: the American crocodile, the diamond-backed terrapin, and the flat-tailed water moccasin.

Of chief importance to Spoonbills are the marine animals: killifishes and aquatic insects and a smaller number of molluscs. Apparently all of these forms breed within the quiet shelter of the pools and their environs. The several varieties of killifishes present are not only amazingly abundant, but the average size indicates that they are immature. The larger ones are only half an inch in length and one-quarter of an inch is more usual. Five species of killifishes have been identified from these pools on Bottlepoint Key, and in the order of their abundance these are as follows:

1. Sheepshead minnow
2. Sail-finned killifish
3. Pale killifish
4. Viviparous top minnow
5. Carp killifish

I did not make any quantitative studies of these killifishes but certainly their total numbers run into the millions. A short haul with a four-foot seine always resulted in a catch of two or three quarts of fish—it cannot be so graphically expressed in any other terms. In no other lo-cation did I find such an abundance of *small* fish.

As to relative numbers of one species to another, the accompanying figure, although not accurate, is my impression of this relationship.

I was aware of seasonal fluctuations among these killifishes. Immature sheepshead minnows (probably the most important single species in the diet of the Spoonbill) appeared to be most numerous during late winter and early spring (including those important weeks when young Spoonbills are in the nests and in these same pools learning to feed for themselves). In August the sail-fin was the most abundant and the pale killifish had greatly increased, although it is doutbul if either of them ever exceeded the sheepshead minnow in numbers. The top minnow may have increased during the summer, but of this I am not certain. The carp killifish was never numerous.

The average salinity of these pools during two winters (1939–40 and 1940–41) and a part of the summer of 1941 was 24.6, which is brackish but of a greater density than many so-called brackish environments (see footnote, p. 63). There may be quite a fluctuation in salinity, depending on the amount of precipitation, direction and force of the wind, and other climatic factors. The average water temperature in the pools was between 80° F. and 85° F. with a record low of approximately 49° F. in December 1939 and a high of 102° F. in August 1941.

In the pools proper there was only one form of aquatic insect, the water boatman. These minute creatures swarmed in vast multitudes, and one scoop of the dip net captured them by the hundreds.

Molluscs were present but in such relatively limited numbers that they did not appear to be an important item in this particular niche. Varieties found in the pools included *Cerithium minimum* and *C. muscarum* (horn shells, an abundant gastropod of that region); a small, thin-shelled bivalve (*Tellina*); and occasionally a bubble shell (*Bulla occidentalis*). The first two are an important food of the American Flamingo.

I have described the *ideal* for Florida Bay. To obtain a composite picture, it will be necessary to mention briefly other types of environment occupied by Spoonbills in that same general region. At the opposite end of Bottlepoint Key the vegetation is chiefly black mangrove, except for a narrow rim of red mangrove on the shore lines. The soil is a black and sticky form of peat interlaced with the intricate root system of black mangrove and studded with the quill-like pneumatophores or breathers of that tree. The water level is at the surface line or may cover the peat to a depth of two or three inches. The black mangroves are stunted and broken from long exposure to hurricanes, gales, the prolonged northers of winter and periodic drenchings of salt water. One of the larger trees had an extreme height of ten feet to the top of the tallest living branch, and the base had a circumference of four feet ten and one-half inches. A ring-count sample indicated that it was probably in the neighborhood of 140 years old.

In general, the area is made up of thick growths of black mangrove alternated with open spaces which are covered with pneumatophores. Where there are two or three inches of water I found sheepshead minnows and viviparous top minnows, chiefly the former. Among the pneumatophores there was an abundance of aquatic insect life, chiefly water boatmen and aquatic beetles. There was also an immense quantity of larval

forms, many of which appeared to be larvae of the sandfly or midge (*Chironomus* sp.).

Salinities and water temperatures varied somewhat from those recorded for the pools at the lower end of the key. The water usually had a lower density than the pools and after a rain was sometimes nearly fresh—but never actually so. The average water temperature was 85° F., seldom less.

Spoonbills came to these areas to feed but of course did not nest there because of the lack of adequate cover, etc. Louisiana Herons, Yellowlegs, Killdeers and Black-bellied Plovers also fed there, and many land birds were observed in the upper levels of black mangrove. In winter these birds included the Loggerhead Shrike, Red-wing, Prairie Warbler (which began to sing in January and nested shortly thereafter), and occasionally a Pigeon Hawk, which was observed feeding on migrating dragonflies and on one occasion on a passing flock of Tree Swallows. Mangrove Clapper Rails were more numerous here than at the lower end of the key. A fourth reptile was found only in this environment, a form of the American chameleon.

2. *East Cape Sable*

Strictly speaking, this example of the Spoonbill's niche is a series of ponds and tidal pools near the East Cape Canal. It is *not* a nesting location but is a much-used roost and feeding place not far removed from the old nesting site on Alligator Lake. I did not see this area before destruction of the mangroves by the 1929 and 1935 hurricanes. At present there is scarcely any live vegetation except the ever-present glasswort. The stark and denuded trunks of the dead mangroves give the whole region a somber, depressing appearance; on a dark day it looks like an anteroom to the Inferno. But the strong flow of tide through the canal carries with it an abundance of life and vitality. When the tide runs out, it has left behind multitudes of small organisms which lie trapped in the countless tidal pools and the winding rivulets. Birds swarm in great numbers—herons, ibises, Pelicans, both the White and the Brown, and vast companies of shore birds. Spoonbills are there, too, though irregularly from March until May, when fifty to a hundred immature 'Pinks' roost day and night in the dead trees west of the canal, and spread out over the surrounding terrain to feed on the low tide.

The East Cape tidal pools are made to order for the Spoonbill. In little estuaries, landlocked by the dropping water, I found schools of killifishes milling about in such numbers that the coffee-brown surface was streaked with hundreds of tiny clouds of mud. Four species of killifishes were identified from this region and also large numbers of immature anchovies. Killifishes represented were the following, in order of their relative abundance:

1. Sheepshead minnow
2. Pale killifish
3. Common killifish
4. Banded killifish

Undoubtedly the sheepshead minnow was again the most numerous form, but all of the others except the very handsome banded killifish were almost equally abundant. Incidentally, both the pale and the banded killifish have been generally considered by ichthyologists as quite rare, although the latter may sometimes be abundant locally. Furthermore, the pale killifish was not previously known except from Galveston Bay, Texas (Breder, 1929).[63]

It is especially interesting to note that this region 'in back of' East Cape continues to hold unfailing attractions for birds, including Spoonbills, in spite of the many changes that have occurred there during the last century. When Audubon was at Sandy Key in the spring of 1832, he visited the nearby mainland to secure fresh water from a well that had been dug there, as mentioned in an earlier chapter. This was long before East Cape Canal had been cut, although it is said that the Indians had a canal of sorts leading from the bay into waterways of the mainland east, I believe, of what is now the settlement of Flamingo. The Everglades had not been drained and from Cape

Sable to Lake Okeechobee extended a vast area of fresh-water marsh. At Sandy Key, Audubon saw gallinules, apparently in some numbers, and great flocks of Fish Crows; neither of these birds are seen in that region today. He also found Spoonbills on the shores of Sandy Key, and it seems certain that the Alligator Lake colony was present at that time in all its original glory. After drainage of the Everglades and the construction of canals, the ecology of that region was changed from one of fresh water to one of brackish and salt water. These changes were accentuated by hurricanes like those of 1929 and 1935, which carried marine sediments and organic debris far inland, covering the entire Cape Sable region with a heavy layer of marl.

I found the average salinity in the vicinity of the canal 25.0. Fortunately many of the marine animals, killifishes and aquatic insects in particular, are unusually adaptable to ecological changes of this nature. It has been suggested that wildlife in the Cape Sable region would benefit if the canals were dammed off and the region allowed to return to its original fresh-water status. Certainly this change would require many years to accomplish, if indeed it could ever be brought about. Meanwhile the lifeblood of that entire littoral is contained in the periodic tides, and these must have the canals as the channels of their distribution.

3. Alligator Cove

Still another type of niche is that found along a part of the southwest Florida mainland, of which Alligator Cove is representative. From all accounts, this part of the coast originally harbored large breeding colonies of Spoonbills (Scott, 1889), but today there are none. Whether or not the drainage of Lake Okeechobee or of the Everglades has had a significant effect upon feeding conditions in the nearby interior of the mainland I do not know. Salinities in the coves averaged 25.7, about the same as in the Gulf of Mexico at this point.

I can only describe present conditions in which there are relatively large flocks of Spoonbills, chiefly immature birds, roosting at the heads of coves along the mainland shore and feeding on the

---

[63] In the Spoonbill habitat animals collected are frequently the immature forms and often determination of species is difficult. Two or three forms of killifishes of the genus *Fundulus* from southwest Florida and Florida Bay may show intergrading, and J. T. Nichols (1942) suggests further studies of material from these areas.

littoral during the low tides. In at least one instance an offshore key (Duck Rock) is used as a regular night roost. These immature flocks arrive on that coast in late March or early April, begin to diminish in September, and except for stragglers are absent during most of December and through January, February and early March.

Alligator Cove lies between the mouths of Chatham and Lostmans rivers. The coast north of Lostmans as far as the mouth of Lopez River has a distinct character of its own quite different from that of the shore line south of Lostmans. It is low and muddy; wide areas of mud and oyster bars lie exposed at low tide. The many coves are rimmed with grass against backdrops of red mangrove, and a mile or two may separate them from navigable water when the tide has retreated. South of Lostmans River towering red mangroves, some of them eighty or more feet in height, stand at the very edge of the Gulf, and the coast line is broken by the deep tidal deltas of four strongly flowing rivers. At low tide there are no extensive areas of mud, no low, grass-fringed coves shut off from open water by wide expanses of soft mud. And there are no Spoonbills.

Such coves as Alligator, however, fit very nicely into the Spoonbill's scheme of life. They are shallow enough even at high tide, and slender fingers of water lead from their farthest corners deep into the mangrove-tangled interior. In these retreats the Spoonbills roost when the tide begins to rise; when it is close to low, they come out to the edge of the cove and feed in the tidal pools and along the narrow trickles of water that continue to flow downhill toward the open Gulf. The whole region is an isolated one, and at low tide it is barred to all intruders.

Food is extremely abundant, especially killifishes, small fry and shrimp. When the dropping tide reaches slack, the narrow estuary in Alligator Cove stirs with animation. Sometimes it appears as if its channel contains more animal life than water! The Spoonbills wait patiently until this condition is reached; then, feeding rapidly, they soon gorge themselves. While the tide is falling, some of the Spoonbills wander about the exposed mud of the bottom, picking up fiddler crabs from along the feet of the mangrove roots, or they dip into some of the thousands of tidal pools and nibble on aquatic insects and other organisms to be found there.

Feeding birds include Little Blue Herons, Louisiana Herons, Snowy Egrets and White Ibises, the latter seemingly interested only in fiddler crabs. Swallow-tailed Kites skim gracefully over the tops of the mangroves, their shrill whistles and squeals being almost the only sounds to be heard. When ibises drop into the coves, they grunt unpleasantly; as the Spoonbills march rapidly along the rim of the channel, they, too, grunt in low, preoccupied tones. Raccoons are abundant and frequently join the flocks of feeding birds, crouching on their haunches and fishing tirelessly with their capable forepaws, their glistening eyes shifting from right to left in an absent sort of way.

I found four species of killifishes in these coves and large numbers of immature silversides, anchovies, mullet and mojarras. It seems impossible to form an opinion as to which variety of killifish was the most numerous. The four species were as follows:

1. Sheepshead minnow
2. Pale killifish
3. Long-nosed killifish
4. Common killifish

This southwest coast niche and the one at the East Cape Canal were the only Spoonbill areas that I studied where feeding was governed strictly by the tides. Because of the tides there are only brief periods out of the lunar day in which feeding grounds on the southwest coast east of Pavilion Key (Duck Rock Cove, etc.) were available to Spoonbills. Zero tide is located at a point near the head of Duck Rock Cove and on the edge of a tidal estuary. On a falling tide the birds fed along this estuary a few minutes before the slack. Actually, they might have fed for an hour prior to the flow, but since they were nonbreeding birds and had only themselves to consider, they waited for ideal conditions, i.e. low slack water.

This is an important point because of its relation to the possibility of re-established nesting on that coast. It seems obvious that these tidal coves would be unable to supply proper feeding conditions for a colony in that region; the parent birds would have to secure food at all times of the day and night, presumably from the nearest area of fresh-water marsh inland.

It is frequently mentioned that Spoonbills feed most often at night. Elsewhere I have discussed the possibility that microorganisms and therefore the small fish, crustaceans, etc., that feed on them, are more abundant in shallow waters after dark. It is true, in the case of tidal regions, that nocturnal tides were generally lower than diurnal tides on the southwest coast of Florida during March–July 1941. During five months of the year, diurnal tides are lower; for another five months, the nocturnal are lower. For two months the difference is evenly divided. Spoonbills find the greatest amount of food available on the lower of the two daily lows.

4. San Antonio Bay

The first thing that I noticed about this Spoonbill niche on the Texas coast was the abundance of the little sheepshead minnow, which I had always found wherever Spoonbills occurred in Florida. In Texas these fish were more or less numerous everywhere, but especially in shallow arms of the bay, small bodies of water that often assumed the character of ponds or small lakes. Spoonbills nesting on the Second Chain-of-Islands in the bay fed in these water areas, many of which were located on the mainland of the nearby Blackjack Peninsula.

It is an altogether different environment than any I studied in Florida. That portion of the peninsula is a brackish-water flat, for the most part treeless and with the vegetation mainly saltgrass (*Distichlis*) and *Monanthochloë littoralis*, with clumps of sea ox-eye and saltwort. Here and there are bare mud flats covered with a sparse growth of glasswort, and there are occasional depressions rimmed with smooth cordgrass. Nesting birds included the Willet, Horned Lark, Cherrie's Nighthawk, Texas Seaside Sparrow and one pair of Avocets. Stilts, phalaropes, herons, egrets and ducks fed in the ponds. Three Whooping Cranes remained in the vicinity into May.

In the period from April to June inclusive (1940), the average salinity in the ponds and adjacent water areas was 24.8. Although I found large numbers of immature *Cyprinodon* in the ponds, there were no other killifishes present, nor were there aquatic insects in any abundance or molluscs of direct importance to the Spoonbills. Prawns and silversides occurred in one of the larger areas, Mustang Lake, which is within easy access of the open bay. It was especially noteworthy that the shallows of Mustang Lake were almost entirely deserted by animal life during the day, but fish and prawns alike occurred in these shallows abundantly after dark and during the early morning hours. My first inclination was to suppose that the increased water temperature during the day was responsible for these distributional changes, but subsequent studies suggest that they are more likely to be associated with the presence and absence of food, although actual data on the relative diurnal and nocturnal distribution of microorganisms were not obtained.

Some of the smaller ponds became landlocked during May as a result of evaporation and continuance of drought conditions. Water areas 200 yards in length and 50 yards across were reduced to mud puddles 20 feet in diameter. Many wading birds—Reddish Egrets, Snowy Egrets and Spoonbills—descended on these puddles and literally cleaned them of *Cyprinodon*. When the birds were through with their feast, I waded through the puddles and practically combed them to learn if anything living remained. I found a few of the small razor clams still present (they were eaten chiefly by Shovellers, which by this time had departed), marine worms (*Annelida*) and tiny examples of the sheepshead minnow an eighth of an inch in length.

Spoonbills in this region also fed in the shallow waters of the bay along the shores of Matagorda Island, chiefly on silversides and shrimp. The tides here are negligible, changes in the water level resulting chiefly from wind conditions. My detailed studies were not as extensive as in the various Florida environments, but San Antonio Bay and other waters of the Texas coast have been surveyed by marine biologists interested in fish and oyster production. One of the reports (Galtsoff, 1931) points out that these inshore regions are exposed to great environmental changes, especially in temperature and the concentration of salts.[64] High summer temperature and evaporation on the one hand and on the other an excessive volume of fresh water from the rivers during flood stage result now and then in extreme conditions that cause great mortality among marine organisms. As yet we have not been able to observe the possible effect of these fluctuations on coastal bird life.

5. Matagorda County

There is a fresh-water type of niche in Matagorda County, Texas, on the Hawkins Ranch near Bay City. Actually, the niche is man-made, since overflows from artesian wells are the only water source. In one low spot the overflow formed a marsh habitat that is now quite extensive and grown with a variety of vegetation. Marine organisms inhabit this marsh, including numerous aquatic insects. This area is the location of the breeding colony of Spoonbills and other waders. Although the Spoonbills frequently traveled to the shores of Lake Austin, a tidal area connecting with Matagorda Bay, in order to secure food, they also fed in shallow overflows from other wells on the ranch. Certain of these overflows have formed ponds a few inches deep in which cattle wade about or lie down in order to cool off and escape, in some degree, from flies and other insects. On two occasions I found adult Spoonbills feeding in one of these cattle ponds. It was amusing to see them wading about intent on securing food and describing an irregular zigzag course to avoid the huge steers reclining here and there about the pond. In spite of the seeming incongruity of this spectacle, I found an

[64] Gordon Gunter writes me that "freshets and extreme falls may occur anywhere along this coast, but the extremely high salinities do not occur, except in very local pools, relict from storm tides so to speak, north of the Laguna Madre. Everywhere south of that point may be subject to oversalinity of the water in summer, and in some places the condition may hold on for a period of three or four years. Sometimes the whole Laguna becomes barren of fish life, with the possible exception of *Cyprinodon variegatus* and possibly *Menidia beryllina peninsulae*, which I have taken in water registering 72 parts per thousand saline. Incidentally, the latter species is our common *Menidia*. I doubt that *M. b. beryllina* is present on the Gulf Coast."

abundance of animal life in this particular pond—animals of such minute size that their contrast to the bovine inhabitants seemed remarkable. There were large numbers of back-swimmers (aquatic insects) of the genus *Notonecta*, water boatmen, very small top minnows (*Gambusia patruelis*), a small crayfish, an isopod crustacean (Aega ?), and a small slug.

The only other birds observed in the pond were Snowy Egrets. The nearby nesting colony contained White Ibises, but these fed for the most part on crayfish, which they probed out of the levee banks in adjacent rice fields.

I have described five typical Spoonbill feeding areas; it should be understood that there are many more types. For example, I have omitted several places where I found Spoonbills feeding that superficially seem to be quite different from anything I have described thus far. In detail they are much like the rest: shallow protected waters with an abundance and variety of rather small water animals. On the mainland of Florida, Spoonbills fed occasionally in roadside puddles resulting from excessively high tides. These puddles had ultimately become landlocked and were alive with sheepshead minnows. Similar examples were encountered on Key Largo and also on the shores of San Antonio Bay in Texas.

Dr. Carlos Lehmann of the Instituto Botanico, Bogota, writes me that in certain parts of Colombia he has observed Spoonbills feeding in small fresh-water ponds alongside the highways. The European Spoonbill feeds on mud flats and estuaries. Jourdain lists a variety of small life, "remains of small fish, probably roach. From Continental sources, small fish, mollusca (*Tellina*, water-snails, etc.), tadpoles and spawn, probably small frogs, worms, leeches, newts, insects (*Odonata*, *Trichoptera* and larvae, Coleoptera (especially water-beetles and larvae)) and Crustacea" (Witherby, et al., 1939). Patterson (1907) wrote that on the Norfolk Estuary he observed them eating shrimp and small molluscs. Thorburn (1916), writing of the African Spoonbill, says that Lieut. Comm. Millais found these birds feeding in shallow water on a small species of water insect. Dr. Roberts (1940), also writing of the African

A FOOD CHAIN

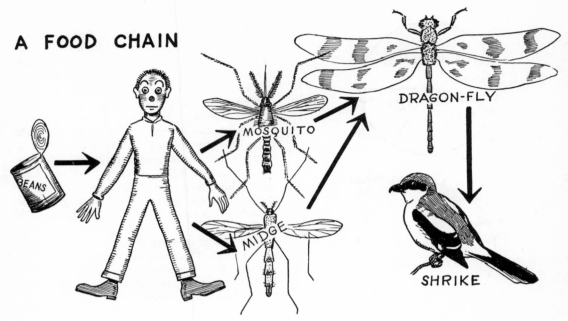

Figure 33.

species, says that they feed on the small water animals that occur in mud and shallow water. In India, the Asiatic race feeds in shallow water on worms, crustaceans, molluscs and water plants (Blanford, 1898). According to Delacour and Jabouille (1931), the Black-faced Spoonbill frequents the edges of mangrove-rimmed shores in French Indo-China and feeds on small insects, crustaceans and vegetation. The two Australian species, the Royal Spoonbill and the Yellow-billed Spoonbill, inhabit large swampy areas and river banks with reedy margins, where they feed on aquatic insects, small fish and molluscs (Cayley, 1931). There is an obvious similarity, then, in the food niche of all Spoonbills, in North America, Europe, Asia, Africa and Australia.

What is our composite picture of the Spoonbill's food niche? Shallow water is universally required, but it may be fresh, brackish or heavily saline (I found Spoonbills feeding in water of greater density than sea water, but such instances were not typical). The kind or even the type of vegetation associated with the shallow waters appears to be of little consequence and a wide vari-

ety of plant life is represented, both marine and fresh water. Shallow water alone, though, is not enough. It must be inhabited by an abundance of animal life, and usually the depth of water is such that the individuals in these animal communities are quite small. The Spoonbill, as I have already stated, will eat almost anything and in that sense is thoroughly omnivorous. Because the form and function of its bill require it to search for food in extremely shallow water, it must capture *quantities* of *small* animals. *They are the only creatures inhabiting such environments.*

This does not mean that Spoonbills would not eat larger objects if they encountered them. Joost ter Pelkwyjk of Utrecht told me of a Spoonbill he found in the Netherlands that had choked to death while attempting to swallow a large eel. He said that their food ordinarily consisted of extremely small fish and crustaceans and also the soft-skinned, worm-like larvae of the midge. Experimentally, I fed food objects of various size to captive Spoonbills and found that they readily swallowed pieces of fish half as big as one's fist. They also ate stale buns and sweet chocolate!

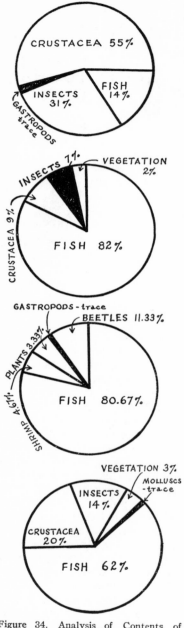

Figure 34. Analysis of Contents of
Spoonbill Stomachs

C. ECOLOGICAL RELATIONSHIPS

If lions lie down with lambs, there must be some good ecological reason for it, which is one way of saying that such an anomaly can probably be explained by correlating the scientific facts involved. In discussing the food of the Spoonbill thus far, I have mentioned a good many different kinds of animals, a number of varieties of fishes, molluscs, crustaceans, insects that live in fresh water, and others that live in brackish water. I have also mentioned several species of birds, reptiles and mammals that appear to have some connection with the Spoonbill's habitat. To each of these animals the Spoonbill is in some way or other related, just as surely as it is related to the habitat itself.

What are these relationships? What is their importance? Unless we know something of the interdependent community life of the Spoonbill's habitat, we can have only a superficial understanding of the bird itself.

1. Food Animals

None of the Spoonbill's relations with other animals are as important as those concerned directly with food, i.e. its relation to those animals upon which it feeds. I have already shown that a link exists between small fishes, crustaceans, *et al.*, and the Roseate Spoonbill. How are each of these various forms related to the Spoonbill and to one another? Of what relative importance is each of them in the life of the Spoonbill?

a. Fish

Evidently fish are the most important Spoonbill food item. An analysis of four Spoonbill stomachs by Cottam and Knappen (1939) and of one additional stomach by F. M. Uhler (*in litt.*) indicates that fish constituted 62% by volume of the total contents. Of the species of fish represented, all were small varieties and the numerical percentage was also high. For example, one young bird from Alligator Lake, Florida, contained more than 246 individual fish, representing 82% by volume of the contents of its stomach. Another Spoonbill, an adult collected at Cape Sable, had only a small amount of material in its stomach, but of the total bulk, fish comprised 42%. Another individual, whose stomach was nearly empty, had fed almost entirely on fish, and the contents were 90% bone fragments of the sheepshead minnow; the remaining 10% was vegetable material. An adult collected in Texas, in a fresh-water habitat, had eaten seventeen individual fishes, one of them a small pin fish and the remainder immature top minnows (*Gambusia patruelis*).

I found the outstanding Spoonbill feeding places in Florida and Texas to be inhabited, as a whole, by twelve species of killifishes, as well as by immature forms of four other groups—silversides, anchovies, mullets, and mojarras. Stomach analyses include six identified species of killifishes and one representative of the porgy family, the pin fish. There were only two species in this list of stomach contents that I failed to find in my habitat studies: the pin fish and a fresh-water form, the star-headed minnow (*Zygonectes notti* Agassiz).[65] The pin fish was probably secured in Lake Austin, Matagorda County, Texas, and the minnow from Alligator Lake [66] or that immediate vicinity.

Of this entire list of fish that are established as Spoonbill food or that are available on known feeding grounds, which varieties seem to be of the greatest importance to the Spoonbill? The answer must be based on a consideration of the distribution and relative abundance of these fish. Although a young Spoonbill in Alligator Lake contained four everglade minnows, I did not find this variety in any feeding grounds that I studied, although I collected it from a fresh-water ditch on the mainland of Florida near Florida City, an area where Spoonbills seldom occur. By contrast, the sheepshead minnow was found at thirty feeding stations, and in both Florida and Texas.

Studies up to this point suggest that the following fish are of importance to the Spoonbill as food.

(1) Sheepshead Minnow

This abundant and adaptable species ranges from Cape Cod to Mexico. Throughout the range of the Spoonbill it was the most widely distributed and numerous fish encountered. I found it in nearly all Spoonbill feeding areas studied, actually in thirty different locations. Some of these were virtually fresh water (Cat-tail Lakes, Florida; Alligator Lake, Florida) and others were tidal regions on the littoral of the Gulf of Mexico (Duck Rock, Florida; Alligator Cove, Florida; Bird Key Bight, Florida). It was the one species that consistently occurred in isolated tidal pools where evaporation had increased the density of the salt water so that it exceeded the density of sea water (areas in Florida Bay).

The sheepshead minnow is a chubby fish, oviparous and omnivorous. At the spawning season, which in Florida Bay appears to begin in late January, the males assume brilliant colors, steel blue above and orange below. Breder (1929) states that their eggs hatch in from five to six days and that maturity is reached in a year. Males reach a length of three inches; females are smaller.

This species feeds to some extent on vegetation, but in captivity I found that they would eagerly accept small particles of shrimp and even the flesh of their own kind. Smith (1907) says that, in aquaria, they will eat their own young. I found evidence to indicate that they feed at times on microorganisms that are attached to marine vegetation. These organisms included a form of protozoan.

One apparent reason for the importance of this fish to the Spoonbill is its wide distribution and abundance. The resistance that it displays toward changes in water density and temperature would seem to be a major factor in its success. Experimenting with the sheepshead minnow in aquaria I found that it survived an abrupt transfer from Florida Bay density (currently 28.5) to rain water, although only one out of nineteen individuals survived an abrupt transfer from bay water to brine (45.4). However, all individuals of this species survived a gradual increase in salinity from bay water to brine, the change being accomplished over a ten-day period. In Florida Bay there are normal fluctuations in density, but these do not reach the extremes tested. Nevertheless, the abundance of this species in that area is significant.

[65] *Fundulus nottii*, Jordan & Evermann.
[66] In Alligator Lake I found only sheepshead minnows and sail-finned killifishes (May 1941).

In my experience, sheepshead minnows were often the only abundant form in extremely shallow, muddy water areas, and they even occurred on flooded roads where there was a water depth of two or three inches in the ruts. Evidently the eggs are deposited in quiet pools of shallow water, and frequently these are the identical pools in which Spoonbills habitually occur. The greatest number of immature sheepshead minnows that I observed anywhere were in pools directly beneath the Spoonbill nesting colony in Florida Bay.

Where newly hatched sheepshead minnows are found in water communities inhabitated by certain aquatic insects, they may be preyed upon by such forms as back-swimmers, predacious diving beetles and others.

(2) Viviparous Top Minnow

This remarkable little fish is found along the South Atlantic and Gulf coasts north to Delaware and rarely to New Jersey. It is also distributed inland as far as Illinois. Jordan (1925) says that it "abounds in all kinds of sluggish water in the southern lowlands, gutters and even sewers included." It is a viviparous species and from ten to thirty young are born at one time, when the young are about one-third of an inch long. The female does not exceed 2.5 inches in length while the male rarely exceeds one inch and is often under 0.75 inches. The species is pugnacious and extremely fecund.

I found these minnows in both fresh and brackish water, and all told they occurred in thirteen Spoonbill feeding areas in both Florida and Texas. Six of these were fresh-water areas and seven were brackish-water areas. They were more numerous in fresh-water habitats and appear to be of greater importance to the Spoonbill in Texas than in Florida.

They feed on mosquito larvae, which are their principal food in some sections. In fact, they have been introduced into malarious and yellow-fever regions. According to Smith (1907) they also eat diatoms, desmids and filamentous algae.

Because of their more habitual occurrence in fresh water, the newly born young are probably more often preyed upon by predacious water insects than are those of the sheepshead minnow.

(3) Sail-finned Killifish

This handsome killifish is distributed from South Carolina to Mexico and is found in fresh, brackish and sea water. Although I discovered it in twelve Spoonbill feeding areas, only two of these were outside the limits of Florida Bay and the Florida keys. Both were Florida locations and both fresh-water habitats—Cat-tail Lakes Canal and a roadside ditch near Florida City.

A viviparous species, like the top minnow, it is not, however, considered as pugnacious or as prolific. Adults reach a length of three inches. In the upper Florida keys, Florida Bay and portions of the Florida mainland, the spawning season appears to begin in February, and at this time the large dorsal fin of the male is exquisitely colored, and in the presence of females is spread in a striking display. The head of the male becomes a golden color and the tail turquoise blue with an edging of black. Some of the males in fresh water are beautifully speckled with brownish and blackish spots.

In aquarium experiments, the sail-finned demonstrated as great a resistance to abrupt changes in density and temperature as the sheepshead minnow. In Florida Bay, where there is a wide fluctuation in salinity, it appears to be second in abundance to the sheepshead minnow. Schools of sail-fins of immature age were numerous in the Bottlepoint Key ponds and along other mangrove shores. In other parts of Florida Bay it seemed to prefer beds of turtle grass. In aquaria, its food habits are similar to those of the sheepshead minnow.

(4) Fundulus Group

Of the genus *Fundulus*, Smith (1907) wrote: "This genus includes some of the best known and most abundant of our 'minnows,' and has numerous members in all parts of the country... Several species abound in water of all degrees of density, while others are confined strictly to fresh or salt water. Some live on muddy bottoms and feed on mud; others swim freely in creeks, rivers, and bays, and subsist largely on insects. All the species go in schools, which sometimes contain thousands of individuals." Jordan (1925) states that these fish occur from Maine to Guatemala and westward to Kansas and southern California.

In my studies of Spoonbill feeding grounds, I collected four species of this genus, three of which were rather widely distributed and sufficiently abundant to be an important food item. One of these was the *pale killifish*, which occurred in eight feeding locations in Florida from Butternut and Bottlepoint Keys in Florida Bay to Duck Rock on the southwest coast. I did not come across it in Texas.

The *long-nosed killifish*, which inhabits the Gulf states from Florida to Texas, was collected in five Florida locations and two in Texas. In Florida it was frequently abundant in Bird Key Bight and Alligator Cove on the southwest coast. The *common killifish* was taken on six feeding grounds in Florida and two in Texas. Its normal distribution extends from the Gulf of St. Lawrence to the Gulf of Mexico and three geographical races are recognized. Breder says that it survives in water that would be fatal to most fishes and shows a remarkable ability to survive changes in both temperature and salinity. Although of great local abundance on the southwest coast of Florida, it was absent from a great many important Spoonbill areas and as a food item it is apparently of minor importance at the present time. The *ocelated killifish* was discovered in only one Spoonbill feeding place, the lagoon on Butternut Key in Florida Bay.

(5) Other Killfishes

There were three additional species of killifishes collected on various Spoonbill feeding grounds. None of these appeared to be sufficiently abundant or distributed widely enough to be of any great importance as a food item. The *banded killifish* occurred in limited numbers on Key Largo and in the general region of East Cape Sable. The *carp killifish* was found in Florida Bay, in ponds on Key Largo and on the southwest Florida coast. Only a few individuals were collected in each of these locations. The *rainwater fish* was found on Key Largo, in the lagoon on Butternut Key in Florida Bay (both of which are brackish to salt-water habitats) and in Wallace Lake, a fresh-water area near the Vingt'un colony in Texas.

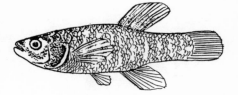

Fundulus heteroclitus
COMMON KILLIFISH

Fundulus pallidus
PALE KILLIFISH

Fundulus similis
LONG-NOSED KILLIFISH

Mollienisia lattipinna
SAIL FINNED KILLIFISH

Figure 35.   Killifishes Found in Roseate Spoonbill Feeding Grounds.

Cyprinidon variegatus
SHEEPSHEAD MINNOW

Gambusia affinis
TOP·MINNOW

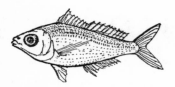

Eucinostomus guta
MOJARRA

Menidia atrimentis
SILVERSIDES

Figure 36.   Other Fish Found in Roseate Spoonbill Feeding Grounds.

(6) Silversides and Other Small Fry

In certain Spoonbill feeding areas, notably though not exclusively the open tidal regions, small examples of silversides, anchovies, mojarras and immature mullets occurred in relatively large numbers. Of these, the *silverside* group was met with most consistently. I found them chiefly on the southwest Florida coast from the Pink Curlew Flats on Big Marco River south to Alligator Cove. Generally, they inhabited the shallowest portions of coves and other semiprotected waters, living in schools in the midst of littoral grasses. The specimens collected were generally so immature that identification as to species was impossible. In Florida Bay there were limited numbers of one of these silversides, referred to as the slender white fish or bristle herring.

In Texas, silversides were abundant in Mustang Lake near the Second Chain-of-Islands. In Cuthbert Lake, Florida, there was a freshwater form of silversides, probably *Menidia peninsulae atrimentis*.

Silversides feed on plankton, small crustaceans, molluscs and insects.

Mojarras were more important in Florida Bay than the silversides, but were lacking on the southwest coast with the exception of Alligator Cove. I did not find them on the Texas coast, that is, in the Spoonbill feeding areas that I examined. The Florida Bay species usually encountered was the *mojarra de ley*. In locations such as the southern shore of Stake Key in Florida Bay, the young of this species were sometimes the most numerous fish in quiet waters among aerial roots of the red mangrove. Mojarras are omnivorous.

Anchovies were collected at Alligator Cove and in the vicinity of the East Cape Canal, both in Florida, where they occurred in schools of small immature individuals. It is probable that they also occur at times in other tidal regions on the Florida west coast. I did not find them in Spoonbill feeding areas on the Texas coast, although Gunter (1938, 1941) has indicated that the little anchovy probably has the greatest numbers and largest species mass of any fish of the Gulf bays. However, as Gunter has advised (*in litt.*), it is a

Plate 17.   The female does most of the nest-building, but the twigs are broken off and carried to her by the male.

Plate 18.   Poised, dignified, beautiful, these Spoonbills looked no different in the distant Pleistocene.

plankton feeder that is more often found in open water than close to shore. Spoonbills feeding on the shores of San Antonio Bay, Aransas Bay, etc. probably take this species now and then.

Evidently anchovies feed for the most part on small organic plankton such as copepods. As a group, they are preyed upon by other fish, spanish mackerel, blue fish, etc.

Mullets are the only fish of commercial value that may be taken by the Spoonbill as food. In spite of their general abundance, I found schools of immature individuals on only two Spoonbill feeding grounds. One of these was Alligator Cove on the southwest Florida coast and the other Ratiseau's Pond close to Redfish Point on Copano Bay, Texas. The Florida specimens were extremely young and more nearly the usual size of fish captured by Spoonbills than those taken from the pond in Texas. The latter were identified as striped mullet.

The food of mullet is varied and may change with the age of the individual. Breder (1929) says that the very young feed on "readily assimilated plankton" and the adults on marine vegetation. Smith (1907) tells of twelve mullet that contained amphipods, annelid worms, small shrimps, bivalves and serpent stars (Ophiurae).

There is no indication that Spoonbills feed to any great extent on mullet,[67] except perhaps seasonally.

b. Crustaceans

Second in importance to fish as a Spoonbill food are crustaceans: shrimps, prawns, and less

frequently crayfish, fiddler crabs and smaller examples such as isopods and amphipods.[68] An analysis of five stomachs indicated that crustaceans made up 20% by volume of the total contents, but one stomach contained no crustaceans whatever and in three others the percentage was relatively small. In other words, whereas fish may always be an important food, crustaceans may only be important locally, depending on local conditions.

A Spoonbill collected in a fresh-water habitat in Texas had eaten one small crayfish and one isopod crustacean (Aega ?). This bird had evidently been feeding in a brackish bay nearby, as it also contained five small shrimps (*Peneus* sp.) and five prawns (*Palaemonetes* sp.). Bulked together, these few crustaceans, twelve in number, totaled 55% by volume of the entire stomach contents.

A nearly grown young Spoonbill in the Alligator Lake colony in Florida had been fed more than 152 shrimps (*Palaemonetes exilipes*) (Howell, 1932), and it is interesting to speculate that, since these could be identified as to species, they must have been given to the young bird with little or no predigestion.[69] They made up 9% of the contents

---

[67] Apparently, predatory fishes store greater quantities of vitamins than those that feed largely on vegetation, which is the case with the adult mullet. Arthur H. Schmidt of Marineland, Florida (*in litt.*), found that captive porpoises, if fed fish such as mullet on a year-around diet, broke out in sores due, possibly, to an evolvement of the sebaceous glands. When fed on predatory fishes such as blue fish, trout, jacks, whiting and croakers, these sores never appeared. Both vitamins A and D belong to the oil-soluble group and may well be present in quantities in killifishes, silversides, anchovies and mojarras. It is thought that vitamin A assists in resisting infection and in human beings a slight deficiency in this vitamin causes so-called 'night blindness.' Vitamin D is concerned with the metabolism of calcium and phosphorus.

[68] Isopods collected in Florida Bay near the Spoonbill colony included the following species:

1. *Cirolana parva* Hansen
2. *Rocinela signata* S. & M.
3. *Excorallana tricornis* (Hansen)
4. *Exosphaeroma faxoni* Rich.
5. *Sphaeroma quadridentatum* Say.
6. *Cleanitis planicauda* Benedict

Some of these were found on mangrove roots, others on wharf pilings or on the shells of small bivalves (*Pinctada radiata* Leach). Many were taken from sponges.

Amphipods were more abundant throughout the eastern Florida Bay region but identifications have not been completed.

[69] Cottam and Williams (1939) state that, while fish-eating birds normally have rapid digestion, some of them may have a "mechanism" for controlling the digestive organs and possibly also the rate of digestion. "It seems probable that fish-eating birds and others have the power to contract the base of the gullet leading into the cardiac unit of the stomach and prevent digestive fluids from coming in contact with the food." The authors noted that some gulls and pelicans fly great distances from feeding grounds to the nesting colony and, on arrival, regurgitate insects, fish, etc., that "showed scarcely any signs that digestion had even started." Of course, both pelicans

by volume, this one bird having been fed the in-
credible total of 494 animals.

An adult Spoonbill from the Cape Sable area
contained one small crustacean, but there was so
little else in the stomach that this comprised 16%
by volume of the total. Another Florida specimen
did not have any evidence of crustaceans in its
stomach when collected.

On the Florida feeding grounds small prawns
(*Palaemonetes carolinus* Stimpson), averaging no
more than 25 or 30 mm. in length, are extremely
abundant in many of the areas, particularly tidal
estuaries near the East Cape Canal and along the
southwest coast. These small prawns appeared
to be scarce in Florida Bay, but I found them
numerous in semitidal pools and ponds on Key
Largo and Plantation Key, areas in which Spoonbills occasionally fed. Doubtless, where they
occur in abundance they are an important Spoonbill food. In Florida Bay, a larger prawn (*Peneus
brasiliensis* Latreille) was commonly observed but
not particularly numerous in the bay proper.
The only place where I found them in numbers
was in Tavernier Creek; there I saw considerable
numbers moving with the outgoing tide toward
the Atlantic Ocean. At such locations along the
Florida keys, this form is commonly trapped in
large numbers and sold as bait, chiefly to snapper
fishermen. I was told that they appear in great
numbers in creeks and inlets during winter following a period of strong northwest winds.

On the Texas coast, prawns of the genus *Peneus*
are commonly distributed, although Gunter believes that snapping-shrimp are more abundant.
Probably both forms are important Spoonbill
food. I found *Peneus brasiliensis* Lat. in Mustang
Lake, Texas, a major feeding place.

The crustacean most frequently collected and
most abundant as to mass on Spoonbill feeding
grounds was the small prawn *Palaemonetes carolinus* Stimpson. I found these decapods in widely
divergent areas in Florida (*Pink Curlew Flats*,

and Spoonbills have a throat pouch which may be utilized
in transporting food short distances, but which may be
more important as a receptacle from which the young
obtain their food. However, the chief point of interest
here is that food may be given to young birds without
having been partially digested. Probably this would
apply only to larger young.

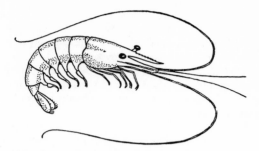

Figure 37.   Prawn, *Palaemonetes carolinus.*

*Duck Rock, Alligator Cove, East Cape Canal, Cat-
tail Lakes Canal, Cuthbert Lake, Low Key* and
Dove Creek Slough) in salt, brackish and fresh
water. They were also collected from brackish
tidal pools on the Texas coast in which Spoonbills
feed (*Ratiseau's Pond*, Copano Bay). Like the
sheepshead minnow, its small size, abundance,
ability to withstand temperature and salinity
fluctuations and wide distribution make it a 'key
industry' food animal as far as the Spoonbill is
concerned.

Other decapoda, of much less importance but
taken occasionally, include:

Hippolyte pleuracantha Stimpson (Florida Bay)
Callinectes sapidus Rathbun (yg.) (southwest coast)
Eurytium limosum Say (Duck Rock)
Uca speciosa (Ives) (Duck Rock)

The last two are very likely important food of the
White Ibis.

c. Insects

The delicate nature of the Spoonbill's manner
of feeding is no better exemplified than by a
consideration of the importance of insects as
food items. The analyses made of five Spoonbill stomachs show that insects constituted 14%
by volume of the aggregate total. An adult
in Texas had eaten more than seventy insects.
More than sixty of these were back-swimmers
(*Notonecta* sp.) and at least ten were water boatmen. Bulked together, these insects comprised
31% by volume of the total contents of this bird's
stomach.

A young Spoonbill in the Alligator Lake colony

had been fed a total of 95 insects comprising 7% by volume of the stomach contents. Five different forms were represented: ground-beetle, trace; predacious diving beetle (*Thermonectes basilaris*), 49; water-scavenger beetle (*Tropisternus glaber*), 23 plus; water boatmen, 21 plus; pseudoscorpion, 1. Two Spoonbills taken in Florida did not contain any insects.

In the field I found abundant populations of aquatic insects in many areas where Spoonbills habitually fed. In shallow-water habitats on Key Largo and on some of the keys in Florida Bay, water boatmen and coleopterous beetles were fairly abundant, particularly in open pneumatophore flats on which there was a water depth of from one to three inches. Usually immature examples of the sheepshead minnow were found in the same habitats and very often there was an abundance of various larval forms floating or suspended in the water. Water boatmen were the most abundant and widely distributed insect within the Spoonbill range, and their greatest local abundance that I observed occurred in shallow pools in Bottlepoint Key, Florida Bay. Fair numbers of corixids were always encountered at low tide in shallow puddles along the southwest coast of Florida from the vicinity of the East Cape Canal to Big Marco River.

In Texas my observation of aquatic insects in localities where Spoonbills fed was limited to fresh-water habitats. Birds from the Vingt'un colony on Galveston Bay flew east to reed-lined ponds beyond Smith Point. At one of these ponds, Wallace Lake, I found Spoonbills feeding with Black-necked Stilts, Killdeers, Solitary Sandpipers, Green Herons and Snowy Egrets. In the reeds were many Red-wings and grackles. The lake was only a short distance from the shore of East Bay, in the midst of coastal prairie where herds of cattle are grazed. I estimated the salinity at 3.7. Narrow-leaved cattails were abundant.

There was a good deal of aquatic vegetation in the lake, and the principal animal inhabitants appeared to be top minnows, rainwater fish, small prawns (*Palaemonetes* ?) and at least two aquatic insects—water boatmen (*Trichocorixa verticalis* Fieb) and water-scavenger beetles (*Berosus striatus* Say).

In Matagorda County, Texas, the nesting colony in Green Marsh was likewise inhabited by aquatic insects, including another species of water-scavenger beetle (*Tropisternus mexicanus* Cast.) and also water tigers, the larval form of the predacious diving beetles (*Cybister fimbriolatus* Say), and numbers of giant water bugs.

In discussing the importance of certain fish in the life of the Spoonbill, I mentioned that the young of these fish are sometimes preyed upon by aquatic insects. Most of the insects found in Spoonbill feeding habitats are predacious, but this is not true of the most abundant of these forms, the *water boatman*. The corixids feed on minute plant and animal particles that they obtain from the organic ooze. Their front legs are flat and spoon-shaped and, when feeding, they keep them in continuous motion so that a stream of ooze comes in contact with the large mouth opening. This opening is equipped to take small bits of algae and diatoms from the ooze as it passes over the mouth. Living for the most part on the bottom of quiet pools, water boatmen must come to the surface every few hours to renew their air supply. However, they can carry extra air under their wings, and it is thought that, if forced to do so, they might remain under water as long as four or five hours. When I found them on the southwest coast in shallow puddles at low water, I wondered how such tiny creatures could survive the strong flow of tide as it rose and fell. Evidently the answer lies in their ability to store an air supply and in the grappling function of their claw-tipped middle legs.

Adult water boatmen can fly, which may account in part for their wide distribution. While I was studying their relation to the Spoonbill environment in Florida Bay, they frequently appeared at night around my lantern at camp and in the light of the store windows in Tavernier on nearby Key Largo.

The *back-swimmers* (*Notonecta* sp.) were numerous in some of the Texas Spoonbill areas, and it will be recalled that one bird had consumed more than sixty of them at a single meal. They are more of a surface insect than the water boatman, swimming on their backs with their heads down and the tip of the abdomen exposed so as to secure air. Back-swimmers are highly predacious and are able to kill young fish larger than themselves.

Water-scavenger beetles of two species were collected in Wallace Lake and Green Marsh, Texas. Twenty-three were contained in the stomach of a Spoonbill in Florida. In a report on the life history of this genus and its economic relation to fish breeding, Wilson (1924) found that the chief food of the larvae of these beetles consists of snails (*Physa* and *Planorbis*), and midge larvae (*Chironomus* sp.) However, these beetle larvae also eat young fish whenever they have the opportunity and are likewise confirmed cannibals, attacking and eating each other voraciously when acceptable food is not abundant. On reaching a length 30 mm.,[70] they begin to seek larger prey, attacking other beetle larvae, dragonfly nymphs, tadpoles and small fish. By the time they reach 40 mm. their diet is quite mixed and they will eat anything they can capture. The adults feed largely on vegetable matter, only taking animal food occasionally.

These Hydrophilidae are eaten by Roseate Spoonbills, and, according to Wilson and others, by Green Herons, Horned Grebes, Black Terns, Cinnamon Teal, Pintails, Wood Ducks, and by the common bullfrog. They migrate from one locality to another by flying and at such times unbelievable numbers are killed by striking against street lights and buildings. Many are also destroyed by storms, and on the Great Lakes they have been found washed ashore in considerable numbers. Wilson concludes that beetles of this genus may be a serious menace to pondfish culture.

I have mentioned that Spoonbills may take various larval forms, as they are known to do in Holland, but it is difficult to know just how much of this material is consumed. Spoonbills feeding among the pneumatophores of the black mangrove where larvae are abundant could hardly avoid taking large quantities. The most numerous larvae collected from such environments on keys in Florida Bay were apparently those of the tiny *Diptera*, known commonly as the midge or

[70] Of one hundred fishes, crustaceans, insects and gastropods in one Spoonbill stomach, all were much less than 30 mm. in length, most of them less than 20 mm.

sand fly. Midge larvae feed on algae, bits of organic matter, diatoms or tiny crustaceans. In turn, they are eaten by fishes, water insects and various birds.

Insects other than water insects are taken occasionally as food by Spoonbills. I have already mentioned a ground beetle and a pseudoscorpion contained in stomachs that were analyzed. At the Second Chain-of-Islands in Texas I saw Spoonbills picking around on the dry ground as if trying to capture something, and now and then they seemed to be successful. On examining this area I found crickets to be quite numerous and also small grasshoppers. Probably both forms would be eaten when readily available.

d. Molluscs

Although molluscs are sometimes prominently identified with shallow waters in which Spoonbills reside, they may be of only minor importance as food. In the five stomachs that have been analyzed two contained molluscs, and in both cases only one individual was represented. A Texas adult had eaten a small slug and a young bird in Florida had been fed another gastropod (*Amnicola* sp.), a fresh-water snail.

I found molluscs especially numerous in Spoonbill habitats in Florida, and in Florida Bay in particular. The eastern part of Florida Bay in the vicinity of Bottlepoint Key is generally quite shallow, with water depths that rarely go beyond five and six feet. There is no periodic rise and fall of tide. Long shoals or banks of marl extend irregularly between many of the mangrove keys and much of the time are exposed above the surface of the bay. Contiguous to these shoals there are so-called marl flats that may be several acres in extent. The average water depth on these flats is usually less than a foot and in many portions only two or three inches. The principal marine vegetation is turtle grass.

Most of the molluscs were found at depths no greater than five inches. I collected many samples from various depths and kept a comparative record of live molluscs. These samples were standardized as to size of area dredged. The following list gives average counts for the different depths and different character of the bottom.

Depth	Character of Area	Average No. of Live Molluscs	Average No. of Genera	Dominant Form
1/2″–5″	Broad marl flat; fairly hard bottom; scattered grass	1220	6	*Cerithium minimum*
1″–2 1/2″	Narrow marl flats with soft bottom; no grass	68	6	*Modulus modulus*
2″–2 1/2″	Broad marl flat; soft bottom; no grass	258	4	*Cerithium minimum*
2 1/2″–6″	Broad marl flat; fairly hard bottom; scattered grass	150	9	*Modulus modulus*
3″–5″	Semienclosed slough; soft bottom	1072	5	*Anomalocardia cuneimeris*
4 1/2″–5 1/2″	Broad marl flat; fairly hard bottom; no grass	129	8	*Cerithium minimum*
4 1/2″–5 1/2″	Broad marl flat; fairly hard bottom; sparse grass	88	6	*Cerithium muscarum*
5″–7″	Broad marl flat; fairly hard bottom; scattered grass	227	5	*Pinctada radiata*
2′	Edge of shoal; heavy grass on bottom	83	7	*Pinctada radiata*
3′	Edge of shoal; heavy grass on bottom	76	1	*Pinctada radiata*
6′	Open bay; marly bottom with sparse grass	75	1	*Pinctada radiata*
6 1/2′	Open bay; marly bottom; no grass	0	0	....

It will be seen that the greatest number of molluscs were obtained from a depth of one to five inches. The bottom, which sloped gently from a narrow beach toward the open bay, was fairly hard and covered with a scattered growth of turtle grass. Spoonbills fed here occasionally but seemed to prefer an adjacent area where the depth was normally one to two and one-half inches. This area sloped away from a shore line of inundated red mangroves rather than from a beach;

the bottom was soft and without grass. In this location the average number of live molluscs per sample was sixty-eight, and in place of *Cerithium* the dominant form became *Modulus*.

From my observations in the field, it would seem that the following molluscs might be taken occasionally as food by Spoonbills in the Florida Bay habitat:

Horn shells { *Cerithium minimum* Gmelin
Cerithium algicola C. B. Adams
Cerithium muscarum Say

Measure shell, *Modulus modulus* Gray
Bubble shell, *Bulla occidentalis* Adams
Anomalocardia cuneimeris Conrad[71]

These were the only molluscs that occurred on the Florida Bay feeding grounds in sufficiently available numbers as to result in their being taken now and then. I do not believe that Spoonbills deliberately seek out molluscs in preference to other animals.

On the southwest Florida coast the dominant mollusc was the smallish oyster, generally called coon oyster, growing either on mangrove roots and pilings or on bars in shallow tidal waters. There were few gastropods. In tidal pools on Duck Rock, however, I observed prosperous colonies of little black horn shells, a form I also found in other west-coast areas north to Little Patricio Island below Charlotte Harbor. It may be taken occasionally as food.

On the Texas coast quite a different sort of oyster community is encountered. Other molluscs associated with them are for the most part bivalves, particularly cockles, scallops, mussels and clams. It is doubtful if Spoonbills find much opportunity to feed upon molluscs on this coast. Some areas had numbers of small amphibious gastropods of the genus *Littorina* which might occasionally be taken as food.

One of the most favorable Spoonbill localities on the Texas coast appears to be in the neighborhood of Mesquite Bay, located between San Antonio Bay and Aransas Bay. According to Galtsoff (1931), Mesquite Bay produces oysters of superior quality; he feels that this is undoubtedly due to favorable food conditions in those waters.

[71] No common name. A tiny bivalve of the Venus family (Veneridae).

He also mentions that diatoms (*Bacilaria para-doxa*, and Biddulphia) were extremely abundant. It seems significant that the Mesquite Bay region is a center of nesting activity for many species of water birds, including the largest colony of Roseate Spoonbills in this country. Apparently salinities in Mesquite Bay are favorable to the welfare of many types of marine organisms, perhaps for the most part those that feed on diatoms and other plankton. Galtsoff recorded the range of annual fluctuations of salinity from 5.03 to 20.10, and a variation in water temperature from 10° to 30° C. (50° to 87.1° F.).

2. Vegetable Material

Vegetable material made up 3% by volume of the aggregate total of the contents of five stomachs. One Florida bird had consumed wood pulp which made up 10% of the stomach contents. An adult from Cape Sable contained three tubers of a sedge, and because the stomach was nearly empty, this material comprised 42% of the stomach contents. A young bird in Florida had swallowed a pine-cone fragment, the plant fiber of a sedge and some wood pulp and vegetable debris, constituting 2% by volume of the stomach contents. It also contained a feather fragment.

I did not observe Spoonbills taking vegetable material, but there is considerable evidence in addition to the above records that other Spoonbills include vegetable matter in their diet. Jourdain (1939, Witherby, *et al.*) mentions plant fibers, including the fruit of a bur-reed, the carpel of a pondweed, and various marsh grasses. This refers to European Spoonbills collected in the British Isles. Of the Spoonbill on the continent, Jourdain says simply that "their diet includes some vegetable matter." Forbes (Butler, 1896–98) says "the European Spoonbill seems to eat a good deal of vegetation and grasses." Arrigoni degli Oddi (1929) states that this same species eats the "young roots of aquatic plants and other vegetables for which it swims and digs." He also mentions frogs, fishes, etc. Whymper (1909) tells of a Spoonbill in Egypt that brought its head to the surface with long strings of grass and other water weeds held in the bill. Referring to the Asiatic species, which occurs in India, Blanford (1898)

says that water plants are included in the diet, and, according to Delacour and Jabouille (1931), the Black-faced Spoonbill sometimes eats "vegetation."

3. Food of Birds of the Same Habitat

There are a number of water birds that occupy food niches similar in many ways to that of the Spoonbill. In Florida the more important species in this group are the Louisiana Heron, Little Blue Heron, Green Heron, Snowy Egret, Yellow-legs, Black-bellied Plover, Semipalmated Sandpiper, Turnstone, and Least Tern. On the Texas coast birds prominently identified with Spoonbill feeding areas are the Snowy Egret, Reddish Egret, Black-necked Stilt, Willet, Shoveller, and Wilson's Phalarope. The last two occur in the Spoonbill habitat on that coast only during the early portion of the Spoonbill nesting season.

Most of these other birds stalk their prey (a notable exception would be the Shoveller). The herons spear or snatch fish and other small animals with a rapid, dartlike motion of the head and bill. Yellow-legs sprint through the shallow water, striking to right and left with quick grasping motions. Sandpipers dabble and probe in the mud, or search minutely among rocks, shells and sea wrack. Plovers are expert at sudden stops and quick striking motions. Turnstones root through the sea wrack, turn over shells, driftwood, etc., or dig in the wet sand in order to obtain molluscs. The Least Tern dives into the water, specializing in the surprise attack. Stilts are principally insect feeders and obtain them by wading nervously through shallow-water areas. The Wilson's Phalarope is more of a shore feeder than the other members of its family and seeks its food by searching along muddy shore lines or whirling in its remarkable fashion on shallow ponds and similar water habitats.

Briefly stated, the chief food of these birds [72] may be summarized as follows:

a. Louisiana Heron

Chiefly killifishes. "Probably eats more fish than other small herons." Of forty-eight stom-

[72] Unless otherwise stated, data on food habits from Bent, *U. S. Natl. Mus. Bulls.*, 126, 135, 142, 146 (1923–29).

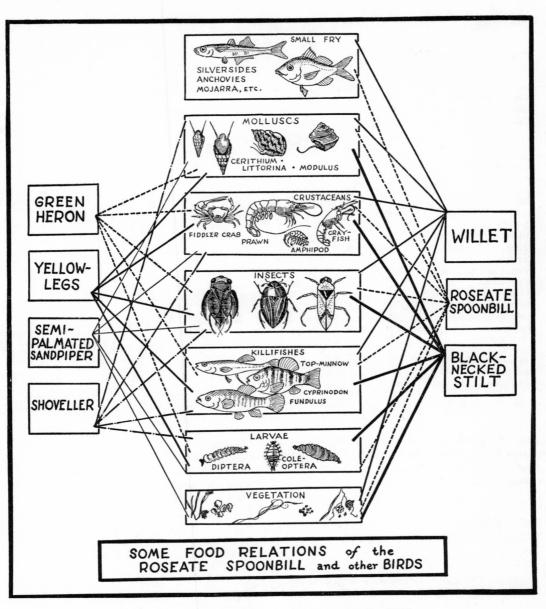

Figure 38. Some Interrelationships of the Spoonbill's Food Niche.

	Roseate Spoonbill	Green Heron	Lesser Yellow-legs	Greater Yellow-legs	Black-necked Stilt	Shoveller	Semipalmated Sandpiper	Willet	Louisiana Heron	Little Blue Heron	Black-bellied Plover	Least Tern	Wilson's Phalarope	Snowy Egret
Water boatmen	X	?	X	?	?	?	?	?	?	?	?	?	?	...
Back-swimmers	X	?	X	?	?	?	X	?	?	?	?	...	?	...
Water-scavenger Beetles	X	?	?	?	?	?	X	?	?	?	?	...	?	...
Predacious Diving Beetles	X	?	X	?	?	?	?	?	?	?	?	...	X	...
Aquatic Insects in general	X	X	X	X	X	X	X	X	X	X	X	X	X	X
Crickets	?	X	...	...	...	...	...	...	...	...	...	...	...	...
Grasshoppers	?	X	X	...	X	...	...	...	...	...	...	...	...	...
Other Insects	X	X	X	...	X	X	X	...	...	...	?	...	...	...
Insect Larvae	X	X	X	X	X	X	X	...	...	X	?	...	X	...
Killifishes and Minnows	X	X	X	X	X	X	...	X	X	X	...	X	...	...
Small Fry	X	X	X	?	?	X	...	X	...	X	...	X	...	...
Molluscs	X	X	X	X	X	X	X	X	...	...	X	...	X	X
Fiddler and Mud Crabs	?	X	X	?	...	...	...	X	...	X	X	...	...	X
Prawns and Shrimps	X	X	X	X	...	X	...	...	X	...	...	X	...	...
Crayfish	X	X	?	?	X	...	...	...	X	X	...	...	...	X
Isopods and Amphipods	X	...	?	?	...	...	...	...	...	...	?	...	X	...
Beach Fleas	?	...	?	?	?	...	X	...	...	...	?	...	X	...
Marine Worms	...	...	X	X	...	X	...	X	X	...	X	X	?	...
Earthworms	...	X	?	...	...	...	...	...	...	...	X	...	...	...
Frogs and Tadpoles	...	X	...	...	...	X	...	...	X	...	...	...	...	...
Snakes	...	X	...	...	...	...	...	...	X	...	...	...	...	...
Lizards	...	X	...	...	...	...	...	...	...	...	...	...	...	...
Spiders	X	X	X	...	...	...	...	...	X	...	...	...	...	...
Vegetable Material	X	...	...	...	X	...	X	X	...	...	X	...	X	...
Sand or Gravel	...	...	...	...	...	...	X	...	...	...	...	...	...	...
Small Mammals	...	X	...	...	...	...	...	...	...	...	...	...	...	...

Figure 39. Food Relations of the Roseate Spoonbill and Thirteen Other Water Birds (Based on Analyses of Stomach Contents).

achs examined, thirty-eight contained killifishes, amounting to 68% of the aggregate total. Other food: shrimps, crayfishes, marine worms, spiders, water insects.

b. Snowy Egret

The principal food is composed of small crabs, snails, crayfish, and aquatic insects.

c. Little Blue Heron

Feeds chiefly on crayfishes and small fish, which are mainly minnows and killifishes. Also water insects and occasionally frogs and snakes; fiddler crabs are taken now and then.

d. Green Heron

In 202 stomachs examined (Howell, 1932), fish made up an aggregate total of 40% by volume.

Most of them were killifishes. Crustaceans, chiefly prawns and crayfish, made up 24% and insects, including water beetles, grasshoppers and crickets, comprised 27%. In addition, a few spiders and snails had been eaten.

At Orange Lake, Florida, a fresh-water habitat, this species consumed insect larvae, frogs, lizards and crabs. They will also feed upon tadpoles, earthworms, snakes and small mammals.

e. Greater Yellow-legs

Killifishes, including the common killifish and the top minnow. Likewise aquatic insects, insect larvae, snails, worms and crustaceans.

f. Lesser Yellow-legs

Chiefly insects, including ants, bugs, flies and grasshoppers. Also small crustaceans, small fishes and worms. Four stomachs examined by Wetmore[73] in Puerto Rico contained 57.5% in the aggregate of water boatmen, and two of the stomachs contained nothing else but the corixids. The remaining 42.5% was made up of crustaceans, including several crabs.

Danforth[74] examined nine stomachs taken in Puerto Rico; these contained various insects and insect larvae, blood worms, snails, spiders and fish scales. The larvae of predacious diving beetles made up 26.6% of all the animal material. Among the insects were numbers of back-swimmers.

g. Semipalmated Sandpiper

Feeds mostly on animal matter, such as insects; small molluscs, especially amphibious snails of the genus *Littorina;* worms and crustaceans like the beach flea. The insects include water scavenger beetles, back-swimmers, small flies, fly larvae and occasionally mosquito larvae. Bits of seaweed and sand are also consumed.

h. Black-bellied Plover

This bird feeds on snails and other molluscs, crabs, marine worms and insects. Under certain conditions it takes earthworms, seeds and berries.

i. Willet

The Willet feeds on aquatic insects, marine worms, small crabs (including fiddlers), small molluscs, fish fry and small fish. Some vegetable matter is taken, such as roots, grasses and seeds.

j. Black-necked Stilt

Feeds mainly on insects, especially aquatic bugs and beetles. Also takes dragonfly nymphs, caddis-flies (the larvae of which are extremely abundant and are eaten by many fish), may-fly nymphs, flies, bill bugs, mosquito larvae and grasshoppers. Sometimes they eat crayfish, snails and tiny fishes; rarely the seeds of aquatic plants.

k. Wilson's Phalarope

Feeds on mosquito larvae, the larvae of crane

flies (which are injurious to grass crops), predacious diving beetles and other aquatic insects, both bugs and beetles. Also small crustaceans, including amphipods and brine shrimps (*Artemia*), the eggs of water fleas, and the seeds of various aquatic plants.

In Texas this species swam in the wave of Shovellers that were feeding on small razor clams and marine worms and apparently obtained morsels cast aside by the ducks.

l. Shoveller

Feeds on small fishes, frogs, tadpoles, shrimps, leeches, aquatic worms, small molluscs, and insects, including aquatic insects as well as their larvae and pupae.

m. Least Tern

This is the only tern that appeared to feed regularly in shallow-water areas along with the Spoonbills. It subsists mainly on fish—for the most part killifishes, anchovies, silversides and small menhaden. Also occasionally on shrimps, marine worms and insects.

I have listed thirteen species that, in my experience, occurred more or less frequently on Spoonbill feeding grounds. It has seemed worth while to describe the food of each of these birds in order to demonstrate how similar it is to that of the Spoonbill. All birds mentioned, including the Spoonbill, feed on water insects, the only item consistently taken by every species. Most of them also eat killifishes and molluscs. Next in importance are crabs (including fiddler crabs) and marine worms, although the latter are not recorded as a Spoonbill item. Next are shrimps and prawns.

Not one food item known to be in the diet of the Spoonbill fails to be listed in the food of one or more of these other birds. However, there are quite a number of food animals on the total list that have not been recorded for the Spoonbill (snakes, lizards, flies, dragonfly nymphs, may-fly nymphs, mosquito larvae, earthworms, frogs, small mammals, etc.).

I saw nothing that suggested any sort of competition for food, in the sense that the demands of one species rendered it difficult for another

[73] 1916, *U. S. Dept. Agr. Bull.* 326.
[74] 1925, *Jour. Dept. Agr. of Porto Rico*, **10**: 1.

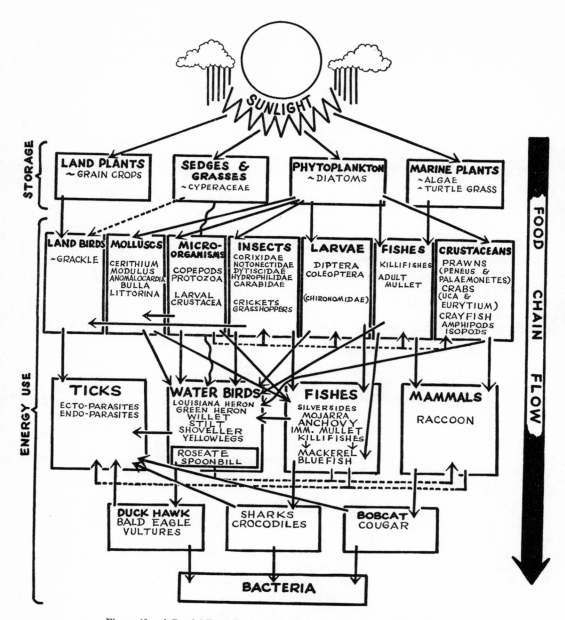

Figure 40.   A Partial Food Cycle of Which the Roseate Spoonbill Is a Member.

species to obtain enough to eat. On the other hand, more detailed studies of the entire animal community might reveal a temporary situation of this sort from time to time. It is not as simple a matter as it might seem to relate the feeding habits of every member of this community to that of every other member. A preliminary attempt to show some of these relationships has been made in the food-cycle diagram.

D. Summary

1. The spatulate-shaped mandibles of the Spoonbill are a delicate instrument, adapted to taking minute animal life from mud and shallow water. They appear to be supplied with sensi-tive nerve ends and blunt processes to aid in transferring prey to the throat. Their efficient use is limited to shallow waters.

2. The food niche of the species may be varied in many details but is fundamentally the same in widely separated regions.

3. The Spoonbill is related not only to a type of environment but to a variety of food animals (fish, crustaceans, insects, molluscs) that inhabit this environment and that show many inter-relationships among themselves.

4. Thirteen species of birds are discussed, all of which occupy food niches similar to that of the Spoonbill. They are not competitors but 'com-panions.'

Part VII. Plumages and Molts

To THE average person, the color of the Roseate Spoonbill is its most attractive and most important feature. Among Spoonbills of the world, ours is the only species with brilliantly colored plumage. For the most part, the feathers of other Spoonbills are white, and brilliant hues are limited to the bill, throat, legs, and other soft parts. Much of our enthusiasm for the Roseate Spoonbill derives from its magnificent pinks and carmines; those who have seen the faded specimens in some of the zoos can appreciate how relatively unspectacular it is without them.

Our Spoonbill is one of those birds that requires about three years to attain adult plumage; as a result, there is a sequence of immature plumages that at first glance appears quite confusing. Although we can give a fairly satisfactory description of these sequences and fit them more or less into an average pattern, there are still some points that will require special study if they are to be cleared up entirely. These will be referred to in the course of the present discussion.

Aside from our natural interest in the plumage of the Spoonbill for its beauty alone, there is a very practical reason for acquainting ourselves with the progression of the various molts and the resulting plumage changes. As with the Herring Gull, which also requires about three years to attain adult plumage, we can recognize the approximate age of an individual if we know the average pattern of plumage changes. Many of the Spoonbills that we see in this country are immature examples. In both Florida and Texas, flocks that are present during the summer months are predominantly immature and in total numbers are more numerous at such time than the native United States breeding birds. Our interest in the life history of these flocks is considerable. We want to know where they have come from, what age groups are represented and to what areas they will return. Plumage studies are the only way in which we can study age groups.

A. Plumages and Molts as an Index to Age

According to Bent (1926) and other authorities, the Roseate Spoonbill undergoes one partial molt and three complete molts in acquiring the adult plumage. On the average this entire process requires thirty-three to thirty-six months. Thereafter, there are two molts annually: (1) a partial molt, prior to the nesting season, by which the bird acquires a plumage that is uniform for both sexes and for all breeding adults; (2) a post-nuptial molt four months later, which is complete and replaces the feathers that have been worn and frayed during the exigencies of the nesting cycle.

The accompanying diagrams of the plumage cycles of Roseate Spoonbills in Florida Bay and in Texas are similar to those presented by Dwight (1925) for "any large gull that breeds in the Northern Hemisphere" and "any large gull that breeds in the Southern Hemisphere." These two groups, represented by the Herring Gull and the Kelp Gull, evidence what Dwight termed four-year plumage cycles, i.e. the birds do not attain adult plumage until the fourth year. Two diagrams are necessary in the case of these two groups of gulls because the breeding season in the two hemispheres is reversed. In the case of the Spoonbill, at least two diagrams are necessary because of the great difference in the time of breeding between the Florida Bay and the Texas colonies, where most of my field studies were conducted.

The diagrams present the plumage sequences of an *average* individual; in all probability, progression toward maturity is delayed in some individuals and advanced in others, just as Dwight found in the gulls.

Six well-defined age groups can be described. The principal plumage and soft-part characteristics of each age group are indicated on the diagrammatic drawings.

1. *Natal Down* (from hatching to about three to four weeks)

Skin of body, including bill and feet, bright salmon pink. Body at hatching entirely covered with sparse growth of short white down.

At about one week the thin growth of down shows a gradual increase in length and density until it becomes thick and woolly.

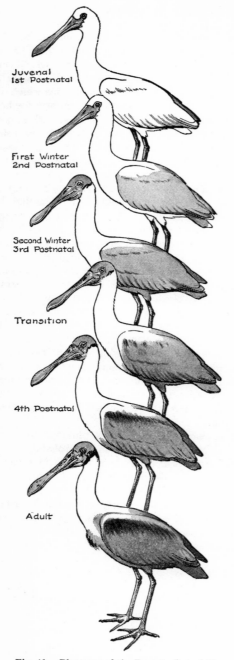

Juvenal
1st Postnatal

First Winter
2nd Postnatal

Second Winter
3rd Postnatal

Transition

4th Postnatal

Adult

Fig. 41.   Plumages of the Roseate Spoonbill

Wing quills appear at an early age. The young bird leaves the nest at an age of approximately five or six weeks; before that the first or juvenal plumage is acquired.

2. Juvenal or First Postnatal (from about one month to undetermined age under one year)

The juvenal plumage is attained gradually and its duration is more or less indefinite, because it is continued with minor changes in the first winter or second postnatal plumage.

Spoonbills approximately one month old are chiefly white in appearance and are well feathered, although the short growth on head and neck may still contain down.

Crown, cheeks and throat are covered with white feathers, and there is a slight suffusion of pink on the feathers of the tail and under the wings.

The primary wing coverts and greater wing coverts are dusky tipped, but this is not always very apparent. The dark tips of the primaries are quite prominent.

The iris is yellow, the smooth bill is a light yellow, sometimes dirty yellow, the legs brownish, and the feet and toes a darker brown.

3. First Winter or Second Postnatal (a continuation of the juvenal, retained until age thirteen to fourteen months)

In this plumage there are progressive changes toward maturity. A *partial molt* results in a pinker coloration on mantle and breast; the pinkish tail of the juvenile becomes pale buff. The dusky-tipped wing coverts disappear, apparently before the bird reaches one year of age.

Other characteristics remain more or less unchanged, including the dark-tipped primaries, although these are not as blackish as in the early juvenile.

In some of the first winter juveniles a little trace of carmine appears in the lesser wing coverts and upper tail coverts before the bird reaches the age of one year. This is not usual and seldom prominent.

The iris is yellow, possibly with changes toward amber. The bill is dirty yellow to dull greenish. *The head remains feathered.*

4. Second Winter or Third Postnatal (from about fifteen months to twenty-one to twenty-four months)

This plumage is a result of the *first complete molt*, which takes place shortly after the bird has reached one year of age and which brings it into the present plumage at about fourteen or fifteen months of age.

For the first time the head, crown, cheeks and throat are bare, and around the ear openings and back of head a thin line of black skin is visible.

There is a deeper pink on the wings, tail and body, although the neck and upper breast remain white.

The skin of the head is a blue-green color and the iris is apparently an amber color. The bill begins to lose its yellow cast and becomes dull greenish or bluish. More flesh color appears in the legs.

5. Fourth Postnatal (duration usually from twenty-one

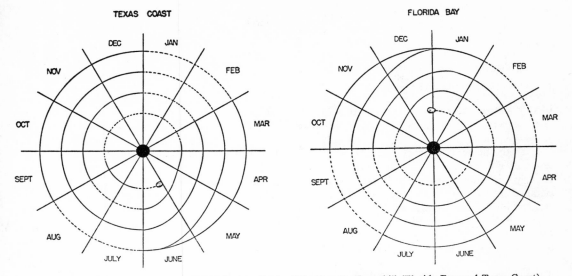

Figure 42.   Diagrams of the Four-Year Plumage Cycle of the Roseate Spoonbill (Florida Bay and Texas Coast). Solid Lines Represent Periods of Stable Plumage; Broken Lines Periods of Molt.

to thirty-three months; sometimes from twenty-four to thirty-six)

A *second complete molt* results in the present plumage, in which the bird has a definite carmine 'drip' on the lesser wing coverts. The wings and under parts become a deeper pink, including the upper and lower tail coverts, which may also show some carmine.

The tail is buff. Some trace of carmine streakings may appear on the upper breast.

The bare skin of the head is greenish; the covering of the bill rougher and somewhat varied with greenish and blackish, as in the adults. The iris is reddish. The legs become a dull red and the feet blackish.

6. *Adult Plumage* (acquired at thirty-three to thirty-six months)

A *third complete molt* takes place when the bird is approaching three years of age, and the result is the adult breeding plumage. *The species is not known to breed except in this plumage;* it exhibits a number of characteristics that are definitely lacking in the fourth postnatal plumage, which superficially resembles the adult.

There is a larger area of carmine in the lesser wing coverts and this drip is of a richer, deeper hue. The upper and lower tail coverts are likewise an intense carmine. The tail is rich ochraceous buff, almost an orange. The back, wings and lower breast attain a richer degree of pink.

On the upper breast there is a prominent patch of stiff curly feathers of a carmine color surrounded by a suffusion of pink and ochraceous buff. There are also prominent

areas of ochraceous buff at the shoulders. At the back of the neck there are usually streakings of carmine, in rare instances large enough to form a small crest.

The bare head varies from a pale or apple green to a golden buff, the latter possibly in the breeding season only. The bill now has horny excrescences and is varied in color with mottled areas and spots of greenish, blackish and yellow. The black skin area around the ear opening and nape of the neck is more prominent and often quite extensive, sometimes extending in a V-shape well down the back of the neck.

The iris is cherry red or carmine, and the legs lake red. The feet remain blackish, and some blackish is apparent at the leg joints and down the back of the tarsus.

It will be noted that the natal down gives way to feathers rather quickly, and for that matter the white juvenal plumage is not worn very long. It has been mentioned elsewhere in this report that very few Spoonbills in the white juvenal plumage are observed in the so-called summer flocks, either in Florida or in Texas. This need not imply that birds-of-the-year do not wander. The white plumage is never a stable one, but is constantly progressing toward the first winter (sometimes called *second juvenal*) plumage from the time the bird is two or three months of age.

An individual with a considerable amount of

pale pink in the plumage, but retaining the feathered head, is most certainly in the neighborhood of one year of age. The first complete molt apparently begins when the bird is about thirteen or fourteen months old, and those with the head partially bald, with some feathers clinging to the cheeks or crown, are very close to fifteen months of age ($\pm$ 15 months). It is at about this age that they enter the second winter plumage (*third postnatal plumage*).

A study of summer flocks on the southwest coast of Florida indicated that more than 50% were in the third postnatal plumage. From less detailed observations, it seems likely that a similar percentage occurs in the postbreeding season flocks that reach the Texas coast in summer. If this is so it would fit in very well with our conception of the origin of these wandering birds. Apparently the Mexican colonies near Tampico hatch their young Spoonbills about the first of March; according to our pattern of the plumage cycle of the species, the average Mexican birds would be in this third postnatal plumage during the months of June, July, August and September, which is the period when they are present on the Texas coast.

We do not know the origin of the summer birds that begin to appear on the Florida mainland in late March. Peak numbers are probably attained by the end of April, and there is no apparent decrease until the end of August or early September. In other words, the large number of birds in the third postnatal plumage (which is a stable plumage over a period of about four months *on the average*) are in the plumage during April, May, June and July.[75] According to the plumage cycle, these birds must therefore have been hatched about January 1.

If our present understanding of the plumage cycle is correct, the above evidence may prove to be of considerable assistance in solving the mystery of their origin. I do not have complete information on the dates of egg laying in all of the Cuban colonies. The two colonies on the southern shore of Camaguey apparently deposited

their eggs about September 1 and November 1, 1941 (Scaramuzza, *in litt.*). However, the birds of colonies in other parts of Cuba appear to nest both earlier and (possibly) a little later. A recent report (Bruner, *in litt.*) tells of eggs having been seen about August 1 and nestlings in December, and apparently this referred to two different colonies. J. D. Smith (*in litt.*) believes that Spoonbills nest during May in Venezuela. Bond (1936) mentions a nesting colony in the Bahamas in "early February."

A second complete molt begins when the bird is approximately twenty months old, a little later in some individuals; and when it is completed, the appearance of the bird is superficially like that of an adult. According to our plumage cycle, this fourth postnatal plumage is retained for the better part of a year, longer than any other immature plumage. In the summer flocks on the southwest coast of Florida, only 6% of the birds were in this age group, although a number of individuals were observed that seemed to be molting toward this plumage. It may be that there is less of a tendency to wander among birds that are getting close to maturity. This explanation would appear to be more likely than one suggesting that natural losses reduce the number of immature birds as they advance toward maturity. From the evidence of Gross and others with regard to the Herring Gull, it is apparent that in that species the greatest amount of mortality from natural causes occurs during the first year, and the same may be true of Spoonbills.

I have mentioned that birds in the fourth postnatal plumage resemble adults, and reference to the diagrammatic drawings showing Spoonbills in the six age groups will demonstrate the many characters that are absent in this plumage but present in the adult.

The adult plumage is acquired for the first time as a result of a third complete molt, which begins when the bird is approximately thirty-two months of age, perhaps sometimes a little earlier. This initial adult plumage is doubtless still further improved as the bird grows older. This is the opinion of Mr. Bent, who has written me, "I have always supposed that there was

---

[75] Or for two or three months longer. Bent believes this plumage is sometimes worn for approximately six to seven months.

Plate 19.   In its first plumage this immaculate youngster is learning to feed itself and to fly.
It is about six or eight weeks old.

Plate 20. The best evidence of success in restoration of the Roseate Spoonbill would be more of these young birds hatched and reared on our shores.

further progressive improvement, and that the highest perfection of plumage might not be obtained for a year or two more."[76]

B. Determination of Age in the Field

Although the main points have already been mentioned, it may be helpful to emphasize certain outstanding plumage characteristics that can readily be seen in the field and that will serve to indicate the approximate age of the individual. These are as follows:

Juvenal or First Postnatal (from about one month to undetermined age under one year)

Entire plumage white with little evidence of pink except when in flight. Wing tips prominently black; head feathered.

First Winter or Second Postnatal (a continuation of the juvenal, retained until age thirteen to fourteen months)

Head still feathered. Considerable *pale* pink on mantle; tail pale buff but sometimes diffused with pink. Some dusky on wing tips.

Second Winter or Third Postnatal (from twenty-one to thirty-three months; sometimes from twenty-four to thirty-six months)

Hard to distinguish in field from adult except at close range. From a distance appears to have all characteristics but lacks all the following items which are present in the adult bird.

Adult (from thirty-three to thirty-six months)

Head varies from apple green to golden buff. The bill has prominent horn-like excrescences toward base of upper mandible and is in general varied with greenish and blackish hues to tip and splotches toward base. Much rougher in older adults.

The black skin around the ear openings and down back of the neck is more extensive, and beneath it the feathers show a varied amount of carmine mottling.

The mantle is a deeper pink and the drip, which is present in a limited form in the preceding plumage, is now more extensive and of richer color.

The upper and lower tail coverts are a deep carmine and are more extensive than previously. Instead of buff the tail is a rich ochraceous buff, almost an orange.

In front of the shoulders there are suffusions of ochraceous buff, but these tend to be more yellowish than orange in color. At the base of the neck is a patch of stiff curly carmine feathers surrounded by some pink and usually a suffusion of yellowish buff.

Obviously many of these adult characters can-

[76] Audubon (1838) wrote of the adult plumage: "In the third spring the bird is perfect, although it increases in size for several seasons thereafter."

not be seen in the field, but each of them is quite prominent if the observer is close enough. In separating adults from birds in the fourth postnatal plumage, the relative behavior of the birds is an important aid to proper identification. Breeding adults that are flushed from an area in which they are nesting usually disperse with reluctance and sometimes give a low alarm note. Instead of leaving the area entirely, they frequently circle back and seek a perch nearby where the intruder can be observed. This behavior will depend on their place in the breeding cycle. Immature birds are sometimes unaccountably tame, but the experienced observer soon learns to differentiate between the actions of nonbreeding and breeding individuals.

C. Variations

Some of the variations in the appearance of Spoonbills are individual and others are associated with incomplete molts. There are variations in both plumage and color of soft parts, but in the case of the latter it is sometimes difficult to distinguish between actual variation and a difference of opinion as to color. There may also be differences of opinion or of terms used in describing plumage. Compilers may borrow descriptions from other authors without checking the facts and may then include the bad with the good, sometimes repeating mistakes that have already been copied several times. Alexander Wilson (1829) gave the following description of the Spoonbill's plumage: "It is said that the young are a blackish chestnut the first year; of the roseate color . . . the second year; and a deep scarlet the third." Apparently Wilson obtained this singular description from the works of John Latham (1740–1837), and it would appear that somewhere along the line the Spoonbill and the Scarlet Ibis became confused!

There are many actual variations in the plumage, however, and one of these is concerned with the feathers on the back of the head and neck. Many of the museum skins examined show traces of carmine mottling on the back of the head and neck. One young adult female from Alfred Sound, Great Inagua, had these carmine-tipped feathers on the back of the head and neck and

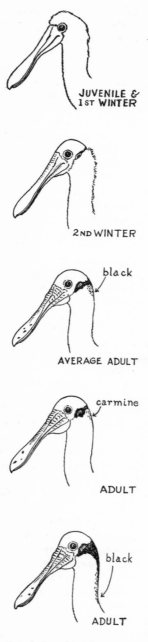

JUVENILE &
1ST WINTER

2ND WINTER

black

AVERAGE ADULT

carmine

ADULT

black

ADULT

Fig. 43.   Relation of Carmine Mottling on the Back of
Head and Neck to Area of Bare Skin Extending Downward from Back of the Head.

also on the *sides* of the neck. Louis Fuertes
painted an adult Spoonbill from Pajaro Island
on the Mexican Gulf coast which had a conspicuous *crest* of carmine feathers at the back of
the head, apparently an unusual variation.

The amount of carmine mottling on the back of
the head and neck, and its relation to the area of
bare skin that extends downward from the back
of the head, is more easily demonstrated in drawings, such as the accompanying sketches.

Another variation is found in the early appearance of carmine among the lesser wing coverts,
the tail coverts and the feathers of the upper
breast. Occasionally individuals in the process
of losing the feathers of the head (entering second
winter plumage) have lesser wing coverts that
show faint tracings of carmine roughly approxi-
mating the area of the drip.

Individuals of the same age group show varying
amounts of carmine in the upper and lower tail
coverts, and this variation is sometimes noted in
an advanced first winter bird. One such individual that still had a feathered head showed
considerable carmine in the upper tail coverts.
The primaries were still quite brown (immature
♂ *from Colombia*). An advanced first winter
bird from Bolivia (*immature* ♀), with the head
partially bare, showed some carmine in the upper
tail coverts and a great deal in the under tail
coverts. This bird had faint traces of pink at
the base of the neck, and there was still a small
amount of brown on the second and third primaries. An advanced second winter bird (*immature* ♀ *from Costa Rica*) had irregular blocks
of carmine on the lesser wing coverts, although
the head and cheeks were still partly feathered.
In this specimen the upper tail coverts were a
rich carmine but there were only traces of this
color in the under tail coverts.

A specimen from Colombia (*adult* ♂) appeared
to have all of the adult characters except the
curly patch of feathers at the base of the neck.
Probably the length of these feathers and the
intensity of their color varies with age.

A bird from Cuba (immature ♂) was almost
entirely brown except for the shafts of the flight
feathers, which were an intense pink. Another
specimen from Florida had patches of brown

feathers in the wings. This bird was apparently in advanced second winter plumage. The brown tips of the primaries are sometimes retained by birds in their third year. A specimen in one of the museum collections was labeled " ♀ adult" but had brownish traces at the tips of the primaries, buff tail, pale tail coverts and lacked the curly carmine feathers on the upper breast. It was apparently a bird in the fourth postnatal plumage, with variations. Adult characteristics included a fairly extensive drip and faint streaks of carmine on the back of the neck.

Pearson (1921) saw a melanistic specimen in a flock of forty-three Spoonbills that he observed near Aransas Pass on May 25, 1920.

There are age differences in the color of the soft parts, and there may also be individual variations. In addition, seasonal changes occur among the breeding adults. Birds in the Second Chain colony in Texas had uniform apple-green color on the bare skin of the head, while others in the same colony showed a golden brown color around the ear opening and under the eye, although the upper portion of the head was buff merging to green. I do not believe that these are sex differences. Most of the apparent variations in soft-part colors in the literature are merely a result of one author saying that the legs are red and another specifying lake red. One writer speaks of the iris of the adult as cherry red while another insists that it is carmine.

D. WINTER ADULTS

Arthur C. Bent in his account of the Roseate Spoonbill (1926) suggests that adults may have a winter plumage resembling the second winter plumage of immature birds. This plumage would be acquired, presumably, in the postnuptial molt, but a lack of material showing this molt in the adult prevented Mr. Bent from reaching any definite conclusions regarding the existence of any such plumage change. I have corresponded with Mr. Bent on this subject, and he writes: "I have always supposed there was a winter plumage of the adult . . . and that a partial prenuptial molt, which may occur as early as December, produces the full brilliancy of the adult nuptial plumage. I was never able to prove this

because I had no specimens of known age to show it."

One reason Mr. Bent advanced for suggesting the possibility of a winter plumage was the fact that birds in 'full nuptial plumage' were exceptional in November and December. This would probably hold good for the mainland of Florida at the present time, since Spoonbills are absent for the most part during those months and stragglers are apt to be immature birds. In Florida Bay, adults in full breeding plumage arrive in October, pair in November and lay their eggs in December.

In Texas, breeding flocks reach the vicinity of the colony as early as late February and appear to be in breeding plumage, although the flight feathers are molted after their arrival. In early April 1941, I found great windrows of flight feathers on the beaches near this colony and American Egrets in several instances used them to line their nests. These adults were evidently completing the prenuptial molt. According to our plumage cycle for the Texas Spoonbills, adults would begin their postnuptial molt early in July and by September would be in the so-called winter plumage. There are concentrations of Spoonbills in the Bahia Grande area near Brownsville in September and sometimes for several weeks thereafter; but an examination of the plumages of these birds would prove nothing because we do not know if they are made up of summer birds from Mexico or birds from the Texas colonies that are en route south.

The Florida Bay adults presumably begin their postnuptial molt in February and would be found in the winter plumage by early April. I do not know if these adults from Florida Bay summer on the southwest coast of Florida or not, but the fact remains that the number of individuals in adult plumage on that coast in summer is very small and the greatest number of birds are in the second winter plumage, which corresponds to that of the winter adult. At Little Patricio Island (below Charlotte Harbor) on August 8 (1941) I saw three adults, two of which appeared to be molting. The small nesting group reported at this location apparently hatched their young in May so that the adults would enter the winter

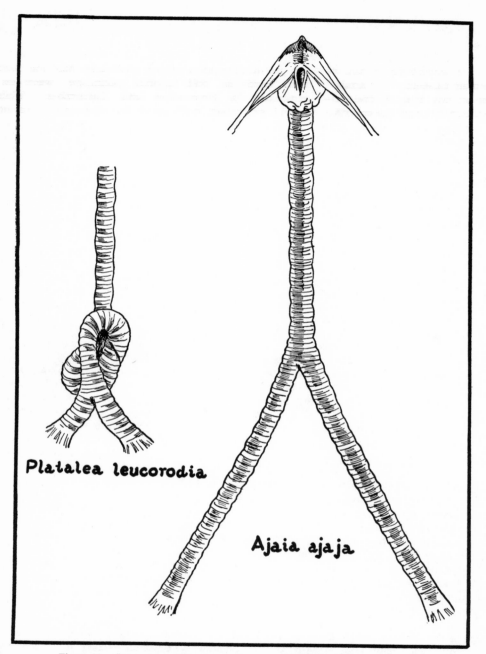

Platalea leucorodia

Ajaia ajaja

Figure 44.   Comparison of Trachea in European Spoonbill and Roseate Spoonbill.

plumage about the first of August. The individuals that I observed showed signs of molt as mentioned, but there was no indication that a drastic change in the pattern of the plumage was under way.

Obviously the picture is somewhat confused and there is no conclusive evidence one way or the other. The observation of banded birds whose ages are known may settle the question at some future time, and meanwhile, the possibility that the species has a winter adult plumage must remain in doubt.

E. HUDSON'S 'PALLID SPOONBILL'

William Henry Hudson was convinced that there were two species of Roseate Spoonbills in South America. Baird, Brewer and Ridgway (1884) submitted his arguments "without at all sharing in this belief." Hudson said that in the Argentine he observed on the pampas two or three hundred pale Spoonbills with "feathered heads and black eyes" for every one bird with all the characteristic marks of the adult "*Platalea ajaja.*" The characteristic marks he described as "bright wing spots, the tuft on the breast, horny excrescences and other marks."

In his 'Birds of La Plata' (1920) Hudson speaks of the young as having a head that is completely feathered and of the birds in general being pale-plumaged. It is not clear that he was acquainted with the various immature plumages of the species or the fact that it requires three years to attain adult plumage! In referring to his belief that there were two species of Spoonbills in Argentina, he reduces the ratio in this 1920 edition and says "for one bird with all these characteristic marks of the true *Platalea ajaja,* which has a yellow tail, we meet on the pampas with not less than a hundred examples of the pale-plumaged bird without any traces of such marks and with a rose-coloured tail; and the disparity in number between mature and immature birds of one species could not well be so great as that."

It is not infrequent on this continent to find large flocks of Spoonbills composed for the most part of immature birds, but in Mr. Hudson's dilemma we can see possible arguments in favor of Mr. Bent's belief that there may be a winter

adult plumage! However, it appears that Hudson's new species always had a feathered head, which would, of course, eliminate such additional arguments.

In his earlier discussion of the possible existence of another race of Spoonbills in South America, Hudson did not limit himself to a consideration of the plumage alone. He dissected both 'varieties' and found that the tracheae were different. In three adult Spoonbills (then called *Platalea ajaja*) he noted that the trachea was simple and bifurcated outside the body cavity, but in thirty of the suspected new race he did not find this form of trachea. Unfortunately, he does not tell us what form of trachea he did find in these birds!

In the Sixteenth Century the Italian naturalist, Aldrovandi, described the trachea of the European Spoonbill,[77] which is convoluted in the form of a figure eight and which bifurcates inside the body cavity. Willoughby, in the Seventeenth Century, apparently dissected young European Spoonbills that he took from the nest and found the trachea unlike that of the adults of that species. The inference is that in the young it was simple and without convolutions, although Willoughby does not happen to provide any further details.

It would appear from all this that the form of the trachea in Spoonbills may show age differences, and this fact would account for Hudson's findings. Doubtless these matters will be settled for us some day by dissection.

F. SUMMARY

1. The Roseate Spoonbill undergoes one partial molt and three complete molts in acquiring adult plumage, a process requiring from thirty-three to thirty-six months. Adults have two molts annually.

2. The six plumages from natal down to adult may serve as an index to the age of an individual, and this knowledge is an important aid in the solution of distributional problems.

3. Variations in plumage may be individual in character or associated with incomplete molts.

---

[77] Yarrell, 1841, 'History of British Birds,' II.

These occur in both the plumage and in the color of the soft parts.

4. There may be a 'winter adult' plumage, but satisfactory proof is of this lacking.

5. Hudson's description of the 'Pallid Spoonbill' indicates confusion with different age groups, although certain physiological differences claimed by him await further investigation.

Part VIII. The Future

THE decimation of Spoonbills on our Gulf coast was the result of progressive destruction which began faintly in the 1830's, grew apace in the 1850's and swept through Florida and along the Texas coast like a plague between 1865 and 1890. The shy, wilderness-seeking Spoonbill hadn't much chance in resisting this onslaught. It must have tried, must have returned again and again to coasts that became less and less hospitable until at length it returned no more, except in pitifully small numbers.

Events have shown that the return of breeding Spoonbills to Texas and Louisiana in the 1920's and 1930's is attributable to the fortunate existence of a nucleus in Mexico, able to wander north and east along the Gulf and Texas lagoons. The National Audubon Society offered these flocks protection and encouragement, and they have prospered remarkably.

What is the trouble in Florida? So far as the mainland is concerned, it is not an exaggeration to say that there has been no restoration of breeding Spoonbill populations. But, on its wild southwest coast, quite a few nonbreeders appear annually—comprised almost entirely of immature birds. The year 'round there are relatively few adult Spoonbills on the mainland; a few adults return each fall to nest in Florida Bay, but the colony there has never been large and, even with protection, has not managed to increase. This is far from saying that the protection given is not of utmost importance; to save what little is left, while seeking ways and means of assuring increase, is essential.

It is clear that plans for the future must give consideration to the entire range of the species. Our present knowledge of the Spoonbill's distribution and habits suggests strongly that we must look to Cuba and South America for rehabilitation of the species as a nester in Florida. Apparently most of the spring and summer birds that inhabit the southwest coast of Florida come from breeding concentrations to the south. Many of them may come from Cayo Romano or from the colonies near Baragua, in Cuba, possibly even from Laguna Tacarigua on the north coast of Vene-

zuela. Questions as to their exact source we are as yet unable to answer. Neither can we state with assurance what can be done, over and beyond furnishing protection, to encourage adult Spoonbills to move northward into deserted breeding range in Florida.

For many years the National Audubon Society has been the outstanding champion of the Roseate Spoonbill. The Society has had increasing coöperation from federal and state agencies and from various organizations and individuals, but it seems likely that for some time to come it will have to continue to be the chief watchdog of the Spoonbill's welfare. In the interest of that welfare, the following recommendations are submitted:

1. We must continue to provide guardianship for existing United States breeding colonies and important concentration and feeding areas. This means that we must employ, equip and supervise an adequate force of wardens.

2. We should initiate, as promptly as possible, field research in those countries to the southward on which the United States seems dependent for breeding Spoonbill repopulation. Special consideration should be accorded the condition, habits and distribution of Spoonbill colonies in Cuba, possibly in certain of the other West Indies, and in northern South America. This research should be followed by the establishment of warden-patrolled sanctuaries where critically needed in those regions, for we cannot help but feel that an increase in the size of the Cuban and certain South American colonies would in time cause restoration of the Spoonbill to former abundance in the state of Florida.

3. We must continue to seek official action establishing as inviolate sanctuaries, on a more permanent basis, all important Spoonbill breeding, roosting and feeding areas in Texas, Louisiana and Florida. The present short-term leases, permitting coincidental mineral exploration, and authorities granted by resolution subject to cancellation, lack, in most cases, the desirable degree of permanence. Some of the areas will be threatened from time to time with commercial exploita-

tion and, barring more satisfactory arrangements, will, indeed, be exploited.

4. We must continue to be alert to population shifts and their causes, and provide protection for all new breeding colonies.

5. Steps should be taken to secure more adequate legal protection in many countries to the southward, including those whence adult Spoon-bills may in time come to repopulate Florida colonies. State legal protection accorded the Spoonbill today in Florida, Louisiana and Texas should be supported and strengthened in effect by inclusion of this bird in the definition of migratory birds in the Migratory Bird Treaty with Mexico; such action would give our federal government jurisdiction that it does not now possess.

Appendix

A. LOCAL AND FOREIGN COMMON NAMES FOR THE SPOONBILLS

Roseate Spoonbill (*Ajaia ajaja*)

Rosy Spoonbill
Rose or Rosy-colored Spoonbill
Rose-coloured Curlew (Audubon)
Pink (Florida)
Pink Curlew (Florida)
Pink Spoonbill (Preble, 1842)
Pink-bird (Louisiana)
Pinkie (Louisiana)
Red Spoonbill (rare)
Flamingo (Texas)
American Spoonbill
Skatule (Louisiana)
Alaloolasetteé (Seminole Indian)
Tlauhquechul (Mexico, Seventeenth Century)
Garza Colorado (Mexico)
Garza Rosada (South America)
Espatula (Mexico and South America)
Pato cucharo (Colombia)
Planeta (Chile)
Espatula rosada (Argentina)
Spatule (West Indies)
Colhereiro (Brazil)
Colherado (South America)
Sevilla (Cuba, South America)
Cuchareta (South America)
Ayaya (South American Indian)

European or White Spoonbill (*Platalea l. leucorodia*)

Common Spoonbill (England)
Banjo-bill (England)
Spooney (England)
Shoveler (Sixteenth Century England)
Shovelard (Aristotle and Sixteenth Century England)
Popelar (Sixteenth Century England)
Spatule Blanche (France)
Lepelaar (Netherlands)
Spatola (Italy)

African Spoonbill (*Platalea alba*)

Lepelaar (South Africa)
Loffelreiher (German)
La Spatule (French)
Da-dosa (Mandingo)

Black-faced Spoonbill (*Platalea minor*)

La Petite Spatule (French Indo-China)
Japanese Spoonbill (Japan)

Australian Spoonbills (*Platalea regia* and *Platibis flavipes*)

Black-billed Spoonbill (*P. regia*)
Royal Spoonbill (*P. regia*)
Yellow-billed Spoonbill (*P. flavipes*)
Yellow-legged Spoonbill (*P. flavipes*)
Kotuku ngutupapa (Maoris)

B. LIST OF SCIENTIFIC NAMES OF PLANTS AND ANIMALS MENTIONED IN THE TEXT

1. PLANTS

Bur-reed	*Sparganium* sp.
Cattail, narrow-leaved	*Typha angustifolia* L.
Cordgrass, smooth	*Spartina alterniflora* Lois.
Cypress, bald	*Taxodium distichum* (L.) Rich.
Elder, marsh	*Iva frutescens* L.
Elder, southern	*Sambucus Simpsonii* Rehd.
Glasswort	*Salicornia* sp.
Grass, —	*Monanthochloë littoralis* Engelm.
Grass, panic	*Panicum amarulum* H. & C.
Grass, turtle	*Thalassia* sp.
Hackberry	*Celtis mississippiensis* Bosc.
Hackberry, desert	*Celtis pallida* Torr.
Mangrove	*Rhizophora* sp.
Mangrove, black	*Avicennia nitida* Jacq.
Mangrove, red	*Rhizophora mangle* L.
Morning glory	*Ipomoea* sp.
Oak, willow	*Quercus phellos* L.
Ox-eye, sea	*Borrichia* sp.
Pine	*Pinus* sp.
Pondweed	*Potamogeton* sp.
Saltgrass, seashore	*Distichlis* sp.
Saltwort	*Batis maritima* L.
Sedge	Cyperaceae
Willow, sand-bar	*Salix longifolia* Muhl.

2. CRUSTACEANS

Crayfish	*Cambarus* sp.
Snapping-shrimp	*Crago* sp.

3. INSECTS

Ants	Hymenoptera
Back-swimmer	Notonectidae
Beetles	Coleoptera
Beetle, predacious diving	Dytiocidae
Beetle, water-scavenger	Hydrophilidae
Bill-bug	Calandrinae
Caddis-fly	Trichoptera
Crane-fly	Tipulidae
Cricket	Gryllidae
Dragonfly	Odonata
Flies	Diptera
Grasshopper	Acrididae
Ground-beetle	*Bembidium* sp.
May-fly	Plectoptera
Midge	Chironomidae
Water boatman	Corixidae
Water-bug, giant	*Belostoma* sp.

4. MOLLUSCS

Clam.................Plecypoda
Cockle................Cardium
Horn shell, black.......*Cerithium minimum nigrescens* Menke
Mussel...............Mytilidae
Oyster, coon..........*Ostrea* sp.
Razor clam...........*Tagelus* sp.
Scallop..............Pectinidae
Slug.................*Gastropoda*

5. FISH

Anchovy..............Engraulidae
Anchovy, little........*Anchovia mitchilli* (Cuvier & Valenciennes)
Blue fish.............*Pomatomus saltatrix* (Linnaeus)
Croaker..............Sciaenidae
Fish, rainwater........*Lucania parva* (Baird & Girard)
Herring, bristle........*Atherina stipes* Müller & Troschel
Jack.................Caranx
Killifish.............Poeciliidae
Killifish, banded.......*Adinia multifasciata* Girard
Killifish, carp..........*Cyprinodon carpio* Günther
Killifish, common......*Fundulus heteroclitus* (Linnaeus)
Killifish, long-nosed.....*Fundulus similis* (Baird & Girard)
Killifish, ocelated......*Fundulus ocellaris* Jordan & Evermann
Killifish, pale..........*Fundulus pallidus* Evermann
Killifish, sail-finned.....*Mollienisia latipinna* Le Sueur
Mackerel, spanish.......*Scomberomorus maculatus* (Mitchill)
Menhaden............*Brevoortia tyrannus* (Latrobe)
Minnow, everglade......*Jordanella floridae* Goode & Bean
Minnow, sheepshead....*Cyprinodon variegatus* Lacépède
Mojarra..............Gerridae
Mojarra de ley........*Eucinostomus gula* (Cuvier & Valenciennes)
Mullet...............Mugilidae
Mullet, striped........*Mugil cephalus* Linnaeus
Pin fish...............*Lagodon rhomboides* (Linnaeus)
Silversides............Atherinidae
Stickle-back...........Gasterostidae
Top minnow...........*Gambusia* sp.
Top minnow, viviparous.................*Gambusia patruelis* (Baird & Girard)
Trout................Salmonidae
White fish, slender......*Atherina stipes* Müller & Troschel
Whiting..............*Menticirrhus* sp.

6. REPTILES

Alligator..............*Alligator mississippiensis* (Daudin)
Chameleon............*Anolis* sp.
Crocodile.............*Crocodylus acutus* Cuvier
Moccasin, flat-tailed water...............*Tropidonotus compressicaudus* (Kennicott)

Terrapin, diamond-back. *Malaclemys pileata* subsp.

7. BIRDS

Avocet...............*Recurvirostra americana* Gmelin
Bunting, Reed.........*Emberiza schoeniclus schoeniclus* (Linnaeus)
Bunting, Snow.........*Plectrophenax nivalis subnivalis*
Cormorant, Double-crested.............*Phalacrocorax auritus auritus* (Lesson)
Cowbird.............*Molothrus ater ater* (Boddaert)
Crane, European........*Grus grus grus* (Linné)
Crane, Whooping.......*Grus americana* (Linnaeus)
Crow.................*Corvus brachyrhynchos*
Crow, Fish.............*Corvus ossifragus* Wilson
Crow, Hooded........*Corvus cornix cornix* Linnaeus
Cuckoo, Maynard's.....*Coccyzus minor maynardi* Ridgway
Curlew...............*Numenius* sp.
Duck, Wood..........*Aix sponsa* (Linnaeus)
Eagle, Bald...........*Haliaeetus leucocephalus leucocephalus* (Linnaeus)
Egret, American........*Casmerodius albus egretta* (Gmelin)
Egret, Reddish.........*Dichromanassa rufescens rufescens* (Gmelin)
Egret, Snowy..........*Egretta thula thula* (Molina)
Flamingo.............*Phoenicopterus ruber* Linnaeus
Flicker...............*Colaptes auratus luteus* Bangs
Gallinule..............Gallinulinae
Goose, Canada.........*Branta canadensis canadensis* (Linnaeus)
Goose, Gray..........*Anser anser* (Linné)
Grackle..............Icteridae
Grackle, Great-tailed....*Cassidix mexicanus mexicanus* (Gmelin)
Grebe, Horned........*Colymbus auritus* Linnaeus
Grouse...............Tetraonidae
Gull, Herring..........*Larus argentatus smithsonianus* Coues
Gull, Kelp............*Larus dominicanus* Lichtenstein
Gull, Laughing........*Larus atricilla* Linnaeus
Hawk, Duck..........*Falco peregrinus anatum* Bonaparte
Hawk, Marsh.........*Circus hudsonius* (Linnaeus)
Hawk, Pigeon.........*Falco columbarius columbarius* Linnaeus
Heron, Black-crowned Night..............*Nycticorax nycticorax hoactli* (Gmelin)
Heron, Cocoi..........*Ardea cocoi* Linné
Heron, Green.........*Butorides virescens virescens* (Linnaeus)
Heron, Grey..........*Ardea cinerea cinerea* Linné
Heron, Little Blue......*Florida caerulea caerulea* (Linnaeus)
Heron, Louisiana.......*Hydranassa tricolor ruficollis* (Gosse)

Heron, Ward's.........*Ardea herodias wardi* Ridgway
Ibis, Scarlet...........*Guara rubra* (Linnaeus)
Ibis, White............*Guara alba* (Linnaeus)
Ibis, White-faced Glossy.*Plegadis guarauna* (Linnaeus)
Ibis, Wood...........*Mycteria americana* Linnaeus
Killdeer..............*Oxyechus vociferus vociferus* (Linnaeus)
Kite, Swallow-tailed....*Elanoides forficatus forficatus* (Linnaeus)
Lark, Prairie Horned....*Otocoris alpestris praticola* Henshaw
Mockingbird..........*Mimus polyglottos polyglottos* (Linnaeus)
Nighthawk, Cherrie's...*Chordeiles minor aserriensis* Cherrie
Owl, Eagle............*Bubo bubo bubo* (Linné)
Owl, Great Horned......*Bubo virginianus virginianus* (Gmelin)
Owl, Short-eared.......*Asio flammeus flammeus* (Pontoppidan)
Paroquet, Carolina......*Conuropsis carolinensis carolinensis* (Linnaeus)
Pelican, Brown........*Pelecanus occidentalis occidentalis* Linnaeus
Pelican, White.........*Pelecanus erythrorhynchos* Gmelin
Penguin, Gentoo.......*Pygoscelis papua papua* (Forster)
Phalarope.............Phalaropodidae
Phalarope, Northern....*Lobipes lobatus* (Linnaeus)
Phalarope, Wilson's.....*Steganopus tricolor* Vieillot
Pheasant..............*Phasianus* sp.
Pigeon, Passenger......*Ectopistes migratorius* (Linnaeus)
Pigeon, White-crowned..*Columba leucocephala* Linnaeus
Pintail...............*Dafila acuta tzitzihoa* (Vieillot)
Plover, Black-bellied...*Squatarola squatarola* (Linnaeus)
Quail.................Odontophorinae
Rail, Mangrove Clapper................*Rallus longirostris insularum* Brooks
Red-wing.............*Agelaius phoeniceus phoeniceus* (Linnaeus)
Robin................*Turdus migratorius migratorius* Linnaeus
Robin, British.........*Erithacus rubecula melophilus* Hartert
Sandpiper............Calidridiinae
Sandpiper, Semipalmated..............*Ereunetes pusillus* (Linnaeus)
Sandpiper, Solitary......*Tringa solitaria solitaria* Wilson
Shoveller.............*Spatula clypeata* (Linnaeus)
Shrike, Loggerhead.....*Lanius ludovicianus ludovicianus* Linnaeus
Skimmer, Black.......*Rynchops nigra nigra* Linnaeus
Skylark..............*Alauda arvensis arvensis* Linnaeus
Snipe.................*Capella* sp.
Sparrow, Cape Sable Seaside.............*Ammospiza mirabilis* (Howell)
Sparrow, English.......*Passer domesticus domesticus* (Linnaeus)

Sparrow, Nuttall's......*Zonotrichia leucophrys nuttalli* Ridgway
Sparrow, Song.........*Melospiza melodia* subsp.
Sparrow, Texas Seaside..*Ammospiza maritima sennetti* (Allen)
Spoonbill, African.......*Platalea alba* Scopoli
Spoonbill, Asiatic.......*Platalea leucorodia major* Temminck and Schlegel
Spoonbill, Black-billed..*Platalea regia* Gould
Spoonbill, Black-faced...*Platalea minor* Temminck and Schlegel
Spoonbill, European.....*Platalea leucorodia leucorodia* Linné
Spoonbill, Japanese.....*Platalea leucorodia major* Temminck and Schlegel
Spoonbill, Lesser.......*Platalea minor* Temminck and Schlegel
Spoonbill, Red Sea.....*Platalea leucorodia archeri* Neumann
Spoonbill, Roseate......*Ajaia ajaja* (Linné)
Spoonbill, Royal........*Platalea regia* Gould
Spoonbill, White........*Platalea leucorodia* subsp.
Spoonbill, White Nile...*Platalea leucorodia archeri* Neumann
Spoonbill, Yellow-billed...............*Platibis flavipes* (Gould)
Spoonbill, Yellow-legged...............*Platibis flavipes* (Gould)
Starling...............*Sturnus vulgaris vulgaris* Linnaeus
Stilt, Black-necked.....*Himantopus mexicanus* (Müller)
Stork, Black...........*Ciconia nigra* (Linné)
Stork, White..........*Ciconia ciconia ciconia* (Linné)
Swallow, Tree........*Iridoprocne bicolor* (Vieillot)
Teal, Cinnamon.......*Querquedula cyanoptera* (Vieillot)
Tern, Black...........*Chlidonias nigra surinamensis* (Gmelin)
Tern, Caspian.........*Hydroprogne caspia imperator* (Coues)
Tern, Common.......*Sterna hirundo hirundo* Linnaeus
Tern, Gull-billed.......*Gelochelidon nilotica aranea* (Wilson)
Tern, Least...........*Sterna antillarum antillarum* (Lesson)
Thrush...............*Hylocichla* sp.
Tinamou..............*Eudromia elegans* subsp.
Turkey, Wild..........*Meleagris gallopavo* subsp.
Turnstone............*Arenaria interpres morinella* (Linnaeus)
Vulture, Black.........*Coragyps atratus atratus* (Meyer)
Warbler, Prairie.......*Dendroica discolor* subsp.
Willet................*Catoptrophorus semipalmatus semipalmatus* (Gmelin)
Woodpecker, Ivory-billed...............*Campephilus principalis* (Linnaeus)
Wren, House..........*Troglodytes aedon aedon* Vieillot
Yellow-legs, Greater.....*Totanus melanoleucus* (Gmelin)
Yellow-legs, Lesser......*Totanus flavipes* (Gmelin)

8. MAMMALS

Armadillo............*Dasypus novemcinctus texanus* (Bailey)	Porpoise...............Delphininae
Bobcat.................*Lynx rufus* subsp.	Raccoon...............*Procyon* sp.
*Horse, Pleistocene.....*Equus* sp.	Raccoon, Florida.......*Procyon lotor elucus* Bangs
*Mammoth...........Mannuthinae	Skunk................Mephitinae
Mongoose.............*Herpestes* sp.	*Tiger, sabre-tooth......*Smilodon californicus*

* = extinct.

Bibliography

(Many authorities have been given a complete reference in the body of the text or in the form of a footnote. Otherwise the author's last name and the publication date appear in the text in parentheses and refer to the following bibliography.)

ANONYMOUS
1879. (Cor. in *Forest and Stream*) Florida Birds. *Oölogist*, 5 (5): 40.

ALLEN, ROBERT PORTER
1935. Notes on the Roseate Spoonbill on the Gulf Coast. *Auk*, 52 (1): 77–78.
1938. Black-crowned Night Heron Colonies on Long Island. *Proc. Linn. Soc. New York*, 49 (1937): 43–51.

ALLEN, ROBERT PORTER AND FREDERICK PAUL MANGELS
1940. Studies of the Nesting Behavior of the Black-crowned Night Heron. *Proc. Linn. Soc. New York*, 50–51: 1–28.

ARRIGONI DEGLI ODDI, ETTORE
1929. Ornitologia Italiana. Milano. P. 460.

AUDUBON, JOHN JAMES
1834. Ornithological Biography. Edinburgh. The Florida Keys. 2: 312–316, 345–349.
1838. Ornithological Biography. Edinburgh. Roseate Spoonbill. 4: 188–197.
1839. Ornithological Biography. Edinburgh. American Flamingo. 5: 255–264.

BAILEY, ALFRED MARSHALL AND EARL G. WRIGHT
1931. Birds of Southern Louisiana. *Wilson Bull.*, 43 (2): 140.

BAILEY, MRS. FLORENCE AUGUSTA (MERRIAM)
1916. Meeting Spring Halfway. *Condor*, 18 (4): 155.

BAILEY, HAROLD HARRIS
1925. The Birds of Florida. Baltimore. Pp. 31–32.

BAIRD, SPENCER FULLERTON, THOMAS MAYO BREWER AND ROBERT RIDGWAY
1884. The Water Birds of North America. Boston. 1: 100–106.

BANNERMAN, DAVID ARMITAGE
1930. The Birds of Tropical West Africa. London. 1: 123–125.

BARBOUR, THOMAS
1923. The Birds of Cuba. Cambridge, Mass. Pp. 31–32.

BARNES, CLAUDE TEANCUM
1919. Roseate Spoonbill in Utah. *Auk*, 36 (4): 565–566.

BARTON, BENJAMIN SMITH
1799. Fragments of the Natural History of Pennsylvania. London.

BARTRAM, WILLIAM
1791. Travels through North and South Carolina, Georgia, East and West Florida, the Cherokee Country. London.

BECKHAM, CHARLES WICKLIFFE
1887. Additions to the Avi-fauna of Bayou Sara, La. *Auk*, 4 (4): 304.

BEECHER, WILLIAM J.
1942. Nesting Birds and the Vegetation Substrate. Chicago. P. 58.

BEETHAM, BENTLY
1927. Among Our Banished Birds. London. Pp. 30–57.

BENNERS, GEORGE BARTLESON
1887. A Collecting Trip in Texas. *Ornithologist and Oölogist*, 12 (6): 81–82.

BENT, ARTHUR CLEVELAND
1923. Life Histories of North American Wild Fowl, Vol. 1. U. S. Nat. Mus. Bull., no. 126.
1926. Life Histories of North American Marsh Birds. U. S. Nat. Mus. Bull., no. 135, 13–23.
1927. Life Histories of North American Shore Birds, Vol. 1. U. S. Nat. Mus. Bull., no. 142.
1929. Life Histories of North American Shore Birds, Vol. 2. U. S. Nat. Mus. Bull., no. 146.

BEYER, GEORGE EUGENE
1900. The Avifauna of Louisiana. New Orleans. P. 17.

BEYER, GEORGE EUGENE, ANDREW ALLISON AND HENRY HAZLITT KOPMAN
1908. List of the Birds of Louisiana, Part IV. *Auk*, 25 (2): 173.

BISSONNETTE, THOMAS HUME
1930. Studies on the Sexual Cycle in Birds, I. Sexual Maturity, Its Modification and Possible Control in the European Starling (*Sturnus vulgaris*). *Am. Jour. Anat.*, 45: 289–305.
1937. Photoperiodicity in Birds. *Wilson Bull.*, 49 (4): 241–270.

BLANCHARD, BARBARA D.
1941. The White-crowned Sparrow (*Zonotrichia leucophrys*) of the Pacific Seaboard: Environment and Annual Cycle. *Univ. Calif. Pub. Zoo.*, 46 (1): 1–178.

BLANFORD, WILLIAM THOMAS
1898. Fauna of British India. London. 4: 366–367.

BOND, JAMES
1936. Birds of the West Indies. Philadelphia. Pp. 34–36.

BOWDISH, BEECHER SCOVILLE
1909. Ornithological Miscellany from Audubon Wardens. *Auk*, 26 (2): 117, 126–127.

BREDER, CHARLES M., JR.
1929. Field Book of Marine Fishes of the Atlantic Coast. New York.

BRYANT, HENRY
1859. In *Proc. Boston Soc. Nat. Hist.*, 7 (10): 5–21.

BUTLER, AMOS WILLIAM
1898. The Birds of Indiana. Indianapolis. Pp. 643–644.
1930a. Roseate Spoonbill in Florida. *Auk*, 47 (1): 75–76.
1930b. Note on the Roseate Spoonbill in Florida. *Auk*, 47 (3): 416.

BUTLER, ARTHUR GARDINER
1896–98. British Birds with Their Nests and Eggs. London. 4: 46–50.

CARROLL, JAMES JUDSON
1900. Notes on the Birds of Refugio County, Texas. *Auk*, 17 (4): 339.

CAYLEY, NEVILLE W.
1931. What Bird Is That? Sydney, Australia. P. 235.

CHAMBERLAIN, MONTAGUE
1891. A Popular Handbook of the Ornithology of the United States and Canada; Based on Nuttall's Manual. Vol. II, Game and Water Birds. Boston. Pp. 108–109.

CHAPMAN, FRANK MICHLER
1888. A List of Birds Observed at Gainesville, Florida. *Auk*, 5 (3): 269.
1908. Camps and Cruises of an Ornithologist. New York. Pp. 83, 136–148.
1914. The Roseate Spoonbill. *Bird-Lore*, 16 (3): 214–215.
1933. Autobiography of a Bird-Lover. New York. Pp. 203–204.

CHRISTY, BAYARD HENDERSON
1928. A Wading-Bird Rookery. *Auk*, 45 (4): 426–427.

COOPER, JAMES GRAHAM
1877. On Seventy-five Doubtful West-Coast Birds. *Bull. Nuttall Club*, 2 (4): 95–96.

COTTAM, CLARENCE AND PHOEBE KNAPPEN
1939. Food of Some Uncommon North American Birds. *Auk*, 56 (2): 138–169.

COTTAM, CLARENCE AND C. S. WILLIAMS
1939. Food and Habits of Some Birds Nesting on Islands in Great Salt Lake. *Wilson Bull.*, 51 (3): 150–155.

COUES, ELLIOTT
    1887.   Key to North American Birds.   Salem.   2: 868.
DARLING, FRANK FRASER
    1938.   Bird Flocks and the Breeding Cycle.   Cambridge, England.
DAVIS, JOHN H., JR.
    1940.   The Ecology and Geologic Role of Mangroves in Florida.
            Paper from Tortugas Laboratory, 32: 307–409.
DAWSON, CHARLES R.
    1937.   Seminole County Birds.   Florida Naturalist, 10 (2): 40.
DAWSON, WILLIAM LEON
    1923.   The Birds of California.   San Francisco.   4: 1932–1933
DELACOUR, JEAN AND LIERRE JABOUILLE
    1931.   Les Oiseaux de l'Indochine Francaise.   1: 79.
DUTCHER, WILLIAM
    1903.   Report of the A. O. U. Committee on the Protection of
            North American Birds.   Auk, 20 (1): 119.
    1904.   Report of the A. O. U. Committee on the Protection of
            North American Birds for the Year 1903.   Auk, 21 (1):
            129–130.
DWIGHT, JONATHAN
    1925.   The Gulls (Laridae) of the World; Their Plumages,
            Moults, Variations, Relationships and Distribution.   Bull.
            Am. Mus. Nat. Hist., 52 (3): 63–401.
EATON, RICHARD JEFFERSON
    1933.   The Migratory Movements of Certain Colonies of Herring
            Gulls (Larus argentatus smithsonianus Coues) in Eastern
            North America.   Bird Banding, 4 (4): 165–176.
    1934.   The Migratory Movements of Certain Colonies of Herring
            Gulls in Eastern North America.   Bird Banding, 5 (1): 1–
            19; 5 (2): 70–84.
EDWARDS, HELEN M. (MRS. W. H.)
    1930.   Roseate Spoonbill (Ajaia ajaja) Taken in Southern Ala-
            bama.   Auk, 47 (4): 555.
EIFRIG, CHARLES WILLIAM GUSTAVE
    1930.   Seasonal Changes in a Bird Habitat in Texas.   Wilson
            Bull., 42 (4): 239–240.
ELLIS, J. B.
    1917.   Forty Years Ago and Now.   Oölogist, 34 (1): 4.
ELTON, CHARLES
    1927.   Animal Ecology.   New York.
ERRINGTON, PAUL LESTER
    1936.   What Is the Meaning of Predation?   Smithsonian Report
            for 1936, 243–252.
FARGO, WILLIAM GILBERT
    1926.   Notes on Birds of Pinellas and Pasco Counties, Florida.
            Wilson Bull., 38 (3): 146.
    1929.   Winter Bird Life on Indian Key.   Florida Naturalist, 3
            (1): 5.
            Cow and Calf Keys.   Florida Naturalist, 3 (1): 8.
FIGGINS, J. D.
    1923.   The Breeding Birds of the Vicinity of Black Bayou and
            Bird Island, Cameron Parish, Louisiana.   Auk, 40 (4):
            670–671.
FISHER, JAMES
    1939.   Birds as Animals.   London.
FLEISHER, EDWARD
    1920.   Notes on the Birds of Southeastern North Carolina.   Auk,
            37 (4): 565–566, 568.
FORBUSH, EDWARD HOWE
    1929.   Birds of Massachusetts and Other New England States.   3:
            XXVIII.
FOWLER, HENRY WEED
    1906.   Birds Observed in the Florida Keys.   Auk., 23 (4): 397.
GADOW, H. F.
            Migration in Zoölogy.   Encyclopedia Britannica, 11th ed.,
            18: 433–437.
GALSTOFF, PAUL S.
    1931.   Survey of Oyster Bottoms in Texas.   U. S. Dept. Com-
            merce, Bureau of Fisheries, Investigational Report No. 6,
            1: 1–30.
GAMBEL, WILLIAM
    1847–49.   Avifauna of Northern California, Philadelphia, Pa.

GARDINER, LINDA
    1923.   Rare, Vanishing and Lost British Birds, Compiled from
            Notes by W. H. Hudson.   London.   Pp. 6–8.
GRINNELL, JOSEPH
    1902.   Check-list of California Birds.   Pacific Coast Avifauna, no.
            3: 76.
GRINNELL, JOSEPH, HAROLD CHILD BRYANT AND TRACY IRWIN
    STORER
    1918.   The Game Birds of California.   Berkeley, Pp. 262–266.
GRISCOM, LUDLOW AND MAUNSELL SCHIEFFELIN CROSBY
    1925.   Birds of the Brownsville Region, Southern Texas.   Auk, 42
            (4): 436, 524.
GROSS, ALFRED OTTO
    1940.   The Migration of Kent Island Herring Gulls.   Bird Band-
            ing, 11 (4): 129–155.
GUNTER, GORDON
    1938.   The Relative Numbers of Species of Marine Fish on the
            Louisiana Coast.   Amer. Nat., 72: 77–83.
    1941.   Death of Fishes Due to Cold on the Texas Coast, January
            1940.   Ecology, 22 (2): 203–208.
HAVERSCHMIDT, FRANK
    1938.   Spoonbills in Holland.   Bird-Lore, 40 (5): 325–327.
HENNINGER, WALTHER FRIEDRICH
    1917.   The Diary of a New England Ornithologist.   Wilson Bull.,
            29 (1): 4.
HERMAN, WILLIAM CEPHAS
    1931.   Notes and News.   Auk, 48 (2): 332–333.
HIATT, BENJAMIN C.
    1933.   Avocets and Spoonbills on Merritts Island, Fla.   Auk, 50
            (1): 100.
HOLT, ERNEST GOLSAN
    1929.   In the Haunts of the Wood Ibis.   Wilson Bull., 41 (1): 14,
            16, 18.
HOPKINS, E. S.
    1926.   First Egg of 1926.   Oölogist, 43 (1): 12.
HOWELL, ARTHUR HOLMES
    1924.   Birds of Alabama.   Montgomery.   P. 70.
    1932.   Florida Bird Life.   New York.
HOYT, ROBERT DAY
    1906.   Nesting of the Roseate Spoonbill in Florida.   Warbler, 2
            (3): 58–59.
HUDSON, WILLIAM HENRY
    1920.   Birds of La Plata.   London.   2: 125–127.
HUXLEY, JULIAN SORELL
    1916.   Bird-Watching and Biological Science.   Some Observa-
            tions on the Study of Courtship in Birds.   Auk, 33 (2):
            142–161; 33 (3): 256–270.
    1934.   A Natural Experiment on the Territorial Instinct.   Brit.
            Birds, 27: 270–277.
    1938.   Threat and Warning Coloration in Birds.   Proc. 8th Int.
            Orn. Cong., 430–455.
ISLEY, DWIGHT
    1912.   A List of the Birds of Sedgwick County, Kansas.   Auk, 29
            (1): 42.
JENCKS, FREDERICK TINGLEY
    1884.   The Roseate Spoonbill in Florida Rookeries.   Random
            Notes on Nat. Hist., 1 (3): 4; 1 (4): 7; 1 (5): 4–5; 1 (6): 4.
JOB, HERBERT KEIGHTLEY
    1905.   Wild Wings.   New York.   Pp. 31, 54, 58–60, 75, 78.
JORDAN, DAVID STARR
    1925.   Fishes.   New York.
KENNARD, FREDERIC HEDGE
    1915.   The Oklaloacoochee Slough.   Auk, 32 (2): 154–166.
KIRKMAN, FREDERICK BERNULF BEEVER
    1913.   The British Bird Book.   London.   4: 306–316.
KLINE, HORACE A.
    1887.   Florida Bird Notes.   Forest and Stream, 28 (3): 43–44; 28
            (19): 412.
KLINGEL, GILBERT
    1940.   Inagua.   New York.
KLUIJVER, H. N.
    1933.   Bijdrage tot de Biologie en de Ecologie van den Spreeuw

(*Sturnus v. vulgaris* L.) gedurende zijn Voortplantingstijd. Wageningen, Veeman and Zonen.

KNOWLTON, FRANK HALL AND ROBERT RIDGWAY
1909.   Birds of the World.   New York.   Pp. 163–164.

KUERZI, JOHN FRANCIS
1931.   Notes on the Occurrence of *Ajaia ajaja* and Some Other Species in Florida.· *Auk*, 48 (1): 114–116.

LACK, DAVID
1939.   The Behavior of the Robin, I. The Life-History with Special Reference to Aggressive Behavior, Sexual Behavior, and Territory, II. A Partial Analysis of Aggressive and Recognitional Behavior.   *Proc. Zoo. Soc. London*, Series A, 109 (2, 3).
1940.   Pair-Formation in Birds.   *Condor*, 42 (6): 269–286.

LANTZ, DAVID ERNEST
1900.   The Roseate Spoonbill in Kansas.   *Auk*, 17 (2): 171.

LEOPOLD, ALDO
1933.   Game Management.   New York.

LINCOLN, FREDERICK CHARLES
1939.   The Migration of American Birds.   New York.

LONGSTREET, RUPERT JAMES
1929.   Great White Heron and Roseate Spoonbill near Daytona Beach, Florida.   *Auk*, 46 (1): 105.
1930.   Bird Study in Florida.   Daytona Beach, Fla.   P. 35.
1933.   Roseate Spoonbill (*Ajaia ajaja*) in Mosquito Lagoon.   *Florida Naturalist*, 7 (1): 16.

LORENZ, KONRAD Z.
1935.   Der Kumpan in der Umwelt des Vogels.   (Schluss.)   *Jour. f. Ornithologie*, 83: 289–413.
1937.   The Companion in the Bird's World. *Auk*, 54 (3): 245–273.

LORENZ, KONRAD Z. AND NICHOLAS TINBERGEN
1938.   Taxis und Instinkthandlung in der Eirollbewegung der Graugans, I.   *Zeitschr. f. Tierpsychol.*, 2: 1–29.

MASON, CHARLES RUSSELL
1937.   Check List of Seminole County (Fla.) Birds.   *Florida Naturalist*, 11 (1): 18–19.

MAYR, ERNST
1935.   Bernard Altum and the Territory Theory.   *Proc. Linn. Soc. New York*, 45-46: 24–38.

MITCHELL, CATHARINE ADAMS
1931.   Roseate Spoonbills in Florida.   *Auk*, 48 (2): 259.

NEHRLING, HENRY
1882.   List of Birds Observed at Houston, Harris Co., Texas, and Vicinity and in the Counties Montgomery, Galveston and Ford Bend.   *Auk*, 7 (4): 222–223.

NELSON, EDWARD WILLIAM
1930.   Four New Raccoons from the Keys of Southern Florida.   *Smithsonian Misc. Coll.*, 82 (8): 1–12.

NICE, MARGARET MORSE
1937.   Studies in the Life History of the Song Sparrow, I.   *Trans. Linn. Soc. New York*, 4.

NICHOLS, J. T.
1942.   *Fundus pallidus* on the Florida coast. *Copeia*, 1942 (2).

NICHOLSON, DONALD JOHN
1929.   Notes on the Roseate Spoonbill (*Ajaia ajaja*) in Florida.   *Auk*, 46 (3): 381–382.

NICHOLSON, WRAY HAMILTON
1933.   Roseate Spoonbills and White Pelicans in Brevard County, Florida.   *Auk*, 50 (4): 429.

NOBLE, GLADWYN KINGSLEY
1936.   Courtship and Sexual Selection of the Flicker (*Colaptes auratus luteus*).   *Auk*, 53 (3): 269–282.

NUTTALL, THOMAS
1834.   A Manual of the Ornithology of the United States and Canada, vol. 2.   Boston.

OBER, FREDERICK ALBION ("FRED BEVERLY")
1874.   Our Okeechobee Expedition.   *Forest and Stream*, 2 (10): 145–146; 2 (11): 162.

OBERHOLSER, HARRY CHURCH
1938.   The Bird Life of Louisiana.   New Orleans.   Pp. 81–85.

PATTERSON, ARTHUR H.
1907.   Wild Life on a Norfolk Estuary.   London.   P. 101.

PEARSON, THOMAS GILBERT
1897.   *Passer domesticus* at Archer, Fla., and Other Florida Notes.   *Auk*, 14 (1): 99.
1914.   Report of the Secretary: Egret Protection.   *Bird-Lore*, 16 (6): 483.
1915.   Report of the Secretary: Egret Protection.   *Bird-Lore*, 17 (6): 495.
1919.   Roseate Spoonbill in North Carolina. *Auk*, 36 (4): 568.
1921.   Notes on the Bird-Life of Southeastern Texas: *Ajaia ajaja*, Roseate Spoonbill. *Auk*, 38 (4): 516–517.
1925.   The Bird Study Book.   New York.   P. 154.

PEARSON, THOMAS GILBERT, CLEMENT SAMUEL BRIMLEY AND HERBERT HUTCHINSON BRIMLEY
1919.   Birds of North Carolina.   Raleigh.   P. 93.

PEMBERTON, JOHN ROY
1922.   The Reddish Egrets of Cameron County, Texas.   *Condor* 24 (1): 12.
1927.   The American Gull-billed Tern Breeding in California.   *Condor*, 29 (6): 253.

PENNOCK, CHARLES JOHN ("JOHN WILLIAMS")
1919.   Notes on Birds of Wakulla County, Florida. *Wilson Bull.*, 31 (4): 114.
1929.   Vagaries Regarding Bird Life in Florida in 1889 and 1929.   *Florida Naturalist*, 2 (4): 90.

PHELPS, FRANK MILLS
1914.   The Resident Bird Life of the Big Cypress Swamp Region.   *Wilson Bull.*, 26 (2): 88, 90, 94.

PICKWELL, GAYLE BENJAMIN
1931.   The Prairie Horned Lark.   *Trans. Acad. Sci. St. Louis*, 27: 1–153.

PIKE, EUGENE ROCKWELL
1931.   Roseate Spoonbills in Florida.   *Auk*, 48 (3): 423–424.

PREBLE, GEORGE HENRY
1905.   The Diary of a Canoe Expedition into the Everglades and Interior of Southern Florida in 1842.   The United Service, 3rd series, 8 (1): 26–46.

RHOADS, SAMUEL N.
1892.   The Birds of Southwestern Texas and Southern Arizona Observed during May, June and July, 1891. Proceedings of the Academy of Natural Sciences of Philadelphia, Jan. 26, 1892.

RIDGWAY, ROBERT
1895.   Natural History Survey in Illinois, vol. 1, part 1.   The Ornithology of Illinois.   Springfield.   Pp. 102–105.

ROBERTS, AUSTIN
1940.   The Birds of South Africa.   London.   P. 32.

ROWAN, WILLIAM
1929.   Experiments in Bird Migration, I.   Manipulation of the Reproductive Cycle. Seasonal Histological Changes in the Gonads.   *Proc. Boston Soc. Nat. Hist.*, 39: 151–208.
1932.   Experiments in Bird Migration, III. The Effects of Artificial Light, Castration, and Certain Extracts on the Autumn Movements of the American Crow (*Corvus brachyrhynchos*).   *Proc. Nat. Acad. Sci.*, 18: 639–654.

SCHULTZ, FRED W.
1935.   Tampa Bay Rookery Warden's Report.   *Florida Naturalist*, 8 (2): 25.
1936.   Tampa Bay Warden's Report.   *Florida Naturalist*, 9 (4): 81.

SCOTT, WILLIAM EARLE DODGE
1887.   The Present Condition of Some of the Bird Rookeries of the Gulf Coast of Florida.   *Auk*, 4 (2): 137–138; 4 (3): 222, 274; 4 (4): 280–281.
1889.   A Summary of Observations on the Birds of the Gulf Coast of Florida.   *Auk*, 6 (1): 14–15.
1892.   Notes on the Birds of the Caloosahatchee Region of Florida.   *Auk*, 9 (3): 211.

SENNETT, GEORGE BURRITT
1878.   Notes on the Ornithology of the Lower Rio Grande of Texas, from Observations Made during the Season of 1877.   Bull. U. S. Geol. and Geog. Survey of the Territories, 4: 58.

SMITH, HORACE GARDNER
1896. Some Birds New to Colorado. *Nidologist*, 3 (6): 65.
SMITH, HUGH MCCORMICK
1907. The Fishes of North Carolina. North Carolina Geol. and Econ. Survey, 2.
SPRUNT, ALEXANDER, JR.
1936a. The Roseate Spoonbill in Georgia. *Auk*, 53 (2): 203–204.
1936b. The Roseate Spoonbill in South Carolina. *Auk*, 53 (1): 75.
STEPHENS, FRANK
1904. The Roseate Spoonbill in California. *Condor*, 6 (5): 139.
STURGIS, BERTHA BEMENT
1928. Field Book of Birds of the Panama Canal Zone. New York. P. 79.
TAYLOR, GEORGE CAVENDISH
1862. Five Weeks in the Peninsula of Florida during the Spring of 1861, with Notes on the Birds Observed There. *Ibis*, 4: 127–142.
THOMSON, A. LANDSBOROUGH
1926. Problems of Bird-Migration. London. P. 327.
THORBURN, ARCHIBALD
1916. British Birds. London. 3: 12.
TINBERGEN, NICHOLAS
1935. Field Observations of East Greenland Birds, I. The Behavior of the Red-necked Phalarope (*Phalaropus lobatus* L.) in Spring. *Ardea*, 24: 1–42.
1936. Zur Soziologie der Silbermöwe (*Larus a. argentatus* Pontopp.). *Beitr. Fortpfbiol. Vögel*, 12: 89–96.
1939. Field Observations of East Greenland Birds, II. The Behavior of the Snow Bunting (*Plectrophenax nivalis subnivalis* (Brehm)) in Spring. *Trans. Linn. Soc. New York*, 5: 1–83.
VOGT, WILLIAM
1938. Preliminary Notes on the Behavior and the Ecology of the Eastern Willet. *Proc. Linn. Soc. New York*, 49: 8–42.

WARREN, BENJAMIN HARRY
1890. The Birds of Pennsylvania. Harrisburg. P. 54.
WESTON, FRANCIS MARION
1929. Additional Notes from Northwest Florida. *Florida Naturalist*, 2 (2): 56.
WHYMPER, CHARLES
1909. Egyptian Birds for the Most Part Seen in the Nile Valley. London. Pp. 140–141.
WILLIAMS, JOHN LEE
1837. The Territory of Florida: Or Sketches of the Topography, Civil and Natural History of the Country, the Climate and the Indian Tribes, from the First Discovery to the Present Time. New York. Pp. 73–76.
WILLOUGHBY, FRANCIS
1678. The Ornithology of Francis Willoughby. London. Pp. 288–289.
WILSON, ALEXANDER
1829. American Ornithology. New York. 3: 49–51.
WILSON, CHARLES BRANCH
1924. Life History of the Scavenger Water Beetle, *Hydrous* (Hydrophilus) *triangularis*, and Its Economic Relation to Fish Breeding. Bull. U. S. Bureau of Fisheries, 39: 9–38.
WINECOFF, THOMAS E.
1930. Spoonbills at Marco, Fla. *Auk*, 47 (4): 554–555.
WITHERBY, HARRY FORBES, REV. FRANCIS CHARLES ROBERT JOURDAIN, NORMAN FREDERICK TICEHURST AND BERNARD WILLIAM TUCKER
1939. The Handbook of British Birds. London. 3: 118–121.
WOODHEAD, EDGAR S.
1938. 1937 Brevard Rookery Report. *Florida Naturalist*, 11 (3): 61.
WRIGHT, ALBERT HAZEN AND FRANCIS HARPER
1913. A Biological Reconnaissance of Okefinokee Swamp. The Birds. *Auk*, 30 (4): 503.

INDEX

(All italicized cross-references below refer to entries
under the heading of Spoonbill, Roseate.)

CATALOGUE OF DOVER BOOKS

Nature

AN INTRODUCTION TO BIRD LIFE FOR BIRD WATCHERS, Aretas A. Saunders. Fine, readable introduction to birdwatching. Includes a great deal of basic information on about 160 different varieties of wild birds—elementary facts not easily found elsewhere. Complete guide to identification procedures, methods of observation, important habits of birds, finding nests, food, etc. "Could make bird watchers of readers who never suspected they were vulnerable to that particular virus," CHICAGO SUNDAY TRIBUNE. Unabridged, corrected edition. Bibliography. Index. 22 line drawings by D. D'Ostilio. Formerly "The Lives of Wild Birds." 256pp. 5⅜ x 8½.
T1139 Paperbound **$1.00**

LIFE HISTORIES OF NORTH AMERICAN BIRDS, Arthur Cleveland Bent. Bent's historic, all-encompassing series on North American birds, originally produced under the auspices of the Smithsonian Institution, now being republished in its entirety by Dover Publications. The twenty-volume collection forms the most comprehensive, most complete, most-used source of information in existence. Each study describes in detail the characteristics, range, distribution, habits, migratory patterns, courtship procedures, plumage, eggs, voice, enemies, etc. of the different species and subspecies of the birds that inhabit our continent, utilizing reports of hundreds of contemporary observers as well as the writings of the great naturalists of the past. Invaluable to the ornithologist, conservationist, amateur naturalist, and birdwatcher. All books in the series contain numerous photographs to provide handy guides for identification and study.

LIFE HISTORIES OF NORTH AMERICAN BIRDS OF PREY. Including hawks, eagles, falcons, buzzards, condors, owls, etc. Index. Bibliographies of 923 items. 197 full-page plates containing close to 400 photographs. Total of 907pp. 5⅜ x 8½.
Vol. I: T931 Paperbound **$2.50**
Vol. II: T932 Paperbound **$2.50**
The set Paperbound **$5.00**

LIFE HISTORIES OF NORTH AMERICAN SHORE BIRDS. Including 81 varieties of such birds as sandpipers, woodcocks, snipes, phalaropes, oyster catchers, and many others. Index for each volume. Bibliographies of 449 entries. 121 full-page plates including over 200 photographs. Total of 860 pp. 5⅜ x 8½.
Vol. I: T933 Paperbound **$2.35**
Vol. II: T934 Paperbound **$2.35**
The set Paperbound **$4.70**

LIFE HISTORIES OF NORTH AMERICAN WILD FOWL. Including 73 varieties of ducks, geese, mergansers, swans, etc. Index for each volume. Bibliographies of 268 items. 106 full-page plates containing close to 200 photographs. Total of 685pp. 5⅜ x 8½.
Vol. I: T285 Paperbound **$2.50**
Vol. II: T286 Paperbound **$2.50**
The set Paperbound **$5.00**

LIFE HISTORIES OF NORTH AMERICAN GULLS AND TERNS. 50 different varieties of gulls and terns. Index. Bibliography. 93 plates including 149 photographs. xii + 337pp. 5⅜ x 8½.
T1029 Paperbound **$2.75**

LIFE HISTORIES OF NORTH AMERICAN GALLINACEOUS BIRDS. Including partridge, quail, grouse, pheasant, pigeons, doves, and others. Index. Bibliography. 93 full-page plates including 170 photographs. xiii + 490pp. 5⅜ x 8½.
T1028 Paperbound **$2.75**

THE MALAY ARCHIPELAGO, Alfred Russel Wallace. The record of the explorations (8 years, 14,000 miles) of the Malay Archipelago by a great scientific observer. A contemporary of Darwin, Wallace independently arrived at the concept of evolution by natural selection, applied the new theories of evolution to later genetic discoveries, and made significant contributions to biology, zoology, and botany. This work is still one of the classics of natural history and travel. It contains the author's reports of the different native peoples of the islands, descriptions of the island groupings, his accounts of the animals, birds, and insects that flourished in this area. The reader is carried through strange lands, alien cultures, and new theories, and will share in an exciting, unrivalled travel experience. Unabridged reprint of the 1922 edition, with 62 drawings and maps. 3 appendices, one on cranial measurements. xvii + 515pp. 5⅜ x 8.
T187 Paperbound **$2.00**

THE TRAVELS OF WILLIAM BARTRAM, edited by Mark Van Doren. This famous source-book of American anthropology, natural history, geography is the record kept by Bartram in the 1770's, on travels through the wilderness of Florida, Georgia, the Carolinas. Containing accurate and beautiful descriptions of Indians, settlers, fauna, flora, it is one of the finest pieces of Americana ever written. Introduction by Mark Van Doren. 13 original illustrations. Index. 448pp. 5⅜ x 8.
T13 Paperbound **$2.00**

COMMON SPIDERS OF THE UNITED STATES, J., H. Emerton. Only non-technical, but thorough, reliable guide to spiders for the layman. Over 200 spiders from all parts of the country, arranged by scientific classification, are identified by shape and color, number of eyes, habitat and range, habits, etc. Full text, 501 line drawings and photographs, and valuable introduction explain webs, poisons, threads, capturing and preserving spiders, etc. Index. New synoptic key by S. W. Frost. xxiv + 225pp. 5⅜ x 8.
T223 Paperbound **$1.45**

CATALOGUE OF DOVER BOOKS

LIFE HISTORIES OF NORTH AMERICAN MARSH BIRDS. A wealth of data on 54 different kinds of marsh bird (flamingo, ibis, bittern, heron, egret, crane, crake, rail, coot, etc.). Index. Bibliography. 98 full-page plates containing 179 black-and-white photographs. xiv + 392pp. 5⅜ x 8½.
T1082 Paperbound **$2.75**

LIFE HISTORIES OF NORTH AMERICAN DIVING BIRDS. Thirty-six different diving birds including grebe, loon, auk, murre, puffin, and the like. Index. Bibliography. 55 full-page plates (92 photographs). xiv + 239pp. 5⅜ x 8½.
T1091 Paperbound **$2.75**

LIFE HISTORIES OF NORTH AMERICAN WOOD WARBLERS. Covers about 58 types. Index. Bibliography. 83 full-page plates containing 125 black-and-white photographs. xi + 734pp. of text. 5⅜ x 8½.
Vol. I: T1153 Paperbound **$2.50**
Vol. II: T1154 Paperbound **$2.50**
The set Paperbound **$5.00**

LIFE HISTORIES OF NORTH AMERICAN FLYCATCHERS, LARKS, SWALLOWS, AND THEIR ALLIES. Complete information on about 78 different varieties. Index. Bibliography. 70 full-page plates (117 photographs). xi + 555pp. of text. 5⅜ x 8½.
T1090 Paperbound **$2.75**

AMERICAN WILDLIFE, AND PLANTS: A GUIDE TO WILDLIFE FOOD HABITS, A. C. Martin, H. S. Zim, A. L. Nelson. Result of 75 years of research by U. S. Fish and Wildlife Service into food and feeding habits of more than 1,000 species of birds and mammals, their distribution in America, migratory habits, and the most important plant-animal relationships. Treats over 300 common species of birds, fur and game animals, small mammals, hoofed browsers, fish, amphibians, reptiles by group, giving data on their food, ranges, habits and economies. Also focuses on the different genera of plants that furnish food for our wildlife, animals that use them, and their value. Only thorough study of its kind in existence. "Of immense value to sportsmen, naturalists, bird students, foresters, landscape architects, botanists," NATURE. "Undoubtedly an essential handbook," SCIENTIFIC MONTHLY. Unabridged republication of 1951 edition. Over 600 illustrations, maps, etc. Classified bibliography. Index. x + 500pp. 5⅜ x 8.
T793 Paperbound **$2.50**

HOW TO KNOW THE WILD FLOWERS, Mrs. Wm. Starr Dana. A Guide to the names, haunts, and habits of wild flowers. Well-known classic of nature lore. Informative and delightful. Plants classified by color and season of their typical flowers for easy identification. Thorough coverage of more than 1,000 important flowering, berry-bearing and foliage plants of Eastern and Central United States and Canada. Complete botanical information about each important plant. Also history, uses, folklore, habitat, etc. Nomenclature modernized by C. J. Hylander. 174 full-page illustrations by Marion Satterlee. xii + 481pp. 5⅜ x 8½.
T332 Paperbound **$2.00**

HOW PLANTS GET THEIR NAMES, L. H. Bailey. Introduction to botanical nomenclature for the horticulturist and garden-lover. Discussions of Carl Linnaeus, "father of botany," and analysis of his definitions of genus and species, a brief history of the science before Linnaean systematization, a chapter on plant identification, a mine of information on the rules of nomenclature and Latin stems and word-endings used in botanical nomenclature, with pronunciation guides. An important section contains a full list of generic terms of horticultural literature and common Latin words and their English botanical applications and meanings. "Written with knowledge and authority, charm and eloquence and poetic imagination on the varied aspects of the author's specialty," New York Times. 11 illustrations. vi + 181pp. 5⅜ x 8½.
T796 Paperbound **$1.25**

THE CACTACEAE: DESCRIPTIONS AND ILLUSTRATIONS OF PLANTS OF THE CACTUS FAMILY, N. L. Britton and J. N. Rose. Definitive study of plants of the Cactus Family. The authors devoted more than 15 years of research to this monumental task and produced an exhaustive, rigorously scientific account never likely to be superseded. 3 major classifications, or tribes, are recognized, under which they arrange and describe in full detail 124 genera and 1,235 species of cactus from all over the world. Complete data on each species: leaves, flowers, seeds, fruit, distribution, growth, spines, stem structure, economic uses, etc. In addition, 125 keys facilitate identification of genera and species. For teachers and students of botany and forestry, naturalists, conservationists, and nature lovers, this is an indispensable work. Unabridged republication of second (1937) edition. First edition originally published under the auspices of the Carnegie Institution, Washington, D.C. 4 vols. bound as 2. 1279 illustrations, photographs, sketches, etc. 137 plates. Total of xxvii + 1039pp. 8 x 10¼.
T771 Clothbound, 2-volume set **$20.00**

GUIDE TO SOUTHERN TREES, Elwood S. and J. George Harrar. A handy, comprehensive 700-page manual with numerous illustrations and information on more than 350 different kinds of trees, covering the entire area south of the Mason-Dixon line from the Atlantic Ocean to the Florida Keys and western Texas. Descriptions range from the common pine, cypress, walnut, beech, and elm to such rare species as Franklinia, etc. A mine of information on leaves, flowers, twigs, bark, fruit, distribution etc. of each kind of tree. Eminently readable, written in non-technical language, it is an indispensable handbook for all lovers of the outdoors. Revised edition. Index. 81-item bibliography. Glossary. 200 full-page illustrations. ix + 709pp. 4⅝ x 6⅜.
T945 Paperbound **$2.35**

CATALOGUE OF DOVER BOOKS

WESTERN FOREST TREES, James B. Berry. For years a standard guide to the trees of the Western United States. Covers over 70 different subspecies, ranging from the Pacific shores to western South Dakota, New Mexico, etc. Much information on range and distribution, growth habits, appearance, leaves, bark, fruit, twigs, etc. for each tree discussed, plus material on wood of the trees and its uses. Basic division (Trees with needle-like leaves, scale-like leaves, and compound, lobed or divided, and simple broadleaf trees), along with almost 100 illustrations (mostly full-size) of buds, leaves, etc., aids in easy identification of just about any tree of the area. Many subsidiary keys. Revised edition. Introduction. 12 photos. 85 illustrations by Mary E. Eaton. Index. xii + 212pp. 5⅜ x 8.

T1138 Paperbound **$1.35**

MANUAL OF THE TREES OF NORTH AMERICA (EXCLUSIVE OF MEXICO), Charles Sprague Sargent. The magnum opus of the greatest American dendrologist. Based on 44 years of original research, this monumental work is still the most comprehensive and reliable sourcebook on the subject. Includes 185 genera and 717 species of trees (and many shrubs) found in the U.S., Canada, and Alaska. 783 illustrative drawings by C. E. Faxon and Mary W. Gill. An all-encompassing lifetime reference book for students, teachers of botany and forestry, naturalists, conservationists, and all nature lovers. Includes an 11-page analytical key to genera to help the beginner locate any tree by its leaf characteristics. Within the text over 100 further keys aid in easy identification. Synopsis of families. Glossary. Index. 783 illustrations, 1 map. Total of 1 + 891pp. 5⅜ x 8.

T277 Vol. I Paperbound **$2.25**
T278 Vol. II Paperbound **$2.25**
The set **$4.50**

TREES OF THE EASTERN AND CENTRAL UNITED STATES AND CANADA, W. M. Harlow, Professor of Wood Technology, College of Forestry, State University of N. Y., Syracuse, N. Y. This middle-level text is a serious work covering more than 140 native trees and important escapes, with information on general appearance, growth habit, leaf forms, flowers, fruit, bark, and other features. Commercial use, distribution, habitat, and woodlore are also given. Keys within the text enable you to locate various species with ease. With this book you can identify at sight almost any tree you are likely to encounter; you will know which trees have edible fruit, which are suitable for house planting, and much other useful and interesting information. More than 600 photographs and figures. xiii + 288pp. 4⅝ x 6½.

T395 Paperbound **$1.35**

FRUIT KEY AND TWIG KEY TO TREES AND SHRUBS (FRUIT KEY TO NORTHEASTERN TREES, TWIG TREE TO DECIDUOUS WOODY PLANTS OF EASTERN NORTH AMERICA), W. M. Harlow. The only guides with photographs of every twig and fruit described—especially valuable to the novice. The fruit key (both deciduous trees and evergreens) has an introduction explaining seeding, organs involved, fruit types and habits. The twig key introduction treats growth and morphology. In the keys proper, identification is easy and almost automatic. This exceptional work, widely used in university courses, is especially useful for identification in winter, or from the fruit or seed only. Over 350 photos, up to 3 times natural size. Bibliography, glossary, index of common and scientific names, in each key. xvii + 125pp. 5⅝ x 8⅜.

T511 Paperbound **$1.25**

HOW TO KNOW THE FERNS, F. T. Parsons. Ferns, among our most lovely native plants, are all too little known. This modern classic of nature lore will enable the layman to identify any American fern he is likely to come across. After an introduction on the structure and life of ferns, the 57 most important ferns are fully pictured and described (arranged upon a simple identification key). Index of Latin and English names. 61 illustrations and 42 full-page plates. xiv + 215pp. 5⅜ x 8.

T740 Paperbound **$1.35**

OUR SMALL NATIVE ANIMALS: THEIR HABITS AND CARE, R. Snedigar, Curator of Reptiles, Chicago Zoological Park. An unusual nature handbook containing all the vital facts of habitat, distribution, foods, and special habits in brief life histories of 114 different species of squirrels, chipmunks, rodents, larger mammals, birds, amphibians, lizards and snakes. Liberally sprinkled with first-hand anecdotes. A wealth of information on capturing and caring for these animals: proper pens and cages, correct diet, curing diseases, special equipment required, etc. Addressed to the teacher interested in classroom demonstrations, the camp director, and to anyone who ever wanted a small animal for a pet. Revised edition, New preface. Index. 62 halftones. 14 line drawings. xviii + 296pp. 5⅜ x 8⅛.

T1022 Paperbound **$1.75**

INSECT LIFE AND INSECT NATURAL HISTORY, S. W. Frost. Unusual for emphasizing habits, social life, and ecological relations of insects, rather than more academic aspects of classification and morphology. Prof. Frost's enthusiasm and knowledge are everywhere evident as he discusses insect associations, and specialized habits like leaf-mining, leaf-rolling, and case-making, the gall insects, the boring insects, aquatic insects, etc. He examines all sorts of matters not usually covered in general works, such as: insects as human food; insect music and musicians; insect response to electric and radio waves; use of insects in art and literature. The admirably executed purpose of this book, which covers the middle ground between elementary treatment and scholarly monographs, is to excite the reader to observe for himself. Over 700 illustrations. Extensive bibliography. x + 524pp. 5⅜ x 8.

T517 Paperbound **$2.45**

Biological Sciences

AN INTRODUCTION TO GENETICS, A. H. Sturtevant and G. W. Beadle. A very thorough exposition of genetic analysis and the chromosome mechanics of higher organisms by two of the world's most renowned biologists, A. H. Sturtevant, one of the founders of modern genetics, and George Beadle, Nobel laureate in 1958. Does not concentrate on the biochemical approach, but rather more on observed data from experimental evidence and results . . . from Drosophila and other life forms. Some chapter titles: Sex chromosomes; Sex-Linkage; Autosomal Inheritance;; Chromosome Maps; Intra-Chromosomal Rearrangements; Inversions—and Incomplete Chromosomes; Translocations; Lethals; Mutations; Heterogeneous Populations; Genes and Phenotypes; The Determination and Differentiation of Sex; etc. Slightly corrected reprint of 1939 edition. New preface by Drs. Sturtevant and Beadle. 1 color plate. 126 figures. Bibliographies. Index. 391pp. 5⅜ x 8½.   **S306 Paperbound $2.00**

THE GENETICAL THEORY OF NATURAL SELECTION, R. A. Fisher. 2nd revised edition of a vital reviewing of Darwin's Selection Theory in terms of particulate inheritance, by one of the great authorities on experimental and theoretical genetics. Theory is stated in mathematical form. Special features of particulate inheritance are examined: evolution of dominance, maintenance of specific variability, mimicry and sexual selection, etc. 5 chapters on man and his special circumstances as a social animal. 16 photographs. Bibliography. Index. x + 310pp. 5⅜ x 8.   **S466 Paperbound $2.00**

THE ORIENTATION OF ANIMALS: KINESES, TAXES AND COMPASS REACTIONS, Gottfried S. Fraenkel and Donald L. Gunn. A basic work in the field of animal orientations. Complete, detailed survey of everything known in the subject up to 1940s, enlarged and revised to cover major developments to 1960. Analyses of simpler types of orientation are presented in Part I: kinesis, klinotaxis, tropotaxis, telotaxis, etc. Part II covers more complex reactions originating from temperature changes, gravity, chemical stimulation, etc. The two-light experiment and unilateral blinding are dealt with, as is the problem of determinism or volition in lower animals. The book has become the universally-accepted guide to all who deal with the subject—zoologists, biologists, psychologists, and the like. Second, enlarged edition, revised to 1960. Bibliography of over 500 items. 135 illustrations. Indices. xiii + 376pp. 5⅜ x 8½.   **T786 Paperbound $2.25**

THE BEHAVIOUR AND SOCIAL LIFE OF HONEYBEES, C. R. Ribbands. Definitive survey of all aspects of honeybee life and behavior; completely scientific in approach, but written in interesting, everyday language that both professionals and laymen will appreciate. Basic coverage of physiology, anatomy, sensory equipment; thorough account of honeybee behavior in the field (foraging activities, nectar and pollen gathering, how individuals find their way home and back to food areas, mating habits, etc.); details of communication in various field and hive situations. An extensive treatment of activities within the hive community—food sharing, wax production, comb building, swarming, the queen, her life and relationship with the workers, etc. A must for the beekeeper, natural historian, biologist, entomologist, social scientist, et al. "An indispensable reference," J. Hambleton, BₑES. "Recommended in the strongest of terms," AMERICAN SCIENTIST. 9 plates. 66 figures. Indices. 693-item bibliography. 252pp. 5⅜ x 8½.   **T1137 Paperbound $2.00**

BIRD DISPLAY: AN INTRODUCTION TO THE STUDY OF BIRD PSYCHOLOGY, E. A. Armstrong. The standard work on bird display, based on extensive observation by the author and reports of other observers. This important contribution to comparative psychology covers the behavior and ceremonial rituals of hundreds of birds from gannet and heron to birds of paradise and king penguins. Chapters discuss such topics as the ceremonial of the gannet, ceremonial gaping, disablement reactions, the expression of emotions, the evolution and function of social ceremonies, social hierarchy in bird life, dances of birds and men, songs, etc. Free of technical terminology, this work will be equally interesting to psychologists and zoologists as well as bird lovers of all backgrounds. 32 photographic plates. New introduction by the author. List of scientific names of birds. Bibliography. 3-part index. 431pp. 5⅜ x 8½.   **T1128 Paperbound $2.00**

THE SPECIFICITY OF SEROLOGICAL REACTIONS, Karl Landsteiner. With a Chapter on Molecular Structure and Intermolecular Forces by Linus Pauling. Dr. Landsteiner, winner of the Nobel Prize in 1930 for the discovery of the human blood groups, devoted his life to fundamental research and played a leading role in the development of immunology. This authoritative study is an account of the experiments he and his colleagues carried out on antigens and serological reactions with simple compounds. Comprehensive coverage of the basic concepts of immunolgy includes such topics as: The Serological Specificity of Proteins, Antigens, Antibodies, Artificially Conjugated Antigens, Non-Protein Cell Substances such as polysaccharides, etc., Antigen-Antibody Reactions (Toxin Neutralization, Precipitin Reactions, Agglutination, etc.). Discussions of toxins, bacterial proteins, viruses, hormones, enzymes, etc. in the context of immunological phenomena. New introduction by Dr. Merrill Chase of the Rockefeller Institute. Extensive bibliography and bibliography of author's writings. Index. xviii + 330pp. 5⅜ x 8½.   **S299 Paperbound $2.00**

New Books

101 PATCHWORK PATTERNS, Ruby Short McKim. With no more ability than the fundamentals of ordinary sewing, you will learn to make over 100 beautiful quilts: flowers, rainbows, Irish chains, fish and bird designs, leaf designs, unusual geometric patterns, many others. Cutting designs carefully diagrammed and described, suggestions for materials, yardage estimates, step-by-step instructions, plus entertaining stories of origins of quilt names, other folklore. Revised 1962. 101 full-sized patterns. 140 illustrations. Index. 128pp. 7⅞ x 10¾.
T773 Paperbound **$1.85**

ESSENTIAL GRAMMAR SERIES
By concentrating on the essential core of material that constitutes the semantically most important forms and areas of a language and by stressing explanation (often bringing parallel English forms into the discussion) rather than rote memory, this new series of grammar books is among the handiest language aids ever devised. Designed by linguists and teachers for adults with limited learning objectives and learning time, these books omit nothing important, yet they teach more usable language material and do it more quickly and permanently than any other self-study material. Clear and rigidly economical, they concentrate upon immediately usable language material, logically organized so that related material is always presented together. Any reader of typical capability can use them to refresh his grasp of language, to supplement self-study language records or conventional grammars used in schools, or to begin language study on his own. Now available:

ESSENTIAL GERMAN GRAMMAR, Dr. Guy Stern & E. F. Bleiler. Index. Glossary of terms. 128pp. 5⅜ x 8.
T422 Paperbound **$1.00**

ESSENTIAL FRENCH GRAMMAR, Dr. Seymour Resnick. Index. Cognate list. Glossary. 159pp. 5⅜ x 8.
T419 Paperbound **$1.00**

ESSENTIAL ITALIAN GRAMMAR, Dr. Olga Ragusa. Index. Glossary. 111pp. 5⅜ x 8.
T779 Paperbound **$1.00**

ESSENTIAL SPANISH GRAMMAR, Dr. Seymour Resnick. Index. 50-page cognate list. Glossary. 138pp. 5⅜ x 8.
T780 Paperbound **$1.00**

PHILOSOPHIES OF MUSIC HISTORY: A Study of General Histories of Music, 1600-1960, Warren D. Allen. Unquestionably one of the most significant documents yet to appear in musicology, this thorough survey covers the entire field of historical research in music. An influential masterpiece of scholarship, it includes early music histories; theories on the ethos of music; lexicons, dictionaries and encyclopedias of music; musical historiography through the centuries; philosophies of music history; scores of related topics. Copiously documented. New preface brings work up to 1960. Index. 317-item bibliography. 9 illustrations; 3 full-page plates. 5⅜ x 8½. xxxiv + 382pp.
T282 Paperbound **$2.00**

MR. DOOLEY ON IVRYTHING AND IVRYBODY, Finley Peter Dunne. The largest collection in print of hilarious utterances by the irrepressible Irishman of Archey Street, one of the most vital characters in American fiction. Gathered from the half dozen books that appeared during the height of Mr. Dooley's popularity, these 102 pieces are all unaltered and uncut, and they are all remarkably fresh and pertinent even today. Selected and edited by Robert Hutchinson. 5⅜ x 8½. xii + 244p.
T626 Paperbound **$1.00**

TREATISE ON PHYSIOLOGICAL OPTICS, Hermann von Helmholtz. Despite new investigations, this important work will probably remain preeminent. Contains everything known about physiological optics up to 1925, covering scores of topics under the general headings of dioptrics of the eye, sensations of vision, and perecptions of vision. Von Helmholtz's voluminous data are all included, as are extensive supplementary matter incorporated into the third German edition, new material prepared for 1925 English edition, and copious textual annotations by J. P. C. Southall. The most exhaustive treatise ever prepared on the subject, it has behind it a list of contributors that will never again be duplicated. Translated and edited by J. P. C. Southall. Bibliography. Indexes. 312 illustrations. 3 volumes bound as 2. Total of 1749pp. 5⅜ x 8.
S15-16 Two volume set, Clothbound **$15.00**

THE ARTISTIC ANATOMY OF TREES, Rex Vicat Cole. Even the novice with but an elementary knowledge of drawing and none of the structure of trees can learn to draw, paint trees from this systematic, lucid instruction book. Copiously illustrated with the author's own sketches, diagrams, and 50 paintings from the early Renaissance to today, it covers composition; structure of twigs, boughs, buds, branch systems; outline forms of major species; how leaf is set on twig; flowers and fruit and their arrangement; etc. 500 illustrations. Bibliography. Indexes. 347pp. 5⅜ x 8.
T1016 Clothbound **$4.50**

CATALOGUE OF DOVER BOOKS

GEOMETRY OF FOUR DIMENSIONS, H. P. Manning. Unique in English as a clear, concise intro-duction to this fascinating subject. Treatment is primarily synthetic and Euclidean, although hyperplanes and hyperspheres at infinity are considered by non-Euclidean forms. Historical introduction and foundations of 4-dimensional geometry; perpendicularity; simple angles; angles of planes; higher order; symmetry; order, motion; hyperpyramids, hypercones, hyper-spheres; figures with parallel elements; volume, hypervolume in space; regular polyhedroids. Glossary of terms. 74 illustrations. ix + 348pp. 5⅜ x 8.   S182 Paperbound **$2.00**

PAPER FOLDING FOR BEGINNERS, W. D. Murray and F. J. Rigney. A delightful introduction to the varied and entertaining Japanese art of origami (paper folding), with a full, crystal-clear text that anticipates every difficulty; over 275 clearly labeled diagrams of all important stages in creation. You get results at each stage, since complex figures are logically developed from simpler ones. 43 different pieces are explained: sailboats, frogs, roosters, etc. 6 photographic plates. 279 diagrams. 95pp. 5⅝ x 8⅜.   T713 Paperbound **$1.00**

SATELLITES AND SCIENTIFIC RESEARCH, D. King-Hele. An up-to-the-minute non-technical ac-count of the man-made satellites and the discoveries they have yielded up to September of 1961. Brings together information hitherto published only in hard-to-get scientific journals. In-cludes the life history of a typical satellite, methods of tracking, new information on the shape of the earth, zones of radiation, etc. Over 60 diagrams and 6 photographs. Mathemati-cal appendix. Bibliography of over 100 items. Index. xii + 180pp. 5⅜ x 8½.   T703 Paperbound **$2.00**

LOUIS PASTEUR, S. J. Holmes. A brief, very clear, and warmly understanding biography of the great French scientist by a former Professor of Zoology in the University of California. Traces his home life, the fortunate effects of his education, his early researches and first theses, and his constant struggle with superstition and institutionalism in his work on microorganisms, fermentation, anthrax, rabies, etc. New preface by the author. 159pp. 5⅜ x 8.   T197 Paperbound **$1.00**

THE ENJOYMENT OF CHESS PROBLEMS, K. S. Howard. A classic treatise on this minor art by an internationally recognized authority that gives a basic knowledge of terms and themes for the everyday chess player as well as the problem fan: 7 chapters on the two-mover; 7 more on 3- and 4-move problems; a chapter on selfmates; and much more. "The most important one-volume contribution originating solely in the U.S.A.," Alain White. 200 diagrams. Index. Solutions, viii + 212pp. 5⅜ x 8.   T742 Paperbound **$1.25**

SAM LOYD AND HIS CHESS PROBLEMS, Alain C. White. Loyd was (for all practical purposes) the father of the American chess problem and his protégé and successor presents here the diamonds of his production, chess problems embodying a whimsy and bizarre fancy entirely unique. More than 725 in all, ranging from two-move to extremely elaborate five-movers, including Loyd's contributions to chess oddities—problems in which pieces are arranged to form initials, figures, other by-paths of chess problem found nowhere else. Classified accord-ing to major concept, with full text analyzing problems, containing selections from Loyd's own writings. A classic to challenge your ingenuity, increase your skill. Corrected republica-tion of 1913 edition. Over 750 diagrams and illustrations. 744 problems with solutions. 471pp. 5⅜ x 8½.   T928 Paperbound **$2.25**

FABLES IN SLANG & MORE FABLES IN SLANG, George Ade. 2 complete books of major American humorist in pungent colloquial tradition of Twain, Billings. 1st reprinting in over 30 years includes "The Two Mandolin Players and the Willing Performer," "The Base Ball Fan Who Took the Only Known Cure," "The Slim Girl Who Tried to Keep a Date that was Never Made," 42 other tales of eccentric, perverse, but always funny characters. "Touch of genius," H. L. Mencken. New introduction by E. F. Bleiler. 86 illus. 208pp. 5⅜ x 8.   T533 Paperbound **$1.00**

Dover publishes books on art, music, philosophy, literature, languages, history, social sciences, psychology, handcrafts, orientalia, puzzles and entertainments, chess, pets and gardens, books explaining science, intermediate and higher mathematics, math-ematical physics, engineering, biological sciences, earth sciences, classics of science, etc. Write to:

Dept. catrr.
Dover Publications, Inc.
180 Varick Street, N. Y. 14, N. Y.